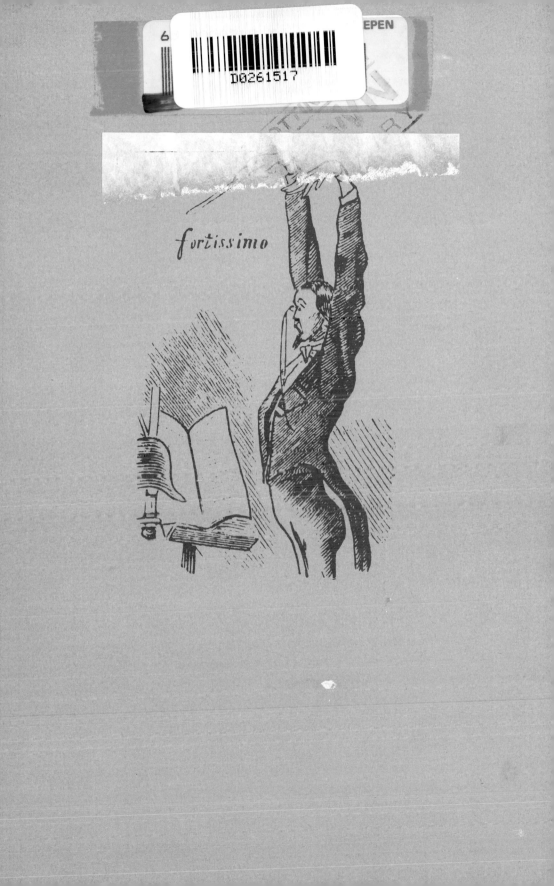

fortissimo

DISCORD

Conflict and the making of music

DISCORD

Conflict and the making of music

NORMAN LEBRECHT

ANDRE DEUTSCH

First published 1982 by
André Deutsch Limited
105 Great Russell Street London WC1

Printed in Great Britain by
Ebenezer Baylis & Son Limited
The Trinity Press, Worcester, and London

ISBN 0 233 97442 3

CONTENTS

ACTS OF AGGRESSION

$\mathcal{O}$n an icy February night a few years before the French Revolution, members of the doomed Parisian gentry trundled out in their carriages for a long-awaited concert by the two greatest living violinists. Their anticipation was sharpened by the knowledge that little love was lost between the Belgian virtuoso Pascal Pieltain and the Italian, Giovanni Mane Giornovichi, more pronouncably known as Jarnovick.

Barely had the two men tuned up and begun their first duet than they quarrelled, each accusing the other of playing out of tune. Tempers flared. Pieltain dropped his bow and threw a punch at Jarnovick, who retaliated by scratching his rival's cheeks with long fiddler's fingernails until the blood flowed. Members of the audience ran forward to pull them apart, but Jarnovick would not be pacified. Arms pinioned behind his back he lunged again at Pieltain, trapping the Belgian's nose between his teeth and refusing to let go until a duel was arranged. With a sabre in his fist, he proceeded to subdue his rival more comprehensively than would have been possible with a violin.

Flushed with glory, Jarnovick sought out the leading swordsman of the age and slapped his face, but the warrior refused to be provoked. 'I love his music too much to fight him,' he observed mildly. Other pillars of society would not tolerate his insolence and had the violinist expelled from France. He embarked on prolonged tours in Germany, Poland and Russia. In 1791 he reached London where, having failed to entrap his conductor at Drury Lane Theatre in a duel, he committed near-treason by stalking out of a recital he was giving for Queen Anne when he caught sight of an adversary in her invited audience. He escaped punishment but lost his own crown soon afterwards in a contest with his compatriot Giovanni Battista Viotti. In defeat he was not humbled. 'My dear Viotti,' he proclaimed loudly to the new champion, 'it must be acknowledged that only we two know how to play the violin.'

Jarnovick's claim to immortality rests on his uninhibited belligerence — his persistence in demonstrating that music, though ostensibly and self-avowedly the most civilized of arts, owes more than is officially acknowledged to underlying sources of tension, aggression and conflict. While others could perform nobler music, Jarnovick's concerts held out the prospect that he might expose the hidden frictions of the art. Discord, he manifested, was integral to harmony. It was the price that must be paid for the tension essential to performance, without which the greatest music would sound impossibly dreary.

Try as they might, musicians have been unable to isolate this tension to the concert hall, or even to their working relationships. It has spilled over first into their private lives, then into their social circle and, ultimately and momentously, into society beyond. The consequences of this diffusion have ranged from marital disturbances to nationwide racial and political persecutions. These reverberations, in turn, have influenced the subsequent works of the musicians with whom they originated. The domestic disruptions that befell Gustav Mahler and Arnold Schoenberg, for example, can be substantially ascribed to musical frictions. The emotional impact of these upheavals are not only audible in their compositions, but served to alter the course of their music, and of modern music altogether.

Yet the role of social discord in the development of music has been minimized by the majority of musical historians, who regard their duty principally to expound on the notes between the staves and the conditions for their performance. They have tended to shy away from the more human aspects of a composer's activities, leaving these sordid details to the fictional devices of the cinema (in *Mahler*, *Lisztomania*, *The Song of Norway*, *Lilac Time*, etc), to playwrights (such as Peter Shaffer in *Amadeus*) and novelists (among whom Thomas Mann, with *Death in Venice* and *Doctor Faustus*, created a musical genre all his own). Dedicated though these fictions may be to eternal truths, some factual ones are inevitably distorted along the way. But if dramatic works cannot do justice to a composer's life, nor can those academic biographies which strip the subject of its vitality. 'I have avoided all biographical details,' writes a respected biographer of the French impressionist composer Claude Debussy, 'which might seem indiscreet. The secrets of his private life belong to those who shared it and those who bear his name.' Those secrets were Debussy's abandonment of his mistress for his bride, and subsequently of his wife for another man's. They resulted in a tragic shooting, a death-bed theft and the desertion of almost all of his friends — events which could not fail to have some effect on the music Debussy was composing at the time. To overlook them is to distort any understanding of both the music and the man; to fictionalize them is to risk sensationalism.

This book, by using original documents and first-hand accounts, hopes to avoid the latter trap. By concentrating specifically on controversy, it also aims to redress in a small way the balance of scholastic distortion and to broaden the appreciation of the vibrant humanity that has expressed itself in music. Unlike Debussy's biographer, I propose, where practicable, to be indiscreet.

Discord of some kind has confronted every great musician. Even Johann Sebastian Bach, who lived on a spiritual plane higher than the average, became embroiled in an eruption of musical passions while working as a young music teacher in Arnstadt. Walking home one

3

evening across the marketplace in the company of his cousin Barbara, he was ambushed by six of his senior students, scarcely younger than himself, armed with sticks. Asking what they wanted, he was told that one of their number, Geyersbach by name, demanded an apology from Bach for having called him 'a nanny-goat bassoonist'. Bach retorted that the epithet had accurately described the young man's prowess. Enraged, Geyersbach hurled himself at the teacher and Bach drew his dagger in self-defence. They were separated, thankfully, before the woodwind player could inflict irreparable damage on the future progress of polyphony. Bach, to add indignity to his physical injuries, was reprimanded by his employers for having allowed his musical emotions to get the better of his educational obligations.

While the fracas harmed Bach's standing with the authorities, it helped attract wider attention to the new musical paths he was beginning to explore. A public which might otherwise have been deterred by radical novelty flocked to hear a musician whose sudden celebrity was founded on a violent incident. Although it would be stretching the point to attribute Bach's eminence to anything other than his creative genius — 'the most stupendous miracle in all music', as Richard Wagner put it in a moment of self-effacement — the brawl did boost his early renown.

It was Wagner who perfected the art of engineering conflicts to draw attention to himself and his music. Despondent after a series of setbacks, and sensing that his concept of opera was too extravagantly original and sumptuously indigestible to win immediate popularity, Wagner contrived to station himself perpetually in the eye of a public storm. He openly insulted every prominent musical personality in Europe, outlawed himself from Germany by joining the 1848 revolutionaries and outraged nineteenth-century sensibilities by living in flagrant sin with the wife of his most fervent supporter. He became a household name, the most famous living German after Bismarck, and the crowds at each new production of his operas were swelled by curiosity-seekers and scandal-mongers. They rarely left the opera house disappointed. Each opera ignited fresh controversy in its own right, whether for the explicitness of its music, its naked espousal of eroticism and incest or its open worship of pagan ideals. The works divided the musical world and provoked its longest and bitterest war, in which none fought more assiduously than the composer himself. Having initiated the hubbub as a means of self-advertisement Wagner became its slave, addicted to its intoxication and able to compose freely only in conditions of maximum turmoil.

The battles he instigated raged on long after his death, their echoes resounding into our own time. France and other allied countries banned his music during both World Wars, deeming it inseparable from the most predatory ambitions of German nationalism. It remains prohibited in Israel, a century after Wagner's death, because of its perceived sympathy with the racial objectives of Nazism. When Zubin Mehta tried to break the taboo in October 1981 by conducting the Israel Philharmonic Orchestra in the Prelude to *Tristan and Isolde*, riots broke out in the audience. Three of his musicians, unable to play music which they associated with the extermination camps, walked out. A second attempt some days later was brought to a halt by 'hysterical screaming and fist fights' in the hall. 'There were two women standing side by side in the middle of the hall shouting at me,' the conductor recalled. 'One demanded that we stop playing this "Nazi" music immediately, the other begged us to carry on.'

The row promoted Wagner once again onto the front pages. 'The cat-calls and scuffles,' observed *The Times* in a memorable leader, 'would not have surprised him, and he would certainly have made matters worse by rushing out an abusive and untruthful pamphlet on the affair.' Even without the composer's intervention, passions ran so high that Mehta backed down and the embargo remained.

Though its outcome was to confirm a ban on his music, the furore increased rather than diminished public curiosity about Wagner — even in Israel. It served to keep music alive, alight and abundant in human interest in an era starved of Wagner's genius and flamboyant pugnacity. Discord in our own times is the life support system of an ailing art. For want of controversial modern masterpieces, musical excitement is generated by the reverberations of unresolved historical dissonances. A stage play on the putative murder of Mozart has inspired more conversation about music than any composition in recent memory. The defection to the West of the son and grandson of Dmitri Shostakovich has won an entirely new following for the works of the vaunted Soviet composer. An immature symphony by Edvard Grieg, locked away in embarrassment by its composer, has become a best-selling record after causing a diplomatic contretemps between NATO and the Warsaw Pact. The world's top conductors have fought over the right to produce the first completed version of Alban Berg's *Lulu*, unfinished for forty years because of a sexual misdemeanour which musicologists have only lately begun to explore. These and similar controversies are the very life's blood of classical music; without them, it would soon be as dead as the daguerrotype, the music hall and the iambic pentameter.

Keeping the fires of discord blazing at the latter end of the twentieth century is the same panoply of forces that has formed the divisions of musical warfare for the past five hundred years. In addition to the demands and overt provocations of composers and performers, there exists a diversity of vested interests, each struggling to gain supremacy through harnessing the energy of musical rapture. In no particular order of merit, these are the legions of musical combat:

— the composer, a backroom inventor of sounds who wants them heard in the open;
— the librettist, champion of the written word against musical encroachment;
— the conductor, nominal commander of mutinous massed bands and enemy of inveterate composers, singers, soloists and managers who dare to challenge his pre-eminence;
— the orchestra, an assembly of individuals united only in their resentment of authority and suspicion of each other;
— the soloist, strung as highly as his instrument;
— the singer, whose emotions, inflamed by dramatic roles, are not readily cooled;
— their husbands, wives and lovers, who are frequently caught up in the musical fray;
— the critics and scholars, observers and occasional instigators of controversy;
— finally, there is the audience, which, having paid for entertainment, demands at the very least diversion.

Together, they continue to make music the most volatile of the arts.

CHAPTER ONE

OPENING SALVOS

*T*o begin, not altogether perversely, at the end. The last of the fighting forces, the audience, while artistically the least significant, warrants immediate consideration simply because it is the largest. Although not noted for its contributions to the advancement of music, the audience is far from being an uncreative element. It has high expectations of concert fare and is as taxing in its demands as the strictest of conductors. When those demands are unmet, it creates.

It is not only in pursuit of perfection, though, that the public attends concerts. Much of the attraction of live music as entertainment lies in its unpredictability, no matter how familiar its programme seems. Concertgoers, while hoping to hear music, would not rule out the possibility of extensive variations to the programme.

It was Mme *Becker's* turn to sing an Air . . . when to the great astonishment of the public she all at once ran off and disappeared into the room adjoining . . . Mme *Becker* had found her breath too short from the effects of dinner and was obliged to have her clothes loosened before she could sing.

Hermstedt now followed with a difficult composition of mine [the writer is the nineteenth-century German composer and violinist Louis Spohr]. Always when appearing in public he went to work with the most nervous precision in everything. However, emboldened to rashness by champagne, he had screwed a new and untried plate to the mouthpiece of his Clarinet and boasted of it to me. I immediately anticipated no good from it. The Solo began with a long sustained note which *Hermstedt* pitched almost inaudibly and increased by degrees to an enormous power, which always produced a great sensation. This time he began in the same way and the public listened to the rising volume of tone with rapt expectancy. But just as he approached the highest power, the plate twisted and gave out a mis-tone like the shrill cry of a goose. The public laughed, and the suddenly-sobered Virtuoso paled with horror.

But with poor *Schwenke* it fared worst of all. The waist buckle of his pantaloons had given way unbeknownst to him during the dinner and shortly after he started playing he felt his pantaloons begin to slip with every movement he made with his bow. Much too conscientious a Musician to omit a note of his part, he waited for the pauses to pull up his nethergarment. His predicament did not escape public notice for long and occasioned considerable merriment. But towards the close of the Pot-pourri, when a 1/16 movement shook him so roughly that the downward tendency of his pantaloons made serious progress

8

and threatened to exceed the limits of propriety, the public could no longer restrain itself.

Spohr does not elaborate on the uproar. Writing his memoirs forty years after the event, its memory was still too painful to bear description. A distinguished music-maker whose lifetime reputation fell not far short of Beethoven's, he was accustomed to being received with honour in the great courts and capitals and public humiliation was a rare and chastening experience. He could console himself only with the thought that no musician, no matter how illustrious, was immune to natural disaster and that no audience would resist an opportunity to convert a lapse into collapse.

Beethoven was playing his new Pianoforte-Concerto, but forgot at the first *tutti* that he was a Soloplayer and springing up, began to direct in his usual way. At the first *sforzando* he threw out his arms so wide asunder that he knocked both the lights off the piano upon the ground. The audience laughed, and *Beethoven* was so incensed at this disturbance that he made the orchestra cease playing, and begin anew. *Seyfried*, fearing that the accident would occur again at the same passage, placed two boys of the chorus on either side of *Beethoven* to hold the lights in their hands. One of the boys innocently approached nearer, and was reading the notes of the piano-part when at the fatal *sforzando* he received from *Beethoven's* out-thrown right hand so smart a blow on the mouth, that he dropped the light in terror. The other boy, more cautious, had followed with anxious eyes every motion of *Beethoven* and, by stooping suddenly at the eventful moment, avoided the slap on the mouth. If the public were unable to restrain their laughter before, they now broke into a bacchanalian roar. *Beethoven* got into such a rage, that at the first chords of the solo, half a dozen strings broke.

That audience uprising drove Beethoven from the concert platform forever. With a valedictory glare at the surging stalls, able to witness the tumult but to hear only a faint echo through his enveloping deafness, he strode from the platform and resolved never to play the piano again in public. Without malicious intent, an audience had permanently silenced Beethoven.

If an audience could put to flight the greatest of musicians through no fault of his own, it needs little imagination to consider what it might do to a performer who roused it to anger through incompetence or impertinence. The latter offence was plainly the more serious, since ineptitude posed less of an affront to public dignity than outright insolence. A performer who insulted an audience could not expect to

9

leave the stage unmolested. The extraordinary violinist Niccolò Paganini, whose unearthly skills were the talk of the whole continent, was lucky to escape with his life from a crowd in his native Italy, after he rallied to the defence of a lady singer it had hooted.

> Maddened with rage, Paganini vowed to avenge the outrage at the end of the concert. As he was about to commence his last solo, he announced to the public that he purposed imitating the notes and cries of various animals. After having imitated the chirping of certain birds, cock-crowing, the mewing of a cat, and the barking of a dog, he advanced to the footlights, and while imitating the braying of an ass, he called out 'This for the men who hissed.' (*Questo è per quelli che han fischiato!*) He was convinced this repartee would excite laughter, and the hissers be hooted; but the pit rose to a man, vociferating, and rushing forward to the orchestra, which they literally scaled. Paganini had only time to escape, by hasty flight, the dangers that menaced him.

During the course of the last century, an element of calculation entered into audience behaviour. Rather than rely on spontaneous unarmed outbursts, members of the audience began to equip themselves in advance with the means of effecting a prompt and efficient disruption. In rural and Mediterranean areas they would carry about their persons reserves of vegetable and animal waste, while in the great urban centres of civilization concert-goers developed a noisier, if less noisome, weapon. It appeared innocuous enough and was carried as a matter of course by most respectable householders. It was a large key, of the kind used to

Audience before . . .

open the imposing iron locks that protected the front doors of well-appointed apartments. Swung on a bunch in a brawl it could leave a nasty weal; applied orally it could cause a musical performance to disintegrate.

A worthy gentleman with the face of a boiled lobster took out his keys to wage a heroic struggle . . . Four keys hung down on a long chain, while this non-appreciator held a fifth one against his lower lip. He then caused streams of air to pass over the hole at its end at an extremely high rate of vibration. The noise thus produced had an implacable quality: it cut right through your stomach. Nor did his spouse desert him in this hour of trial; a large round woman, she was a riding Valkyrie with a bun and a blue dress with yellow flounces. This lady had put two fingers into her mouth; she closed her eyes, puffed up her cheeks and produced a whistle louder than the key had made.

Their clamour took the lead in the wrecking of the 1930 Leipzig première of Kurt Weill's opera, *The Rise and Fall of the City of Mahagonny*. Composed to Bertolt Brecht's sermonizing libretto of Marxist morality, *Mahagonny*'s political message and the racial origin of its composer made it a target for Nazi propaganda long before opening night. The audience arrived prepared for trouble, concealing among its rows a number of professional political agitators. As soon as the first keys were raised to lips pursed with preconceived disapproval, fights broke out throughout the opera house. Members of the audience rushed onto the stage, some to escape the mêlée, others to assault the singers,

and after

who fled in disarray. A large contingent of police arrived and restored calm, but the show had to be abandoned. A second performance was sanctioned only after an emergency meeting of the city council. It went ahead with police lining the walls of the auditorium and the house lights burning throughout.

Three years earlier, in a less ominous social climate, Weill and Brecht had devised a response to a hostile audience. At the first hearing of the laconic songs from *Mahagonny* at a prestigious festival of new music in Baden-Baden, Brecht, anticipating animosity from an audience which included such highbrow musicians as Schoenberg and Otto Klemperer, furnished his singers with whistles and placards emblazoned with anti-audience slogans. 'When they make a noise,' he told the cast, 'you go straight down to the footlights and whistle back!' Lotte Lenya, star of *Mahagonny* and wife of its composer, recalls with satisfaction that she whistled herself red in the face and proudly brandished a placard announcing, 'For Weill!'

But in the face of organized violence at Leipzig, the operatic radicals were helpless. After *Mahagonny* encountered a similar reaction in Berlin, most German cities prudently cancelled their bookings. An exception was Frankfurt-on-Main. There Hitler's followers hurled stink-bombs into the hall and provoked fights in the streets outside in which one Communist student was kicked to death. Audience temperatures, once raised, could rapidly turn dangerous.

The Nazis were not the first to seek to manipulate the aggressions of musical audiences in the interests of a supposedly national cause. Patriotism had long provided a last refuge for musical scoundrels, particularly in circumstances when a local performer was challenged on home ground by a superior foreigner. Unable to defend his or her position on merit, the artist would call on his countrymen's sense of loyalty. It was rarely unanimously forthcoming, though. And while an audience united in antagonism is a fearsome beast, one that is divided into opposing factions is a terrifying menace. In New York in 1849 the National Guard had to be summoned to suppress the consequences of a bid by an undistinguished singer, one Edwin Forrest, to rally his fellow-Americans against an equally nondescript Englishman, William Macready.

On the first appearance of Macready, he was most unmistakably hissed off the stage by those who identified Forrest's grievances with national injuries. A portion of the public, the 'Lower Class', declared that they would permit *no* English actor, *no* Italian Opera, and *no* aristocratic theatre in New York, they being a free and enlightened people. That portion of the public, however, who were called the

'Upper Ten', being likewise a part of that free and enlightened people, declared that they would have whatever amusement they chose to pay for.

In accordance with which determination, a number of gentlemen of high standing invited Mr Macready to perform once more, taking the whole of the seats in the house, and refusing admission to the mass of the general theatre-going public. This proceeding was regarded by them as a positive defiance, and on the evening in question (May 10th, 1849), more than 15,000 of them surrounded the Opera House, and attempted to storm it during the performance. The police-force which had been provided was not strong enough to resist so overwhelming a force and the military were therefore called out.

After vain efforts to restore peace, it was unfortunately obliged, in order to save the building and protect the audience collected inside of it, to fire upon the crowd. After several volleys, a few pieces of artillery were stationed at the different corners of the Astor House, and this led to the gradual dispersal of the mob.

The audience were then permitted to leave, (Mr Macready had already fled,) and immediately after, the Temple of Harmony was transformed into a Morgue for the dead and a hospital for the dying, upon either side.

The next day Max Maretzek, an Austrian conductor, was engaged to rescue New York opera from its nadir and, incidentally, to launch one of its golden ages. 'The blood of those who had been borne into [the opera house] the night previous,' he reported in a letter to his Paris friend Hector Berlioz, 'had not yet been scrubbed from its boards when it passed into my hands.'

Marctzek's sanguinary description was calculated to intrigue the bellicose composer. Sharp-tongued, moody and misanthropic, Berlioz had cultivated a powerful circle of musical enemies in his own country. He was loathed by a conservative establishment, feared by fellow-composers and long shunned by a public too attuned to frivolity to appreciate the grand post-Beethoven idealism of his massive orchestral endeavours. Not until Wagner appeared with his gargantuan schemes did France turn to Berlioz for reassurance. Abroad, by way of contrast, his genius was quickly recognized in Britain, Russia and Germany where, according to the century's foremost critic, 'never was any musical phenomenon greeted with such excitement and enthusiasm'.

Rejection in France brought Berlioz to the brink of despair. He began to imagine that a Machiavellian arch-enemy was conspiring to turn audiences against him. The subject for his paranoia was Luigi Cherubini, a veteran Italian composer whom he had hated ever since he had studied at the Conservatoire, of which Cherubini was the authoritarian Director. The two composers had clashed first over a matter of sexual discrimination. Cherubini, in an act of prudery alien to his French students, had ordained that men and women were to use separate entrances to the academy's library. Berlioz was the first to flout this segregational whim and soon found himself face to face with a lifelong enemy.

> Cherubini was so furious that, for a time, he could not speak, and, when he did, his Italian accent made the whole thing more comical than ever — if possible.
>
> 'Eh! Eh! Eh!' he stuttered, 'so it is you vill come by ze door I vill not 'ave you?'
>
> 'Monsieur, I did not know of the new rule; next time —'
>
> 'Next time? Vhat of zis next time? Vhat is it zat you come to do 'ere?'
>
> 'To study Gluck, Monsieur, as you see.'
>
> 'Vha-Vha-Vhat is your name?' he stammered.
>
> 'My name, Monsieur, you shall hear some day, but not now.'
>
> 'Hotin,' to the porter, 'catch 'im and put 'im in ze prison.'
>
> So off we went, the two — master and servant — hot foot after me round the tables. We knocked over desks and stools in our headlong flight, to the amazement of the quiet onlookers, but I dodged them successfully, crying mockingly as I reached the door:
>
> 'You shan't have either me or my name, and I shall soon be back here studying Gluck.'
>
> That was my first meeting with Cherubini.

Their subsequent encounters were scarcely more amicable. Berlioz delighted in provoking the elderly pedant, while Cherubini did his utmost to block the young man's progress, objecting to performances of his works and vetoing his entries for important competitions. As his disillusionment rose, Berlioz began to see the hand of Cherubini in every setback and to take elaborate precautions against subversion. At the première of his gigantic *Requiem*, employing an orchestra and chorus of four hundred, he insisted on sitting within an arm's length of its conductor, the universally respected François Antoine Habeneck, for fear of sabotage. At the *Tuba mirum*, his worst suspicions were confirmed.

> There are about a thousand bars in my Requiem; will it be believed that at this — the most important of all — Habeneck *calmly laid down his baton and, with the utmost deliberation, took a pinch of snuff.*
>
> But my eye was upon him; turning on my heel, in a flash I stretched out my arm and marked the four mighty beats. The executants followed me, all went right, and my long-dreamed-of effect was a magnificent triumph.
>
> 'Dear me,' bleated Habeneck, 'I was quite in a perspiration; without you we should have been done for.'
>
> 'Yes, we should,' I answered, eyeing him steadily.

Could Cherubini have been behind Habeneck's negligence? The

conductor Charles Hallé, who sat beside Berlioz at the concert, dismissed the incident as no more than an act of thoughtlessness on Habeneck's part. It is the conductor who is always blamed for a breakdown, Hallé argued to his distraught companion, and he would be the last to engineer a disaster deliberately. But Berlioz remained convinced of Habeneck's duplicity and Cherubini's machinations. 'I do not like to think it is so,' he wrote, 'but I have not the slightest doubt. God forgive me if I am wrong.'

Berlioz plotted revenge. His opportunity arose when he discovered that Cherubini's dearest ambition was to recapture the popularity that had deserted him for younger composers. Learning that the old man had invested his last creative energies in a new opera, Berlioz made arrangements to incite the audience against the work and its composer.

It was the first performance of his *Ali Baba*, about the emptiest, feeblest thing he ever wrote. Near the end of the first act, tired of hearing nothing striking, I called out:
'Twenty francs for an idea!'
In the middle of the second I raised my bid.
'Forty francs for an idea!'
The finale commenced.
'Eighty francs for an idea!'
The finale ended and I took myself off, remarking.
'By Jove! I give up. I'm not rich enough!'

He succeeded only in enraging his adversary. The Paris audience which had so violently hissed his own music — seemingly at Cherubini's instigation — refused to be mobilized against the lesser composer's platitudes. What Berlioz failed to realize was that the audience, with a mind of its own, had concluded independently that Cherubini's opera was not worth the effort of disruption. By passive resistance it condemned *Ali Baba* to a fate more awful even than that which Berlioz had desired — to oblivion.

Silence was the audience's ultimate weapon, feared by composers more than any storm of disapproval. Greeted by mute indifference at the Venice première of his opera *Sigismondo*, Gioacchino Rossini turned round and implored his friends in the audience to whistle and shout. They were unable to help. The reactions of the musical audience are not so easily directed, nor are its affections readily held. Though it might give its heart completely to a composer or performer on repeated occasions, this was no guarantee that his next appearance would be met by more than cool neutrality. Maria Callas could be hooted by a La Scala audience that cheered her a month earlier if her singing was thought to fall below her own unique standards. Rossini was forced to run for safety when his hasty newest opera proved not demonstrably different from its predecessor. Worse, if his latest work was too dissimilar from what audiences had come to expect of him, if he happened to create a *Barber of Seville* rather than a cheap melodrama, its very originality could provoke a riot. Even Beethoven had to become accustomed to rejection of each daring new musical step that he made. Two years after his death, a discriminating Paris audience rebelled against his towering C sharp minor quartet, damning it as boring and incomprehensible. Beethoven's followers, Berlioz among them, could defend his reputation only by conceding that the offending work must have been an aberration caused by the great composer's last affliction.

If a confirmed and acclaimed genius risks audience opposition when he departs from his own conventions, attempts by young composers to overthrow the established musical order with brash new notions have provoked the music-loving public into its most savage responses of all. More than mere protests, these demonstrations against radical trends were eruptions of genuine bewilderment and cries of sensory agony. Audiences thus affronted became rampaging armies, massed in defence of their beloved faith. It was to redeem music from infidel experimentation that the people of Paris and Vienna were roused to launch a twentieth-century crusade.

Paris, in the initial third of this century, was host to a united nations of innovatory artists. On the banks of the Seine, Debussy, Stravinsky and Satie revolutionized music; Massine, Isadora Duncan and Nijinsky rewrote the ground rules of ballet; Proust, Cocteau and James Joyce tried out new patterns of literature; while Picasso and Cézanne transformed the visual arts. The irreverence of the radicals for artistic tradition coupled with their openly Bohemian life-style scandalized the Parisian bourgeoisie, though their revulsion was tinged with civic pride that Paris had spawned such cultural effervescence. The emotional conflict that resulted was resolved by a combination of patronage and protest. Respectable citizens would support the young artists by purchasing tickets to new symphonies, ballets and outlandish exhibitions of art, undeterred by the probability of an assault on their most tender sensibilities. When the anticipated monstrosity was unveiled, they could then greet it with a violent protest founded on absolute righteousness. We paid to hear *this*? they would exclaim, tearing their programmes to shreds, hooting at the artists and slamming seats and doors, before storming out happily and cathartically to their suburban homes.

Of the several arts in turmoil, music provided the easiest target for disruption since it was the only one that could literally be shouted down. Music became the forum in which the middle classes could attempt a counter-revolution against the new cultural trends. And it was not only bourgeois art lovers who used music as a target for expressing multiple artistic frustrations. The première of the ballet *Mercure*, with music by the quirky, extravert Erik Satie, was wrecked by a wild-eyed gang of surrealists from the Left Bank, not because of any offence given by its harmonic idiosyncrasies but to demonstrate their objection to their idol, Pablo Picasso, collaborating in so 'decadent' an art.

This was a minor skirmish, though, compared to the conservative eruption at a previous Satie ballet. In fairness to the audience, its composer had intended *Parade* to provoke, with ragtime syncopations and battery of typewriters hammering away at prescribed intervals. Staged in May 1917, with Satie as composer, Cocteau as writer, Massine as choreographer, Picasso as designer, Serge Diaghilev as producer and his Russian Ballet as dancers, its extravagant depiction of a circus society scraped the rawest of mid-War nerves in the audience. 'Bloody Boches,' screamed the spectators, for no good reason except that it was the worst insult imaginable, 'send them to the Front!' When the curtain fell, women ripped lethal hatpins from their headgear and rushed at the ballet's creators as they took their bow. Cocteau said he would rather have faced a German bayonet charge.

Satie, however, enjoyed every minute of the uproar. He could not believe that *le tout Paris* should be trading punches in the aisles all because of him. In a single night he won greater celebrity than he had enjoyed in thirty years as a composer. The Press, ever welcoming to a new villain, discovered rich material in Satie, a bachelor recluse with an eccentric penchant for velvet jackets, black umbrellas and memorably surreal *bon mots* (to Debussy, who called his music 'formless', Satie responded with a piano composition entitled *Pear-Shaped Pieces*). In recognition of his notoriety, public opinion appointed him father-figure to a group of young jazz-influenced composers, whom it stigmatized collectively as *Les Six*. The five men, Georges Auric, Louis Durey, Arthur Honegger, Darius Milhaud, Francis Poulenc, and one woman, Germaine Tailleferre, had little more in common with each other — and less with Satie — than age, time and place, but their individual identities became blurred by the common name which audiences came to associate with outrageous novelty. A première by any of the six, or the seventh, became a signal to concert-goers to prepare a hostile reception which would be launched no matter how innocuous the music proved to be. Darius Milhaud, at the first performance of his affable symphonic suite, was dumbfounded by the reactions it engendered.

My parents came to Paris for the occasion and we shared a ground floor box. I had never for one moment dreamt that my music could possibly be provocative, yet the audience was already restive before the end of the overture, expressing its feelings by cries of: 'Take it away!' and animal noises . . .

With the fugue, an indescribable tumult broke out, a real battle in the course of which Monsieur Franck, the organist from the Temple de la Victoire, had his face slapped by Durey. The sound of the orchestra was swamped; the din grew worse; the police intervened. The balconies were cleared by the *Gardes municipaux*. I had the satisfaction of seeing Monsieur Brancour, the critic of *Le Ménestrel*, 'thrown out' by two policemen.

Yet the audience of the post-War years was no longer the force it had been before 1914, when a less troubled society could devote more of its energies to such luxuries as music-making. It was before the War that the Paris audience achieved its greatest triumphs, winning a reputation that was feared by composers throughout the world. Claude Debussy bore the brunt of its attacks in the 1890s, suffering not only for a smattering of dissonances in his chamber music, but even for the sweet innocence of the *Prélude à l'après-midi d'un faune*, whose fluted opening was drowned in hoots and hisses. In 1902 Debussy had to organize a protection squad of supporters to save his only opera, *Pelleas and Melisande* from demolition by the audience. This group of 'Pelléastres', as they became known, included the young composers Maurice Ravel — who was to succeed Debussy in the next decade as a prime target for opprobrium — Manuel de Falla and Florent Schmitt. The last to join its ranks, in 1909, was the Russian Igor Stravinsky and it soon became apparent that his acerbic gifts would inspire audiences to excesses greater than anything previously experienced.

Stravinsky rose rapidly to notoriety with Diaghilev's Paris productions of his ballets, *Firebird* and *Petrushka*. While composing the second work in St Petersburg, the composer had a dream of 'a solemn pagan rite: wise elders sitting in a circle, watching a young girl dance herself to death. They were sacrificing her to propitiate the god of spring.' This vision was to inspire a ballet score of primitive, barbaric, elemental music, certain to offend bourgeois pretensions. Ravel, when he saw the music, predicted that its première would be 'an event as great as the première of *Pelleas*'. In fact it was incomparably greater, provoking audiences to detonate not just the first but several successive nights with outbreaks of barracking and brawls. 29 May 1913, the première of *The Rite of Spring*, is a date as important to the chronicler of musical warfare as Waterloo's is to the military historian. It was the night the public almost won.

The audience played the role it had to play; it rebelled at once. People laughed, shrieked insults, hissed, imitated the cries of animals, and might have wearied of this sooner or later, if the crowd of aesthetes and a few musicians, carried away by excessive zeal, had not insulted and even manhandled the public of the boxes. The tumult degenerated into a tussle.

Stravinsky playing 'The Rite of Spring' (Cocteau)

Standing in her box, tiara awry, the ancient Comtesse de Pourtalès brandished her fan and screeched until her face turned purple: 'This is the first time in sixty years anyone has dared insult me!' The good lady was sincere; she believed it was all a hoax.

While some blamed Nijinsky's contortionist choreography for the ferocity of the reaction, few doubted that at the root of it all lay the primordial instincts exposed by Stravinsky's music. The composer himself watched the riot from backstage at the Théâtre des Champs Elysées.

I was at Nijinsky's side in the wings. He was standing on a chair, screaming 'sixteen, seventeen, eighteen' — they had their own method of counting to keep time. Naturally the poor dancers could hear nothing by reason of the row in the auditorium and the sound of their own dance steps. I had to hold Nijinsky by his clothes, for he was furious, and ready to dash on to the stage at any moment and create a scandal. Diaghileff kept ordering the electricians to turn the lights on or off, hoping in that way to put a stop to the noise.

But the angry mob was overcome only when Stravinsky's music rose occasionally above the din. The fights that raged throughout the *Rite* and in the streets thereafter became legendary. It seems from numerous literary memoirs that everyone who was artistically anyone was engaged in a brawl. Ravel raised his fist at a fashionable lady who questioned his parentage; Florent Schmitt told a party of hissing society dames that they were 'whores of the sixteenth district'; Cocteau flitted about the stalls looking for fights; and the Ambassador of the Austro-Hungarian Empire delivered a formal diplomatic protest at the Quai d'Orsay over something someone, apparently Ravel, had called him. Stravinsky alone stood above the mêlée. Deeply dejected, he told an interviewer on the following day that he could forgive the audience for not understanding his complex music at first hearing, but not for refusing to hear the piece undisturbed to the end. His previous compositions bore witness to his standing as a serious composer, he protested.

At two o'clock in the morning, Stravinsky, Nijinsky and Diaghilev piled into a cab, together with Cocteau.

No one spoke; the night was cool and mild. By the scent of acacia, we recognized the first trees. Once we reached the lakes, Diaghilev, stuffed into his opossum, began muttering in Russian; I could tell Stravinsky and Nijinsky were listening, and when the driver lit his lamp I saw tears on the impresario's cheeks. He was still muttering, slowly, indefatigably.

'What is it?' I asked.

'Pushkin.'

There was a long silence, then Diaghilev mumbled another short phrase, and the emotion of my two neighbours seemed to me so intense I did not resist my impulse to discover its cause.

'It's hard to translate,' Stravinsky said, 'very hard; it's too Russian, too . . . Russian. But it goes something like this: 'Come with me, come with me to the islands.'

Stravinsky never recovered his exuberance. He was utterly downcast by the uproar he had caused and his later music bears the mark of a man who is constantly glancing over his own shoulder as he strives to remain within the bounds of accepted taste.

Only one man in Paris, it seems, retained his senses of humour and proportion. Maurice Ravel, in wry amusement at the outbursts, raised the ingenious suggestion that *The Rite of Spring* should be performed together with Arnold Schoenberg's song cycle *Pierrot Lunaire*, condemned at its première in Berlin eight months earlier as 'the last word in cacophony and musical anarchy'. *Pierrot*, which had forsaken pure song and was delivered in 'speech-song', when joined with the *Rite* would make, in Ravel's estimation, 'an admirable plan for a concert to stir up a row'.

Two months previously, a Schoenberg concert in Vienna had made world headlines almost as sensational as Stravinsky's. It was a programme in which all the works conformed to a totally new style that he had invented, unlike anything previously imagined. Liberating themselves from the laws of tonality which had governed musical thinking since the Middle Ages, Schoenberg and his followers were no longer constrained to write in a specific key and soared off into virgin realms of atonality. Schoenberg programmed his own *Chamber Symphony, 6 Orchestral Pieces* by his pupil Anton von Webern, two songs by another pupil, Alban Berg, and four further songs by Schoenberg's own former teacher, Alexander von Zemlinsky. It was an exciting venture whose appeal spread beyond the diversified cultural circles that inhabited the capital of the polyglot Austro-Hungarian Empire. It attracted

Zemlinsky and Schoenberg

correspondents from the world's leading musical journals, among them this observer from the New York *Musical Courier*:

> The Grosser Musikvereinsaal audience has an air of expectancy. Vienna prides itself on being 'advanced', and this is no joke either. As for the key — gracious! people wrote in 'keys' far back in 1910. We thought we knew all the discords which human ingenuity could devise, but here even the wisest can learn something. It is without doubt 'original' music.
>
> If this concert was intended to be a 'memorable occasion', it surely succeeded, for it occasioned the greatest uproar which has occurred in a Vienna concert hall in the memory of the oldest critics writing. Laughter, hisses, and applause continued throughout a great part of the actual performance of the disputed pieces. After the Berg songs the dispute became almost a riot. The police were sought and the only officer who could be found actually threw out of the gallery one noisemaker who persisted in blowing on a key for a whistle. But this policeman could not prevent one of the composers from appearing in a box and yelling to the crowd, 'Heraus mit der Baggage!' (Out with the trash!) Whereat the uproar increased. Members of the orchestra descended from the stage and entered into spirited controversy with the audience. And finally the president of the *Akademischer Verband* came and boxed the ears of a man who had insulted him while he was making an announcement.

The litigation that resulted from that night's violence occupied the courts for days on end. A doctor called as witness by one of the rioters testified that the defendant had run amok after the music had afflicted his nervous system so as to induce a state of acute depression. An operetta composer, charged with a breach of public order, pleaded that the sounds were so hilarious that he had roared out aloud. No one, apparently, knew whether to cry or laugh at Schoenberg. Even the public in London, traditionally the most decorous of audiences, could not keep their upper lips stiff.

> It is not often that an English audience hisses the music it does not like [wrote the critic Ernest Newman]; but a good third of the people at Queen's Hall the other day permitted themselves that luxury after the performance of the five orchestral pieces of Schoenberg. Another third of the audience was not hissing because it was laughing, and the remaining third seemed too puzzled either to laugh or to hiss.

Newman reassured his readers that Schoenberg was 'not the lunatic he is generally taken for'. Time alone would tell, 'whether it is our harmonic sense that thinks too slowly, or Schoenberg's . . . that thinks a little too rapidly for the rest of the world.'

Not everyone shared his view. When the work was repeated in London two years later in 1914, its programme had to carry a warning that:

Herr Arnold Schoenberg has promised his co-operation at today's concert on condition that during the performance of his *Orchestral Pieces* perfect silence is maintained.

Schoenberg pretended not to understand the controversy his music kindled. He professed himself to be a composer like any other — perhaps a little more progressive than some — and prophesied that one day milk delivery boys would whistle his tunes. Stubborn and intense, he acknowledged no superior musical authority and refused to make any concession that might have made his output more palatable to public taste. But he remained open to change and, after fifteen years of atonality, elected to modify his compositional method from absolute tonal freedom to a system which organized all twelve tones into formal rows. Dodecaphony, as it was called, or the twelve-tone row, placed emphasis on the order in which notes were composed in a set sequence rather than on the tunefulness of their sound.

As far as the public were concerned, though, it was an even more complex intellectual concept than atonality. Musicians were also among those who rebelled. At the London première of Webern's string trio at the Wigmore Hall in 1938, the cellist, James Whitehead, walked off the stage after a few bars declaring, 'This is mathematics, not music!'

By this time Schoenberg had been so buffeted by audiences that he openly defied them. In Vienna in 1918 he established a Society for Private Musical Performances to which the disinvolved public — and especially newspaper critics — were specifically uninvited. The Society held three aims:

— to arrange clear, well-rehearsed performances of music by Schoenberg and his followers;
— to enable the works to be repeated frequently;
— to remove the performances 'from the corrupting influence of publicity . . . (they must be) unaccompanied by applause or shows of disapproval'.

Uniquely among composers, Schoenberg resolved to exclude the public from the fruits of his mind, having suffered its hostility ever since his very first première, the performance of his melodic and tonally unadventurous sextet *Transfigured Night* in 1902. On what should have been a proud family occasion Schoenberg had to call on his brother Heinrich, a burly singer, to eject disrupters from his début. This first exposure to the public, however, had not been entirely inauspicious,

23

since it brought the young composer to the attention of the dominant musical figure in the Empire, Gustav Mahler, Director of the Vienna Opera. Mahler was impressed by Schoenberg's unwavering certainties and, though he admitted he could not understand his music, reflected that, 'He is young and perhaps he is right. Maybe my ear is not sensitive enough.'

Mahler supported Schoenberg as best he could, giving him money when in need and enhancing his prestige by attending his concerts. On more than one occasion he had to wield his authority against Schoenberg's audience. After angrily silencing hissers during the première of the *Chamber Symphony* in February 1907, he received a warning from the Imperial Court that such conduct was unbecoming to a senior State official. Mahler scorned the caution and presented himself a week later at the next Schoenberg concert, the first performance of his First Quartet, still a tonal work. Mahler's engaging wife Alma recorded the outcome:

> A howling and yelling broke out such as I have never heard before or since. One man stood up in front and hissed Schoenberg every time he came apologetically forward to make his bow, wagging his Jewish head, so like Bruckner's, from side to side in the embarrassed hope of enlisting some stray breath of sympathy or forgiveness. Mahler sprang to his feet and went up to this man. 'I must have a good look at this fellow who's hissing,' he said sharply. The man raised his arm to strike Mahler. Moll,* who was among the audience, saw this and in a second he forced his way through the crowd and collared the man. Moll's superior strength sobered him and he was hustled out of the Bösendorfersaal without much difficulty. But at the door he plucked up his courage and shouted: 'Needn't get so excited — I hiss Mahler *too!*'

But the protection Mahler offered was of limited duration. Ten months later, weakened by a decade of incessant opposition and intrigues in Vienna and tormented by domestic tragedies, he resigned from the Opera and sailed for the United States. Schoenberg was desolate. Mahler had been more than just a powerful friend. He was a father-figure, an adviser, the only man who could restrain Schoenberg from his wildest impulses.

Without Mahler, Schoenberg became increasingly introverted and devoted much of his energy to painting, engaging a Hungarian abstract artist, Richard Gerstl, to give him lessons in technique. Within months Gerstl moved into a studio in the Schoenbergs' house and in summer went on holiday with them. In July 1908 he announced his love for Mathilde Schoenberg, a woman ten years older than himself, and the couple eloped together. Schoenberg was rendered helpless by this second

*Alma's step-father

loss. It was left to his friends, notably to Anton von Webern, to approach Mathilde and persuade her to return to Arnold and their children. Shortly after she did so, Gerstl killed himself with a butcher's knife. He was twenty-five.

In the depths of these emotional crises, Schoenberg finally stepped off the cliff-edge of tonality. His piano pieces Opus 11 were the first to be conceived atonally, but it was the Second String Quartet, though it still bore a key signature, that marked the real point of departure. Dedicated 'To my wife' and replete with harsh dissonances and bitter ironies, it was completed in the month that Mathilde left him and returned. Poignantly, it contains a soprano parody of the Viennese nursery rhyme *Ach du lieber Augustin*, emphasizing its final line, 'alles is hin', all is lost.

The Vienna audience was presented with the Second String Quartet, its first taste of atonality, four days before Christmas of 1908. It was played by the Rosé Quartet, led by Arnold Rosé, Mahler's brother-in-law, but Mahler himself could not be present to shield it from a harsh audience. Relieved of all restraint, the audience gave full rein to its dismay. There was laughter, shouting, booing and cat-calling throughout. Marie Gutheil-Schoder sang the soprano part with tears streaming down her cheeks. She was not the only one who wept.

> Elegant ladies uttered cries of pain, raising hands to their delicate ears. Elderly gentlemen wept tears of anguish at the dissonances,

wrote one journalist. Another Viennese newspaper reported the concert on its crime pages, following what it described as 'scenes unprecedented in Viennese musical history'. Not even the originality of Mozart or Beethoven, it implied, could provoke so uninhibited a reaction.

The crime reporter informed readers that the Quartet was the work of a man who had created a public nuisance on previous occasions. Although exposed to sounds like a cats' chorus, he wrote, the innocent public had remained calm until the end of the first movement, when shouting broke out after some people had expressed approval for the music. The noise rose and fell in *crescendi* and *diminuendi*. In the foyer could be seen the pathetic figure of Ludwig Bösendorfer, owner of the concert hall and manufacturer of the finest pianos, watching helplessly as havoc was wrought in his hallowed premises. A man called out to him: 'They are playing Beethoven after the interval, Ludwig. You had better ventilate the hall first.'

Unforgivably for a man who specialized in detection, the crime writer neglected to seek a motive. Had he been a little more observant, the reporter would have noticed that the uproar began when an immaculately-dressed gentleman stood up in one of the most expensive seats during the second movement and shouted, 'Stop it! Enough!' His neighbour, equally imposing, immediately stood up and yelled, 'Shut up! Carry on playing!' Then everyone else joined in.

A casual investigation would have identified these two leaders of public opinion as precisely that: distinguished music critics, Ludwig Karpath and Richard Specht by name. Unable to contain their opinions for the morning papers, they committed a serious breach of etiquette by forming a common cause with the masses they were employed to inform. In cold print, however, they could wreak greater devastation.

CHAPTER TWO

WAR OF WORDS

George Bernard Shaw

*I*t is Christmas week of 1892 in the Imperial city of Vienna. The pre-festive rush gives way to an incipient hush. Blue-fir trees, yet undecorated, raise their shadows beyond frozen window panes and dust-heavy curtains, within the sitting-rooms of neo-Baroque apartment blocks. The first gifts, heavily beribboned in gaudy wrapping, perch on decoratively precarious side tables. The choir at St Stephen's Cathedral rehearses, though it has no need to, twice through *Silent Night*. The capital of the Holy Roman Empire is about to fulfil one of its last surviving Christian obligations.

In a fourth-floor apartment at Hessgasse 7, an imposing address he can barely afford, Doctor Anton Bruckner prepares to meet his breakfast. He ambles through the shambles of his disordered personal effects, a worn sock here, leaves of a symphonic score there, on his way to a dining-table whose meticulous neatness exudes a silent reproach. Barely have his baggy trousers settled their uncertain folds around the seat of his favourite chair than the ruler of this island of tidiness enters. Frau Kathi Kachelmayer, paragon of a housekeeper who fights a forlorn battle with her employer's worldly unconcern, approaches in all her severity bearing steaming coffee and the morning paper.

Bruckner shakes open his *Neue Freie Presse* at the front page. As he adjusts his pince-nez, he is conscious of a tremor in which anticipation is mixed with dread. For the first time, one of his symphonies has broken through the mass preference for frivolity to the hearts and minds of the Vienna public. They stamped and cheered his Eighth, clamouring for encores and calling the composer time and again to take a diffident bow. He has never known such overwhelming enthusiasm for his abstruse musical offerings. All that is needed to confirm the triumph is a seal of critical approval which only one man can provide.

In the seventeen years that Bruckner has lived in Vienna his most implacable enemy has been Doctor Eduard Hanslick, chief music critic on the *Neue Freie Presse* and arbiter of Viennese taste. For reasons Bruckner cannot fathom, Hanslick abhors his music and ridicules it in front page essays that are read aloud in coffee houses. Now, however, the public has made up its own mind: surely Hanslick cannot ignore its reaction?

Seeking out the inauspicious by-line *Ed. H.* at the foot of the critique, Bruckner takes heart from the final paragraph:

And the reception of the new symphony? A tumultuous ovation, handkerchiefs waving in the standing section, numberless recalls,

28

laurel wreaths. For Bruckner the concert was certainly a great success.

The great composer composes himself, folds the paper to the opening of the article and settles down for a satisfying read.

> The Philarmonic Orchestra devoted its entire concert to a symphony by Bruckner. It is the eighth in the series and similar to its predecessors in form and mood. I found this newest one, as I have found the other Bruckner symphonies, interesting in detail but strange as a whole and even repulsive.

The composer's joy evaporates, his jaw sets, he reads on:

> Bruckner begins with a short chromatic motive, repeats it over and over again, higher and higher in the scale and on into infinity, augments it, diminishes it, offers it in contrary motion and so on, until the listener is simply crushed under the sheer weight and monotony of this interminable lamentation . . .
>
> Also characteristic of Bruckner's newest symphony is the immediate juxtaposition of dry schoolroom counterpoint [a sly reminder of Bruckner's low standing in the professorial hierarchy] with unbounded exaltation. Thus, tossed between intoxication and desolation, we arrive at no definite impression and enjoy no artistic pleasure.
>
> Everything flows, without clarity and without order, willy-nilly into dismal long-windedness. In each of the four movements, and most frequently in the first and third, there are interesting passages and flashes of genius — if only all the rest were not there. It is not out of the question that the future belongs to this *traumverwirrten Katzenjammerstil*. Such a future is unenviable.

Bruckner reads no further. *Traum-ver-wirr-ten Katz-en-jamm-er-stil*, every syllable is a nail in his coffin. Defying literal translation, Hanslick has defined Bruckner's music as bearing the style of a nightmarish hangover, a phantasmagoric sound picture of the morning after the most bibulous of nights before.

The immovable certainty of Hanslick's verdicts, though governed in Bruckner's case by blind prejudice, only added to their impact. Bruckner had reason to fear the critic like the Devil. He estimated that Hanslick's opposition over the years had cost him 100,000 marks in lost income. When, seven years previously, his Seventh Symphony was ecstatically acclaimed at Leipzig, Bruckner had to beg the Vienna Philarmonic not to play it, for fear that 'certain influential criticism' would extend its tentacles to strangle his new-born reputation across the German border. Desperate for justice, he appealed to the highest authority. 'Perhaps your Majesty,' he begged at an audience with the sympathetic Emperor Franz Josef, 'would be kind enough to tell Dr Hanslick not to write such bad criticisms of my work.' He dedicated his Eighth Symphony to the Emperor, but experience swiftly taught him that the critic would not be deterred from attacking even an appurtenance of royalty. Hanslick was Bruckner's fate and the composer was powerless before him.

Eduard Hanslick was the first professional critic of genius. He was clear-thinking, incorruptible and utterly convinced that what he liked was right; all else was an abomination and a fair target. If his judgement was often terribly wrong, it was more frequently tellingly right. The maligned Verdi called him, not without admiration, the Bismarck of music criticism. Tchaikovsky, another victim, called him something untranslatable after Hanslick delivered this assessment of his violin concerto, premièred by Adolph Brodsky in 1881:

> . . . a curious combination of originality and crudeness, of happy ideas and wretched affectations . . . The violin is no longer played but ripped apart, beaten black and blue. Whether it is possible to obtain clarity in these hair-raising difficulties I do not know, but I am sure that Herr Brodsky, trying to do so, has made us — as well as himself — into martyrs . . .
> Tchaikovsky's violin concerto poses for the first time the appalling notion that there can be works of music that stink to the ear.

Tchaikovsky remembered that notice, word for word, to his dying day. When his death occurred prematurely, Hanslick, apparently in remorse for the injuries he inflicted, gave a grudging welcome to the posthumous première of the *Pathétique* Symphony.

> We thank Hans Richter [its conductor] for acquainting us with this original and intelligent composition which, despite unbeautiful purely operatic characteristics and a merciless length, has made a strong impression.

It was unusual for him to display even such qualified mercy, for Hanslick was ruthless to composers whose music he disliked. If he could not crush them in his articles, he would employ against them a second assault wave of innuendo and intrigue on the merry-go-round of social events that whiled away the dying years of the Empire. He lost no opportunity to support Clara Schumann and thwart Franz Liszt, to help Johann Strauss and hinder the unrelated Richard Strauss, above all to advance the career of Johannes Brahms and place obstacles in the path of Anton Bruckner. For the latter pair represented far more than the sum of their compositions. They were knight and knave in Hanslick's most crucial campaign, the total war he waged against the single composer whose charisma and originality threatened to overthrow the most powerful living critic. Richard Wagner challenged the principles that were the foundation of Hanslick's musical world. He proclaimed that Beethoven, by appending a choral finale to his last symphony, had pronounced the last word in the development of the symphony. In future, Wagner declared, all great works of music would have to contain song and drama, more or less on the lines of his own operas.

Hanslick was appalled by this theory, not least because it was so blatantly self-serving. Music, he argued, was not necessarily exalted by its combination with other arts, and was inevitably debased by its subordination to words. He quoted Mozart to the effect that second-rate words could not spoil first-class music, but inferior music would always ruin an opera, no matter how inspired its libretto. Pure music remained the ideal, he declared: the symphony lives on. As for Wagner, his operas were the extravagance of one man's deviation Hanslick fought Wagner unremittingly and with a measure of desperation; he believed that if he lost it would spell the end not only of his power but of musical civilization.

To defeat Wagner, Hanslick seized any means that were to hand. He crowned a reluctant Brahms emperor of the living symphony and denigrated Bruckner for daring to infiltrate 'Wagnerian devices and effects' into the sacred realm of symphonic music. He intrigued ceaselessly against repeated attempts to stage Wagner operas in Vienna and

Hanslick sermonizes to Wagner

preserved for Wagner both his most persuasive written arguments and his wildest invective. Thus, carefully and convincingly:

It is unthinkable that Wagner's method shall be, as he contends, the only valid style from now on, the absolute 'artwork of the future'. When an art arrives at its period of maximum luxury, it is already on the decline. Wagner's opera style recognizes only superlatives; but a superlative has no future. It is the end, not the beginning.

And, without pausing to insert a fresh paragraph, he pursues reason with demagoguery:

From *Lohengrin* on, Wagner broke a new path, a dangerous path, dangerous to life and limb; and this path is for him alone. Anyone who follows will break his neck and the public will contemplate that disaster with indifference.

Behind the rhetoric, Hanslick paid tribute to Wagner's innovations but fought strenuously to quarantine them.

If all other opera composers were to write in [that] style, we listeners would inevitably end up in the madhouse. If Wagner's modifications of [Beethoven's] *tempi* were to be generally accepted, we would soon be joined there by the conductors, fiddlers and wind players.

Brahms, too, was blessed with powerful critics. At twenty-four, Hugo Wolf was rescued from aimlessness by a job as music correspondent for a society gossip magazine, a sinecure secured for him by rich friends who were prominent advertisers in the periodical. Restless and already afflicted with the syphilis that carried insanity and early death, Wolf was prone to intemperate outbursts. He hated the musical establishment which had expelled him from the Conservatory (after he allegedly threatened the life of its Director) and ignored the songs that were beginning to flow from his pen. Refusing to treat his new position as a rung of respectability from which he could advance his career with gentle homilies on musical platitudes, Wolf set his sights on Vienna's most respected composer and unleashed a torrent of venom:

Brahms' *Tragic Overture* brings to mind the entry of a ghost in a Shakespearean drama, startling the murderer by its presence but invisible to all others. We do not know whom Brahms has murdered in his *Tragic Overture*.

And.

> Brahms's Piano Concerto in B flat major was played by the composer. Anyone who can gulp down this concerto with appetite can face a famine without concern. It may be taken for granted that his digestive system is enviable and, in a famine, will function splendidly on the nutritive equivalent of window panes, corks, stove-pipes and the like.

Wolf signed that notice with a skull and crossbones. In another, he declared that Brahms's works only pretended to be music; their composer was the greatest bluffer of the age. Wolf's malice was not altogether unprovoked: 'I once sent him a song,' he claimed, 'and asked him to mark a cross wherever he thought it was faulty. Brahms returned it untouched, saying, "I don't want to make a cemetery of your composition."'

Unlike Wolf, George Bernard Shaw had no personal reason for attacking Brahms. His animosity was stirred by contempt for a Brahms-worshipping English musical hierarchy which, unable to produce an indigenous talent to match Europe's colossi, had fallen into uncritical reverence for visiting celebrities such as the pianist Clara Schumann and the violinist Joseph Joachim, who steered their admirers gently but firmly into the path of their friend Brahms. Shaw's venom, like Wolf's, was intensified by a passionate love of Wagner's operas, anathema to the Brahmsian Brahmins of English music.

He was appointed concert reviewer on the *Star* weekly in 1888, after his editor became alarmed at the young Irishman's fiery political articles. On the music pages, it was felt, he could publish a manifesto of separatism, socialism and anarchy without stirring a murmur of civic rebellion. Ensconced in artistic exile, Shaw looked around him, sighted Authority and proceeded to throw darts at its sacred cow:

> My temper was not improved by Brahms' Symphony in E minor [the fourth]. Brahms takes an essentially commonplace theme; gives it a strange air by dressing it in the most elaborate and far-fetched harmonies; keeps his countenance severely (which at once convinces an English audience that he must have a great deal in him); and finds that a good many wiseacres are ready to guarantee him as deep as Wagner and the true heir of Beethoven. The spectacle of the British public listening with its in-churchiest expression to one of the long and heavy fantasies which he calls his symphonies always reminds me of the yokel in *As You Like It* quailing before the big words of the fool . . .
>
> His symphonies are endured at the Richter concerts as sermons are endured, and his Requiem is patiently borne only by the corpse.

Of the latter work he wrote: 'I do not deny that the Requiem is a solid piece of music manufacture. You feel at once that it could only have come from the establishment of a first-class undertaker.' Its composer was, 'nothing more than a sentimental voluptuary with a wonderful ear'. No section of Brahms's broad and serene output escaped Shaw's notice. In the year that Hanslick suffered his *Katzenjammer*, Shaw discovered the loveliest of Brahms's late chamber works:

> Only the other day I remarked that I was sure to come across Brahms' new clarionet quintet sooner or later. And, sure enough, my fate overtook me last week at Mr G. Clinton's Wind Concert at Steinway Hall. I shall not attempt to describe this latest exploit of the Leviathan Maunderer. It surpassed my utmost expectations: I never heard such a work in my life. Brahms's enormous gift of music is paralleled by nothing on earth but Mr Gladstone's gift of words: it is a verbosity which outfaces its commonplaceness by dint of sheer magnitude.

If the last shot brings to mind, almost plagiarizes, Disraeli's parody of his Liberal opponent ('A sophistical rhetoritician inebriated with the exuberance of his own verbosity'), it indicates something of Shaw's frustration. Although there is always a twinkle in his writing ('how privileged I am,' he remarks, 'to live in an art centre like London, where the nearest opera is at Bayreuth') he was realist enough to know that, to the English, politics were the stuff of life; the arts served only to amuse. Finding Brahms unshaken and his readers unmoved by his diatribes, Shaw began beating at the sides of his cage. 'I hate them . . . hate them all,' he inveighed and, restrained by tough libel laws from having his full say against the living, made a valiant effort to quicken the dead:

> With the single exception of Homer, there is no eminent writer, not even Sir Walter Scott, whom I can despise as entirely as I despise Shakespeare . . . It would positively be a relief to me to dig him up and throw stones at him.

When reproached for the harshness of a musical review, he replied: 'No doubt I was unjust; who am I to be just?'

The worst of such lofty acts of injustice is that the condemned man has no right of appeal, let alone rehabilitation, even on occasions when he is demonstrably innocent of the charges. Singularly unfortunate in this respect was Sergei Prokofiev, whose hangdog expression and brassily assertive music made him an easy target for jaded critics. He was charged twice in as many years by influential critics, for crimes he simply did not commit. In December 1916, a Moscow periodical published the following review by Leonid Sabaneyev:

> At a current Koussevitsky concert, one of the main attractions was the first performance of the *Scythian Suite* by a young composer, Prokofiev, under his own direction . . . If I am asked whether this music gave me pleasure or artistic satisfaction, if it produced a profound impression, I must categorically say no. The composer himself conducted with barbaric abandon.

What might appear to be justifiable criticism is rendered absurd by the fact that the concert in question never took place. Unable to conscript a large enough orchestra in the middle of a war, Prokofiev was forced to call it off at the last moment. In a vain attempt at self-vindication, he took a paid advertisement in Sabaneyev's newspaper, declaring:

> 1 I have never appeared as a conductor in Moscow;
> 2 My *Scythian Suite* has never been performed in Moscow;
> 3 The critic could not have known the work, because the only manuscript score in existence is in my possession

A year later, halfway across the world in New York, where Prokofiev had fled from Lenin's revolution, the authoritative Henry Krehbiel protested to readers of the *Tribune*:

> Why do these Russians give us so much witch music? This new piece is sheerly bestial . . . Mr Prokofiev delights in rending our ears and outraging our sensibilities.

The next day, Krehbiel published a grudging retraction:

> The ear-tearing, nerve-racking description of an orgy of witches (*Hircus Nocturnus*) was the creation of Vasilenko, not Mr Prokofiev. The latter gentleman has artistic sins enough of his own to atone for and ought not to have been saddled with those of another, whose name was overlooked in the dim light of the concert-room. We extend to him our apologies and simultaneously our congratulations that he is not the composer of the musical bestiality which we tried to scourge.

Critics, it seems, cannot lose. When a well-known pianist wrote to the *Manchester Guardian* complaining that Neville Cardus had reviewed him for performing Chopin's Ballade in A flat, not having the intelligence to discern that he was playing the one in G minor, Cardus, who had gone home before it was played, replied.

I must accept his statement that he played the Ballade in G minor. I can only explain my lapse by assuring him that from where I was sitting the music sounded like the Ballade in A flat.

Cardus found a tougher antagonist in Sir Hamilton Harty, the Irish conductor of Manchester's Hallé Orchestra. After grumbling that, 'This young man presumes to be a better conductor than myself,' Harty exploded when Cardus spelled out the exact time in minutes and seconds that he had taken over each movement of a tedious performance of Beethoven's Ninth Symphony. Harty's fulminations were silenced by this rejoinder:

Dear Sir Hamilton:
I do not attend your or anyone else's concerts supported by a stop watch. But I must warn you, as man to man, that if you conduct the Ninth Symphony again in the near future I shall bring with me — less for critical purposes than for those of personal convenience — not a stop watch but an alarm clock.

Robbed of elementary justice, musicians have resorted to dreadful and even criminal methods of retaliation against critics. Few have been more explicit than this memorandum on White House notepaper to a *Washington Post* critic, Paul Hume, from the enraged father of a disparaged concert artist.

Mr Hume:
I have just read your review of Margaret's concert . . . Some day I hope to meet you. When that happens, you'll need a new nose, a lot of beefsteak for black eyes and perhaps a supporter below.
Harry S. Truman
6 December 1950

Outright violence ensued from a review by one Jean Poueigh of Satie's ballet *Parade*. Poueigh committed the *faux pas* of personally congratulating the unpredictable composer on the night of the Paris première and then excoriating his work in an article a week later. Satie, who ignored many reviews more vicious than Poueigh's, saw this as an act of betrayal. He proceeded to pursue the critic with a series of postcards bearing such memoranda as:

Dear Sir, dear friend,
You are not just a c . . ., but an unmusical c . . .
(*Monsieur et cher ami:*
Vous n'êtes qu'un cul, mais un cul sans musique.)

Poueigh sued Satie for libel. The open postcards, he argued, were defamatory; they could have been read not just by the addressee and his family but by the postman, the milkman, even — unthinkably — by his concierge. When the judge concurred with his view and sentenced the composer to a week in prison and a fine of one hundred francs, all hell broke loose in court. Poueigh escaped unharmed, but his lawyer was slapped in the face by Jean Cocteau, Satie's collaborator, who was himself dragged away by the gendarmerie and beaten up in the privacy of the subterranean courthouse cells. Happily, Satie was acquitted on appeal; a criminal record could have resulted in a ban on his music at all national theatres.

Satie might have cited in his defence a French musical precedent for sending critics offensive materials in the mail. Seventy years previously, when Rossini's pastiche *Robert Bruce*, a confection of themes from earlier operas, was attacked by Berlioz as 'sloppy' and by the pianist Stephen Heller as 'corrupt, effeminate, hypocritical, tasteless, trivial, vulgar', Olympe, the second Mme Rossini, could not contain her outrage. She sent a letter to the editor of one offending journal upbraiding him for the insults, impudence and ignorance he had published about her husband's masterpiece and enclosed, for the attention of the reviewers, two large and pungent donkey ears.

Olympe's gesture, like the opera she was defending, was itself not altogether original. It recalled the first known response by a composer to adverse criticism. Johann Sebastian Bach had found himself confronted by a reasonably respectful youth, Johann Adolph Scheibe, whom he had turned down for a job in the Leipzig organ loft. Scheibe moved to Hamburg, where he informed readers of *Der Critische Musicus* that J. S. Bach, while a most dextrous musician, would enjoy a wider following 'if he were more agreeable' socially, as well as less bombastic musically. Bach, he carped, writes for the fingers; he expects poor singers to accomplish with their restricted larynxes what his practised digits can achieve on the keyboard.

His comments sparked off a pamphleteering war with Bach's supporters at Leipzig, an exchange which degenerated swiftly into personal abuse. Bach stood aside from the dispute, but in 1732 brought out a new cantata, which won him a brief reputation as a satirist. Entitled *The Strife Between Phoebus and Pan*, the cantata was founded on a story by Ovid about two judges who have to decide whether Pan or Phoebus has the better voice. The judge who loses is crowned with a pair of donkey's ears.

Gustav Mahler was another who adopted the donkey idiom for critics. Incensed at the hostile reception of his Second Symphony ('musical brutalities' screamed one scribe; 'cynical impudence' scolded another; 'strictly for layabouts and curiosity seekers', declared a third), Mahler interrupted work on his gigantic Third, one of the longest symphonies ever composed, to deliver a riposte. He set to music a folk poem in which a cuckoo and an ageing nightingale approach a donkey for judgement of their respective voices. Inevitably, and to a chuckle from the composer, the donkey pronounces for the cuckoo.

Mahler's contemporary Richard Strauss awarded his critics a dubious place of honour in a symphonic poem with an autobiographical motif, *A Hero's Life*. After the hero-composer announces himself in the opening theme, he is assailed by 'carpers', played by the flutes ('very shrill and biting' writes Strauss), by 'vituperators' (oboes), 'whiners' (cor Anglais) and 'hair splitters', played by the ponderous tubas. The hero ultimately overcomes these nuisances by drowning them in ever louder orchestrations of his personal theme.

Such satires afforded the critics perhaps a twinge of discomfort, but none suffered comparable distress to the injury it was possible to inflict on a composer. Only one musician was able to exact full revenge, an ear for an ear, upon an adverse critic. Richard Wagner, when he wrote *The Mastersingers of Nuremburg*, his only comic opera, used every device at his disposal to ensure that audiences recognized the pedantic, fussy character of Beckmesser as a caricature of Eduard Hanslick.

In 1862, the analytical critic was not yet confirmed as Wagner's sworn enemy. He had written favourably about *Tannhäuser* and had attacked only *Lohengrin*, but this one act of disaffection was seen by Wagner as traitorous. In the first draft of the opera, Wagner actually named Beckmesser 'Hans Lick' and when the work was completed he was not satisfied with exposing the critic to audience ridicule, but contrived to humiliate the unsuspecting butt of his parody in front of his closest friends.

> I had to read *The Mastersingers* aloud to the Standhartner family, as I had done everywhere else. As Dr Hanslick was now supposed to be well disposed towards me, it was considered the right thing to invite him too. We noticed that as the reading proceeded the dangerous critic became more and more pale and depressed, and it was remarked by everyone that it was impossible to persuade him to stay on at the close, but that he took his leave there and then in an unmistakably vexed manner. My friends all agreed in thinking that Hanslick looked on the whole libretto as a lampoon aimed at himself, and had felt an invitation to the reading to be an insult. And undoubtedly the critic's attitude towards me underwent a very remarkable change from that evening. He became uncompromisingly hostile, with results that were obvious to us at once.

Wagner's sublime air of innocence in that recollection, written a decade later, conceals the glee that others observed in him on that fatal evening.

Wagner slays the dragon critic

Hanslick never spoke to Wagner again and devoted the cream of his talent to defeating him. His critique of *The Mastersingers* was studiously disinterested, but by the time of the next Wagner opera he had regained sufficient composure to declaim that

> the Prelude to *Tristan and Isolde* reminds me of the old Italian painting of a martyr whose intestines are slowly unwound from his body on a reel.

The ugliness of his metaphor reflects acutely the intensity of feeling on both sides. Although the conflict generated one of the great comic masterpieces and stimulated widespread interest in music, it also aroused emotions that were distinctly unsavoury. Wagner fought by his own rules, and they were frequently unconventional. He started many fights, some intentionally, others through a blundering, insensitive egotism. Some of his contests were vastly entertaining and enjoyed as much by his antagonists as by himself. Others welled up like bile from the darkest recesses of his soul and kindled the most pernicious of musical vendettas.

CHAPTER THREE

DECLARATION OF WAR

*O*n 3 September 1850, readers of the *Neue Zeitschrift für Musik*, a sober periodical published in Leipzig, were confronted with an article entitled *Judaism in Music*. To the unsuspecting, it probably heralded an analysis of the influence of oriental and synagogue themes on the modern symphony. Few could have dreamed that a magazine so devoted to artistic merit would promote the formula for a political purge of music. The author's pseudonym, K. Freigedank (K. Freethinker), might have suggested liberal tendencies. Instead, he delivered himself of blind prejudice:

> . . . This is not a question of stating anything new but of explaining the unconscious feeling that proclaims itself among people as a rooted dislike of Jewish nature. It is a matter of speaking out about something that really exists, not of breathing life artfully into unreality.

This prologue, artfully and arbitrarily, asserts that racial hatred is a basic human trait, virtually an instinct.

> We have to explain to ourselves the *involuntary repellence* aroused by the nature and personality of the Jews, in order to vindicate the instinctive dislike which we plainly recognize as stronger and more overpowering than our conscious zeal to rid ourselves of it. We are not being truthful to ourselves when we think it necessary to declare immoral and taboo all open proclamation of our natural repugnance against the Jewish nature.

There is no mention yet of music. So far the article is a piece of anti-semitic political propaganda gratuitously inserted in a musical magazine. Only when he has launched into a diatribe of discrimination does the writer begin to broach its relevance to the arts, and even then his principal concern is not music.

> The Jew speaks the language of the nation in which he dwells, but speaks it always as an alien . . . To make poetry in a foreign tongue has always been impossible even to geniuses of the highest order. Our whole European art and civilization have remained to the Jew a foreign tongue.

To support this contention he dismisses Heinrich Heine, the greatest German poet of the age and a Jew by birth, as a highly gifted writer but

42

no true poet; one whose success revealed 'the aridity and jesuitical hypocrisy of contemporary verse'.

> The purely physical aspect of Jewish speech repels us. The first thing that strikes our ear as outlandish and unpleasant in the Jew's production of voice sounds is a creaking, squeaking, buzzing snuffle . . . an intolerably jumbled blabber . . . If the qualities of his dialect make the Jew altogether incapable of giving artistic enunciation to his feelings and impressions through speech, to attain such enunciation through song his aptitude must needs be infinitely smaller. Song is just Talk aroused to highest passion: Music is the speech of Passion.

In that last statement, to anyone who followed revolutionary developments in German music, the author stood revealed. Only one musician in 1850 had the temerity to declare that music and speech had equal potential and should combine as equals to create the greatest artistic impact ever known. The creed of Richard Wagner had not yet taken the world by storm. Only *Rienzi, The Flying Dutchman* and *Tannhaüser* of his operas had been composed; *The Ring* was yet to come. Their author was living in political exile in Switzerland, having fled his post at the opera house in Dresden after the collapse of the 1848 uprisings.

Wagner in 1850 was a bitter man. His career in Germany lay in ruins and elsewhere had not taken root. The great operas he wanted to create lodged stubbornly in his head and he was reduced to writing about ideas that he wanted desperately to express in music. His first marriage was wrecked. His friends were few and distant; his enemies, real and imagined, everywhere. Why he elected at this crisis in his life to attack, not his numerous opponents, but the Jews, who numbered several of his few adherents, is not easily explained. It may have been that, as a refugee from his own land, he resented all the more sharply those traditional 'aliens' who had remained there and prospered, or he may simply have viewed the Jews as the most vulnerable of the German musicians he sought to vilify. It was also an opportunity to slander on ethnic grounds individual adversaries with whom no specifically musical fault could be found. Exactly as he intended, the article aroused a sensation among musicians. It also became the cornerstone of European cultural anti-semitism, gaining ever-greater credibility as its author rose to become, in the eyes of many, the greatest innovator in German culture.

Systematic hatred of Jews, however, was not Wagner's invention. For more than a thousand years, Jews had been cooped up in ghettos, forced to pay punitive taxes and make humiliating obeisances before their Christian neighbours, restricted to a handful of legitimized occupations and periodically expelled or massacred. In the eighteenth and nineteenth centuries, when emancipation opened the ghettos and promised Jews equal citizenship, they burst forth from their confinement with all the force of water from a broken hydro-electric dam. The first generation established industries, banks and companies. The second, having reaped the benefits of a secular education, produced outstanding artists and scientists. The Rothschilds started banks, the Ullsteins newspapers, Reuter the first news agency, Rathenau a major electrical industry. They were followed by a generation of creative genius: Heine, Einstein, Freud, Marx.

In music alone, the second generation after emancipation in central Europe yielded an extraordinary fecundity of talent: Felix Mendelssohn, one of the great Romantic composers, favourite of Queen Victoria; Ignaz Moscheles, outstanding pianist and sometime composer; Giacomo Meyerbeer (born Jakob Beer), son of a Berlin banker, composer of French and Italian operas; Joseph Joachim, the foremost violinist of his time; Jacques Halévy, French opera composer; Jacques Offenbach, German-born composer of French musical comedies; Philipp Spitta, musical scholar and biographer of Bach; Ferdinand Hiller and Stephen Heller, contemporaneous piano virtuosi and composers; Charles-Valentin Alkan, the French composer of almost unplayable piano music — to name but a few who were active around the middle of the last century. Inevitably, their achievements bred new jealousies. Wagner and many other non-Jewish musicians resented this surge of fresh talent with which they had to compete for a livelihood. Personal rivalries with individual Jewish musicians further exacerbated such feelings.

There was an additional, more perverse, musical reason for disliking Jews. Since the Renaissance, music and musicians had been supported either by the Church or by rich aristocrats who sustained them in conditions that varied from the enlightened lassitude that allowed Haydn to compose so copiously to a state of abject servitude. By the turn of the nineteenth century, however, the fortunes of the noble patrons had begun to dwindle and their tastes to decline to cheaper, less artistic pastimes. Fortunately for musicians, the new middle classes in the expanding towns offered an alternative source of income as they started to demand musical entertainment. Their concert-going habit, however, was still in its infancy and required vigorous promotion. Many of the impresarios who helped establish regular concerts were Jewish. So were discernible proportions of the metropolitan audiences they attracted, particularly in such important musical centres as Berlin and Vienna. From dependence on a lordly class, composers and players found themselves relying uneasily for their bread on people they had been taught for generations to despise.

In Wagner's case, he detested any impresario, regardless of his race, who failed to acknowledge his genius, loathed any audience, Jewish or otherwise, which refused to acclaim him. A man of modest stature, his shoulders chipped easily. He was quick to take offence, especially if he felt he was being patronized. Those who tried to help him, impresarios and musicians alike, were frequently rebuffed and those who offered friendly advice quickly became his enemies. Convinced that he alone had been chosen to bring Beethoven's vision to fulfilment, he nourished a special animosity for composers whose careers had advanced beyond his own. In particular, he resented the lofty attitude of Felix Mendelssohn who, though only four years his senior, had shown the most abundant childhood talent since Mozart's and was now the dominant musical personality in Leipzig, Wagner's own home town. Acclaimed by half of Europe, cherished by the Protestant churches whose faith he devoutly espoused, beloved by royalty, adored by audiences, Mendelssohn was still a titanic figure in Germany three years after his sudden death. To Wagner, however, he was a Jew.

> What example can be better than the works of a musician of Jewish birth whom Nature endowed with specific musical gifts as very few before him? All that is apparent in the investigation of our antipathy to Jewish nature; all the contradictoriness of this nature; all its inability to converse with us from an equal footing: all these are intensified to a positively tragic conflict in the nature, life and artistic career of the untimely deceased Felix Mendelssohn Bartholdy.
>
> Mendelssohn has shown us that a Jew may have the amplest of talents, the finest and most varied culture, the highest and tenderest sense of honour, yet these qualities cannot help him even once to evoke in us the deep heart-searching effect which we expect from Art.

Mendelssohn's success, according to Wagner, was transient and illusory. He heaped insult upon injury by placing the high-minded master of Leipzig beside a composer of popular French operas, Giacomo Meyerbeer, coincidentally also a Jew. In so doing, he not only maligned Mendelssohn but pursued a personal vendetta against one of the few musicians who had offered him early encouragement. Ten years previously, he had written to Meyerbeer to ask for help on a visit to Paris, where the opera composer had won great acclaim. Meyerbeer, as Wagner admitted grudgingly in his memoirs, had done his best to assist:

> My favourable opinion was soon confirmed by his kind reception of me. The impression he made was good in every respect, particularly as regards his appearance. The years had not yet given his features the flabby look which sooner or later mars most Jewish faces, and the fine formation of his brow round about the eyes inspired confidence. He did not seem in the least inclined to depreciate my intention of trying my luck in Paris as a composer of opera; he allowed me to read him

my libretto for *Rienzi*, and really listened up to the end of the third act. He kept the two acts that were complete, saying that he wished to look them over, and assured me, when I again called on him, of his whole-hearted interest in my work. Be this as it may, it annoyed me somewhat that he should again and again fall back on praising my minute handwriting.

Meyerbeer helped Wagner find a publisher in Paris and introduced him to the director of the opera, but little came of this. He also advanced his cause in Berlin and Dresden. Wagner had borrowed liberally from Meyerbeer's style in *Rienzi*, his first successful opera, but all the while his benefactor's conspicuous air of achievement and prosperity rankled. So did his neglect to respond promptly to each and every subsequent appeal from his aspiring fellow-countryman. Meyerbeer, to the frustrated Wagner, was usurping the operatic success that should be his. When ultimately, on the verge of his own triumph, Wagner learned of Meyerbeer's death, he recorded his satisfaction that this early benefactor had not lived to see his promise vindicated.

That, however, was fifteen years hence. In 1850, Wagner attacked Meyerbeer for 'deceiving' Paris audiences with a product that was merely a skilful substitute for real Art. He deludes only himself, Wagner fulminated, that self who would dearly love to compose great music but is prevented from doing so by his racial origin.

Judaism in Music aroused a cacophony of acclamation and condemnation across Europe. Its authorship, never properly obscured, was officially acknowledged when Wagner subsequently republished the article under his own name. Its notoriety served to help restore his waning fame and swell the ranks of his supporters. Among those who rallied to his cause were not only fellow-racists whom the article released from their inhibitions, but also, amazingly, a number of Jewish musicians.

The principal opposition came, as anticipated, from the Leipzig establishment which had borne the brunt of the attack. Leaders of the orchestra and Conservatoire, Joseph Joachim at their head, petitioned unsuccessfully for the dismissal of Franz Brendel, publisher of the article, and angrily challenged Wagner's allegation that their music-making was dominated by Jews. Neither they, however, nor any other opponents dared take issue with Wagner's fundamental contention that the Jews, having been excluded from European society for centuries, were incapable of speaking its cultural language without distorting it with extraneous, 'primitive' influences. No one in 1850 would have given any credence to an assertion that a fusion of cultures could create the very greatest art. The American melting pot had not yet produced genius; the lessons of the Islamic Golden Age in Spain had long been forgotten.

Since his opinions were not refuted by facts, Wagner was able to portray the chorus of protest as cries of genuine pain from the vested interests he had exposed. From now on, he and his allies could pose in adversity as martyrs to Jewish political intrigues. Anyone (Hanslick, for example) who attacked Wagner was automatically a Jew, regardless of his parentage. Wagner even persuaded Franz Liszt, never an anti-semite and evidently distressed by his protégé's offensive article, that he had become a target for Jewish counter-discrimination because of his unstinting efforts on behalf of Wagner's music.

So convincing was Wagner's selective reasoning, so charismatic his personality, that Jewish musicians were still attracted to his cause. He accepted their homage as his due and made use of those who could be helpful to him. The popular pianist Carl Tausig became a powerful advocate of his music; another pianist, the star-struck Josef Rubinstein, was persuaded to abandon his career and become a musical house-slave at Bayreuth (he took his life in despair shortly after Wagner's death); the impresario Angelo Neumann did more than any other to achieve performances of Wagner's operas in the capitals of Europe; the conductor Hermann Levi was entrusted with the preparation of the last opera, *Parsifal*. Levi, the son of a rabbi, endured agonies of self-doubt and overt persecution at Bayreuth. In letters to his father, he sought to justify Wagner's prejudices, attributing them to 'the noblest of motives', transcending 'petty hatred of Jews'. A widely-admired conductor, Levi was never treated by the Wagners other than as a racial inferior. On one occasion, arriving late for a meal at their table, he was greeted by a tirade of abuse and innuendo. Even the children were encouraged to be impudent to him. Reproached by the conductor Felix Weingartner for being so submissive, Levi responded sadly: 'It's all right for you in that house; you are an Aryan.' He did walk out on Wagner after the dinner-table incident, and the composer pursued him with telegrams imploring him not to abandon *Parsifal*, though hinting all the while that he might treat him better if Levi converted to Christianity. He declined the suggestion, but returned and made *Parsifal* a personal and Wagnerian triumph. When Cosima Wagner, who called him 'morally unworthy to conduct', forced him some years later to relinquish the opera for one season to another conductor, Felix Mottl, it failed miserably.

As time went on, Wagner and his coterie became ever more violently and explicitly racist. Wagner's acolyte, the conductor Hans von Bülow, who once appealed to Chancellor Bismarck to restrict Jewish activities, wrote to his Master:

> The disease of Judaisation has spread too far . . . We have to wait for the coming of the opposite to a Messiah, namely, one who fastens his own people to the cross.

But Bülow recanted his prejudices, together with his blind Wagner worship, after his wife, Cosima, daughter of Liszt, absconded to become the second Frau Wagner. Cosima, who ruled the Bayreuth kingdom for half a century after the death of its founder, was, if anything, more virulent in her loathing of Jews than either of her husbands. Some suggest that the white heat of her hatred was fanned by the inadequately suppressed knowledge that her own mother, whom Liszt never married, was blessed with Jewish ancestry. Cosima littered her conversation and correspondence with racial jibes. Her hatred of Bolshevism was founded on her conviction that Lenin was a Jew and she contemplated the rise of National Socialism with enthusiastic approval. Hitler became an honoured guest at Bayreuth long before he achieved power and he sanctified Wagner's festival theatre as a shrine of his pan-German ersatz religion.

Wagner's racial theories were to attain their logical — or illogical — objectives in Nazi Germany. His *Judaism in Music*, while not the principal influence on Hitler's racial theories (although some of its heavy phrases were echoed in *Mein Kampf*), had indicated an unsavoury direction, which political opportunists were eager to explore. Where Wagner declared theoretical war on the Jews in music, the Nazis converted his precepts into practical politics. On coming to power in Germany in 1933, and later in the countries of occupation, they hounded Jews out of the orchestras and conservatories to become refugees, prisoners or victims of the murder machine. Among thousands of musicians who perished in the extermination camps were the composers Erwin Schulhoff, Pavel Haas, Hans Krasa, Rudolf Karel and Viktor Ullman, Mahler's niece, the violinist Alma Rosé, Schoenberg's brother, the singer Heinrich, hero of the first-night battles, and Therese Rothauser, Berlin's first Gretel in Humperdinck's fairy tale opera *Hansel and Gretel*. Stefan Zweig, librettist to Richard Strauss, took his own life in remote exile in Brazil; Fritz Löhner, who wrote scripts for Hitler's favourite composer of operettas, Franz Lehár, was killed in a gas chamber.

The Nazi persecution rounded up Jews, live and dead. Works by Jewish composers of all periods and styles were banned from concert halls, music shops and the radio. The imposing statue of Mendelssohn in a Leipzig square was ceremoniously demolished and two irreproachably Aryan composers, Julius Weismann and Rudolf Wagner-Régény, were commissioned to replace his music to Shakespeare's *A Midsummer Night's Dream*. Together with Mendelssohn and his contemporaries were banned such twentieth-century composers as Mahler (whom Hitler is reported to have admired as a young man), Ernst Bloch, George Gershwin, Schoenberg, Milhaud and Kurt Weill. Had the latter four not been Jewish, their music would have been outlawed anyway, along with that of Béla Bartók, Shostakovich, Stravinsky and others, for being too progressive for the simple tastes of Germany's new rulers. 'Art will no longer bear experimentation,' declared Josef Goebbels, Minister of Propaganda.

Wagner became the apotheosis of musical creation. While Hanslick's writings were burned, the subjected musicians of Germany were given Wagner as their model and ordered to emulate him. Themes from *The Ring* cycle were woven into a *Nibelungen March*, whose playing was reserved by law for important Nazi Party meetings, at which its performance was compulsory. When Stalin in 1940 wanted to demonstrate the warmth of his non-aggression treaty with Nazi Germany, he did so by ordering the first Russian performance of Wagner for fifteen years. It did not save him from Nazi invasion six months later.

Banning so many composers created some problems for the Nazis, who found themselves hard-pressed to fill programmes without repeating the symphonies of Beethoven, Brahms and Bruckner *ad nauseam*. Their dilemma might have been greater still but for an elaborate exercise in obfuscation.

In 1935, an Austrian musicologist revealed that Johann Strauss the Son, 'the Waltz King', whose works were proclaimed typically Aryan by the Nazis, was descended from a Jewish great-great-grandfather. Marriage records at St Stephen's Cathedral in Vienna showed for all to see that on 11 February 1762, Johann Michael Strauss, a baptised Jew, son of Wolf and Theresia Strauss, both Jewish, had married Rosalie Buschinin and set about siring one of the great empires of popular music.

As soon as Austria was absorbed into Nazi Germany in 1938, Ministry of Propaganda officials summoned a meeting of scholars in Vienna. They were ordered, on pain of brutal retribution, to forget anything they had heard about Strauss's origins and to discuss them with no one, not even among themselves. While the meeting was taking place, other officials were raiding the cathedral. Wedding Book No. 60, the source of the embarrassment, was seized and transported to Berlin. There it was photocopied and the copy returned to the vaults of the cathedral with all references to Strauss's ancestors deleted. The music of the Strauss family was made safe once again for German ears.

The most acute musical embarrassment of all for the Nazis was caused by another Strauss. The outstanding German composer, Richard Strauss, one of few who did not leave the country when Hitler took over, had gratified the régime by accepting the presidency of its Reich Music Chamber. He pleased it less by persisting in working with an Austrian Jewish librettist, Stefan Zweig. Forced to accept Zweig or lose Strauss, the Nazis bit on the bullet and agreed to let their opera, *The Silent Woman*

(*Die Schweigsame Frau*), be premièred at Dresden in June 1935. Initially, they kept Zweig's name off the advertisement hoardings, but backed down when Strauss threatened to resign. The opera received an immensely successful première. Zweig stayed away; so, for different reasons, did the Nazi hierarchy. Its second performance was sparsely attended, opera-goers having apparently been discouraged by the hint of official disapproval. A month later came news of Strauss's resignation from his official posts and confirmation that *The Silent Woman* was banned. A zealous Gauleiter had intercepted a private letter from Strauss to Zweig in which, begging him to continue their harrassed collaboration, the composer had committed heresy. 'Do you believe,' Strauss wrote, 'that Mozart composed as an "Aryan"? Do you believe that I am ever, in any of my actions, guided by the thought that I am "German"?'

By virtue of his worldwide fame, Richard Strauss escaped the punishment that befell lesser mortals, but was treated thereafter with suspicion. In marked contrast, across the great dictatorial divide in the Soviet Union, fame no longer afforded protection. Those who offended Stalin suffered, whatever their eminence at home or abroad. In the mid-1930s, while the Nazis were consolidating their control over German music, the Soviet leader turned his attention to the arts with a proclamation which left no doubt as to his cultural preferences or his intentions.

Like his fellow-dictator Hitler, Stalin had strong but simple musical tastes. He favoured Georgian folksongs and nineteenth-century Russian classical masterpieces and, like any musical enthusiast, sought to persuade the widest possible audience to share his tastes. In the month that Hitler came to power in Germany, Stalin sounded the first chords of his musical campaign. There appeared in Moscow the first issue of *Sovyetskaya Muzyka* (*Soviet Music*), a periodical that pledged to combat 'musicians who are smuggling in the ideological baggage of the rotten bourgeois world' as well as 'leftist distortions of Marxism-Leninism, vulgarization and pseudo-simplification'.

In the following year, while Alban Berg was struggling to obtain a German première for his *Lulu Suite*, the Soviet composer Dmitri Shostakovich basked in the triumphant world première in Leningrad of his unashamedly modernist opera, *Lady Macbeth of Mtsensk*. Like *Lulu*, it was lurid and violently erotic, a russification of Shakespeare's theme, in which Lady Macbeth plots with her lover to murder her merchant husband, is banished to Siberia for the crime and there murders her lover when she finds him betraying her with another murderess. It had taken him three years to compose and contained some of the most explicit scenes ever seen or heard in an opera, with both copulation and assassination depicted realistically. Shostakovich, the shy, baby-faced hero of Soviet music, said he had tried to write a modern Russian *Carmen*. While he acknowledged the influence of Mahler and Berg and was hovering on the very periphery of tonality, his music was quintessentially as Russian as Rimsky-Korsakov's. Nor could it be claimed that he was other than a faithful son of the Revolution; his latest symphony had been entitled the *May First Symphony* inciting in its choral finale to, 'Burn the old! Ignite the flames of new reality!'

The Soviet press proclaimed *Lady Macbeth of Mtsensk* another 'success of Socialist construction, of the correct policy of the Party'. It was despatched to the West to show what 'a Soviet composer brought up in the best traditions of Soviet culture' could achieve. Deterred by the Soviet propaganda, American critics expressed reservations. One called it 'a bed chamber opera', another 'pornophony'; but New York audiences loved it.

Stalin, occupied by affairs of state, did not get round to seeing the opera until two years after its première. The delay must have annoyed him because Stalin liked a good opera, particularly a good Soviet opera. He liked opera enough to command that favourite works of the pre-Revolutionary period should not be abandoned, but, where necessary, should be re-scripted and staged for the proletarian masses. Mikhail Glinka's *A Life for the Tsar*, the tale of a serf who rescued the founder of the Romanov dynasty which Stalin had helped to overthrow, was transformed on the dictator's orders into *Ivan Susanin*, the saga of an eponymous peasant who did his patriotic Russian duty by saving his country's leader. (Hitler, similarly, had two of Handel's philo-semitic operas metamorphosed from *Israel in Egypt* to *Mongol Fury* and from *Judas Maccabaeus* to the absurdly Prussian *Wilhelm von Nassau*.)

January 1936 promised to be a good month for Stalin with two new Soviet operas to be seen. The first was just what he liked, written to the narrow measure of his tastes. It was a folkloric score by Ivan Dzerzhinsky to the novel *And Quiet Flows the Don*, the saga of Cossack life which won its author Mikhail Sholokhov the Nobel Prize for Literature for a work he is widely suspected to have stolen from another, liquidated, writer. Stalin loved it and the newspapers publicized his delight. Some days later, he stiffened his moustache again in anticipation of seeing the latest opera by the foremost Soviet composer, *Lady Macbeth of Mtsensk*. He left before the end.

Since composing the opera, Shostakovich had married, was writing his Fourth Symphony and had joined a delegation to Turkey to show off the vigour of Soviet music to the perennial Sick Man of Europe. On his return, he toured the Russian provinces. On 28 January 1936, he wandered down to the newsagent at the railway station in Archangel in the frozen north to pick up a newspaper and found that *Pravda*, on page three, reported a drastic change of climate.

In an unsigned article entitled *Chaos Instead of Music*, the Party declared war on Shostakovich by name and on any other Soviet composer who dared write music that did not please The Great Leader and Teacher:

> As culture continues to advance in our land, there has been an increasing demand for good music and good operas . . . Several Soviet theaters have presented the opera *Lady Macbeth of the District of Mtsensk* by Dmitri Shostakovich. Officious music critics have praised the opera to the skies, spreading its fame far and wide. But audiences were bewildered by a stream of deliberately discordant sounds in the music. Melodic fragments, bits of musical phrases popped up on the surface here and there but were immediately drowned, emerging only to disappear once more in the general uproar. To follow this sort of music is difficult, and to enjoy it is impossible . . . Singing is replaced by screaming. If by some lucky chance the composer happens to hit upon an attractive melodious tune, he hastens, as though horrified by such a calamity, to plunge back into the jungle of musical confusion, at times degenerating into complete cacophony . . . All this is done not because of the composer's lack of talent, not because of his inability to express simple and profound emotions in musical tones. No, his music is distorted deliberately . . . It is a leftist bedlam instead of human music. The inspiring quality of good music is sacrificed in favor of petty-bourgeois formalist cerebration, with pretense at originality by cheap clowning. This game may end badly.

The last phrase was ominously explicit. Thousands of Russian creative artists and writers had already learnt how badly it could end in Siberia; tens of thousands of others were soon to join them in the Great Purges.

> The peril of such distortion for Soviet music is clear, Leftist monstrosities in the opera are derived from the same sources as leftist monstrosities in art, in poetry, in pedagogy and in science. The petty-bourgeois 'innovations' lead to the renunciation of true art, true science, true literature . . . *Lady Macbeth* is highly successful with the bourgeois audiences abroad. It may be that this success is owing to the fact that Shostakovich's opera is utterly devoid of all political meaning, and that it titillates the perverted tastes of the bourgeoisie with its fidgeting, screaming, neurasthenic music.

The article was not just inspired but almost certainly dictated by Stalin himself. The Russian word for 'chaos', used in the title, was a favourite of the tyrant's and he had used it only the day before in a signed *Pravda* article on the teaching of history. Shostakovich, in his memoirs, posthumously smuggled out of Russia, says he knew instantly

52

who the writer was. Some people, he remarks, thought the criticism was 'written by the well-known bastard Zaslavsky. It might have been written down by Zaslavsky [a *Pravda* staff hatchet-man], but . . . the article has too much of Stalin in it. There are expressions even Zaslavsky would not have used; they were too ungrammatical.'

The opera was immediately taken off. Shostakovich was transformed overnight from a Soviet hero into a virtual pariah. His friends and followers put a safe distance between themselves and one to whom the Great Leader had assured a bad end. One faithful friend wrote to Stalin pleading that Shostakovich was not altogether corrupt: Comrade Stalin might revise his opinion if he went to see the composer's ballet *Bright Stream*, which was playing at the Bolshoi. Satisfied with his first effort as a music critic the Great Teacher booked seats for the ballet. He liked it no better than the opera and said so some days later in another unsigned article.

Shostakovich quickly withdrew his Fourth Symphony from rehearsal, for fear of provoking immediate retribution. Other composers also felt the heat. A new musical term, 'formalism', had been coined in Stalin's article, whose meaning was unclear except that Stalin intended it to be pejorative. Any music he and his circle disliked was condemned from now on as formalist. Communist parties abroad seized on the latest slogan from Moscow with fervour: they, too, were enthusiastically anti-formalist. They, too, hated Shostakovich, whom only weeks earlier they had praised. They, too, loved Georgian folk songs. Sergei Prokofiev, now under siege in Russia, came closest to an accurate definition: 'Formalism is music that people don't understand at first hearing.'

Desperate to protect themselves, Soviet composers began dedicating reams of compositions to Stalin. There were odes to Stalin, hymns to Stalin, paeans to the Great Leader and Teacher. The Armenian composer Aram Khatchaturian produced a symphonic *Poem About Stalin*, ending in the choral finale:

Leader of our land! Higher than the mountains rises your glory among nations! Like the sun itself you spread your light through space! The whole world will soon open its eyes and raise your banner! . . . Your name will be our banner forever, O Comrade Stalin!

When the Leader turned sixty in December 1939, the veteran symphonist Nikolai Miaskovsky wrote him a *Birthday Overture*; for the same occasion Sergei Prokofiev was induced to write *Zdravitsa*, a cantata of fulsome birthday greetings in the six recognized languages of the Soviet Union.

Shostakovich alone abstained from sycophancy. When the first wave of terror abated he found himself surprisingly safe, but impoverished. His works were rarely played or recorded and if his name was advertised at a concert it would be qualified as 'enemy of the people Shostakovich' or some such soubriquet. Mindful of the family he had to support, he made a solitary concession to Stalin in his Fifth Symphony, a tuneful, optimistic, colourful composition, humbly entitled *A Soviet Artist's Response to Just Criticism*. Performed in Leningrad late in 1937, it was accepted by the Party as an act of contrition. After two years of ostracism, the greatest living Soviet composer was rehabilitated for a while.

Others had been less fortunate. Those destroyed in Stalin's first rampage against the arts included one of Shostakovich's sponsors, the theatre director Vsevolod Meyerhold, who had commissioned several of his early works, and one of his favourite poets, Nikolai Oleinikov.

When the Germans launched their invasion, the Party relaxed its vigilance on composers, partly as a means of winning sympathy from music lovers in the West. Shostakovich was officially resurrected and paraded as a war hero, a symbol of Russian resistance to Nazism. He named his Seventh Symphony for his besieged home city of Leningrad and appeared on the cover of *Time* magazine in a fire-fighter's hat against a backdrop of smoking ruins.

The repression was resumed, however, as soon as the war was over. In 1947, incensed by the paucity of musical tributes to the thirtieth anniversary of the Bolshevik Revolution, Stalin set Andrei Zhdanov, his cultural executioner, upon the musicians. Zhdanov had distinguished himself in the 1930s by purging Leningrad with conspicuous brutality of its Trotskyists, revisionists and undesirables. Later he exercised his nefarious talents against practitioners of literature, theatre and cinema. Ostensibly, the target of Zhdanov's campaign was a lame opera by a forgettable Georgian, Vano Muradeli — *The Great Friendship*, composed in honour of the Communist anniversary and of Stalin's home state. Zhdanov, and probably Stalin as well, previewed the opera at a closed performance at the Bolshoi Theatre in November 1947. A violent row erupted after the performance, so violent that the Director of the Bolshoi had a heart attack and died on the spot. Confronted with official displeasure, Muradeli 'confessed' that he had fallen under the influence of formalism, as practised by the famous 'Big Four': Shostakovich, Prokofiev, Khatchaturian and Miaskovsky. His statement was the excuse for Zhdanov to launch Stalin's second musical purge.

Without prior announcement, works of the indicted composers disappeared from the concert repertoire. A number of musicians were arrested, none of them prominent, but sufficiently well known to spread fear in the musical world. In January 1948, the leaders of Russian music were summoned to the Kremlin to face the Central Committee of the Communist Party, Zhdanov presiding. He began by reciting word for

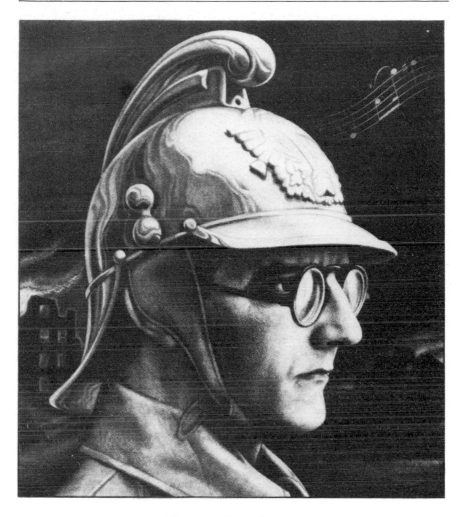

Fireman Shostakovich

word the text of *Chaos Instead of Music* and demanded to know why the assembled composers had not paid heed. What followed was an extraordinary discussion, lasting three days, in which the nation's musical élite grovelled in obsequious self-justification. Even Shostakovich admitted that he had 'deviated towards formalism and begun to speak a language incomprehensible to the people'. Prokofiev, who had recently returned to Russia of his own free will from the West, was exposed to the same terror as his colleagues. Prevented by illness, he said, from attending a disciplinary meeting, he sent a letter apologizing for many of his great works:

55

There have been formalist elements in my music for the last fifteen or twenty years. The infection must have been caused through contact with Western currents. After *Pravda*'s criticism of Shostakovich's opera in 1936, I gave much thought to the whole question, and came to the conclusion that formalism was wrong . . .

As a result, I looked for a clearer musical language, and one with more content. In a number of my subsequent works I tried to get rid of formalist elements, and I believe I succeeded to some extent . . .

I never had the slightest doubt about the importance of melody, and consider it by far the most important element in music.

Zhdanov's conclusions were published in a Central Committee decree that was to govern Soviet music until Stalin's death, mirroring the original *Pravda* article:

The Central Committee considers that the failure of Muradeli's opera is the result of his having followed the formalist road — a road that has been so pernicious to the work of Soviet composers . . .

Despite warnings, and despite the Central Committee's recent decisions on literature, the cinema, and the theatres, Soviet music has failed to pull itself together. The occasional successes of a few composers who have written songs which became popular with the people, and the music written for some films, etc., do not alter the general picture.

The state of affairs is particularly bad in symphonic and operatic music. The Central Committee has in mind those composers who persistently adhere to the formalist and anti-people school — a school which has found its fullest expression in the works of composers like Comrades Shostakovich, Prokofiev, Khatchaturian, Shebalin, Popov, Miaskovsky, and others. Their works are marked by formalist perversions, anti-democratic tendencies, which are alien to the Soviet people and their artistic tastes.

Zhdanov set about his persecutions energetically but not for long. He died in August 1948 in mysterious circumstances, initially blamed on the so-called Doctors' Plot, but now believed to have been on the orders of Stalin, who felt that his henchman was becoming too powerful. His work was carried on posthumously within the Composers Union by Tikhon Khrennikov and other functionaries, who seized the opportunity to advance their music at the expense of their betters. Shostakovich retreated again into obscurity; Prokofiev died, within an hour of Stalin, on 5 March 1953.

Slowly, as the Soviet Union emerged from its darkest age, the restrictions on musicians were lifted and the decrees annulled. Shostakovich became respectable again, but never recovered his early spirit, never lost his fear of the system. His clandestine memoirs, whose authenticity is hotly disputed by Moscow, are the frightening testimony of a broken man. His Fourth Symphony, withdrawn in 1936, was not performed until 1962.

Although Stalin has been discredited, he established a governmental precedent that the State could dictate how its musicians performed. His successors in the USSR and the satellites of Eastern Europe have not needed to use overt brutality to impose their will. With uncommon efficiency, they have centralized the practice of music to assume control over what should be played and by whom within their boundaries and which of their subjects should be allowed to travel beyond them. Musicians who do not fall in line with the dictates of the bureaucrats who run the State concerts and music businesses are simply given fewer concert bookings and prevented from making records.

Nowhere has Stalin's doctrine of musical taste control enjoyed greater ascendancy since his death than in China during the Cultural Revolution of the 1960s. Mao's followers trotted out Stalin's arguments to justify the persecution; music, it was argued, must be written to please the masses. Red Guards roamed the country with purifying vengeance. At one conservatory, pianists were ordered to entertain the young redeemers with classical music. When they finished the programme, their fingers were broken. Western music was banned. Beethoven, previously hailed as a revolutionary composer, was declared decadent and his music not played again until 1977. Only eight operas, all celebrating the Cultural Revolution, were permitted and the Peking Opera, the country's best known cultural institution, was singled out for special treatment by a failed actress and singer who had become a star in the political firmament. The official news agency painted a grim picture of the role of the opera cast.

Revolutionary mass criticism has enabled the theatre's revolutionary masses to bring about a tremendous change in their mental outlook. Led by the workers' propaganda team, they often go to factories, mines and rural people's communes to take part in manual labour and receive re-education by the proletariat.

As Chairman Mao degenerated into feeble senility, China found itself under the domination of a clique led by his wife Jiang Qing, a prima donna in the most literal sense with a captive audience of one thousand million. Her reign, in common with that of most divas, was brief and violent.

CHAPTER FOUR

BATTLE CRY

*O*f all the musical instruments invented by man, none has ever approached the popularity of the human voice. It produces the simplest of sounds and the most instinctively appealing: the only musical tone that is literally 'divine'. Few composers have resisted the temptation to harness it.

Unlike any other instrument, the voice is inseparable from its player. Cased within the human frame, it is wrapped within a personality and dressed in a temperament. The voice cannot afford to be impersonal or it would be musically anonymous, and the larger the voice, the larger the temperament it requires to sustain it. When one such personality tries to dominate a small stage at the same time as another, the outcome is often calamitous:

> In the middle of the third act, when Don José, the tenor Ravelli, was about to introduce an effective high note which generally brought down the house, Carmen rushed forward and embraced him. Being interrupted at the moment of his effect, he was greatly enraged, and made to throw Madame Hauk into the orchestra. But she held firmly on to his red waistcoat, he shouting all the time, '*Laissez moi, Laissez moi!*' until all the buttons came off one by one, when she retired hastily to another part of the stage. Ravelli rushed forward and exclaimed, '*Regardez, elle a déchiré mon gilet!*' and with such rage that he brought down thunders of applause, the people believing this genuine expression of anger to be part of the play.

The curtain came down and the combatants retired to prepare for the fourth and final act of Bizet's opera. Minnie Hauk, the all-American girl who was playing Carmen on that wintry Chicago night, retreated to her corner in some trepidation:

> I went behind the scenes, and when the act was over Ravelli careered around the stage like one possessed of a devil, screaming in French at intervals, 'I will kill her, I will kill her!'
> They all came running to my dressing-room, begging me not to appear in the last act in which Don José kills Carmen. 'He will surely do something dreadful to you,' they cried, 'for he is full of fury against you!'
> But, to the disappointment of everybody, Ravelli had calmed down, and the fourth act passed off naturally enough . . .

Naturally, the matter could not rest there. Into the hustings rode

Madame Hauk's husband and protector, the Baron de Hesse Wartegg, mounting an epistolary charge against the innocent manager of the opera company:

CHICAGO,
FEBRUARY 9TH, 1886

DEAR COLONEL MAPLESON,

The vile language, the insults, and threats against the life of my wife in presence of the entire Company, quite incapacitate her from singing further, she being in constant fear of being stabbed or maltreated by that artist, the unpleasant incident having quite upset her nervous system. She is completely prostrate, and will be unable to appear again in public before her health is entirely restored, which under present aspects will take several weeks.

As a matter of duty, I trust you will feel the necessity to give ample satisfaction to Miss Hauk for the shameful and outrageous insults to which she was exposed last night, and Mr Ravelli can congratulate himself on my absence from the stage, when further scenes would have occurred.

I fully recognize the unpleasant effect this incident may have on your receipts, more especially so should I inflict upon him personally the punishment he deserves.

I am, dear Colonel Mapleson,
Very truly yours,
E. DE HESSE WARTEGG.

Ravelli was bound over by magistrates to keep the peace towards his leading lady. James Henry Mapleson, meanwhile, teetering towards bankruptcy, reflected upon the impotence of an imperious imperial Englishman who is forced to earn his keep at staging operas:

What could the public think of an Opera Company in which the tenor was always threatening to murder the prima donna, while the prima donna's husband found himself forced to take up a position at one of the wings bearing a revolver with which he proposed to shoot the tenor the moment he showed the slightest intention of approaching the personage for whom he is supposed to entertain an ungovernable passion. Ravelli was afraid of Minnie Hauk's throttling him while engaged in the emission of a high B flat; and Minnie Hauk, on her side, dreaded the murderous knife with which Ravelli again and again had threatened her. Love-making looks, under such conditions, a little unreal. 'I adore you; but I will not allow you under pretence of embracing me to pinch my throat!' 'If you don't keep at a respectful distance I will stab you!'

While Ravelli was over-excitable and Hauk rather less innocent than she sounds, such explosions of temperament could overcome the mildest of singers. The tenor Beniamino Gigli, who possessed the sunniest nature and voice, confessed that even he succumbed once in his life to the lures of temperament. Singing in New York in 1925, with the sensuous Czech soprano Maria Jeritza, he found himself 'becoming every bit as temperamental as she was . . . in her presence I always felt tension'. Rehearsals passed without incident, but on the first night of Giordano's melodramatic opera *Fedora*, 'she hurled herself on me with such abandon in the betrothal scene that I was able to withstand the impact only by bracing myself firmly against a wing support.'

He kept his feet for the first performance, but the next night, 'she wriggled so violently in my supposedly loving arms that I actually did stagger, making the audience roar with laughter at what should have been an intensely tragic moment.' On another evening when Gigli's top hat fell off his head, Jeritza surreptitiously kicked it halfway across the stage.

The Italian bided his time for two weeks of performances. Then, in a scene where, after discovering her to be a spy, he was supposed to thrust the heroine away from him in disgust, he pushed her with such force that she was propelled almost into the orchestra. Aghast, Gigli offered to help her to her feet but Jeritza spurned his arm, got up and sang on to the end of the scene, before bursting into tears.

Backstage, she went wild. Gigli, she said, had tried to murder her. She commanded her husband, a Baron like Hauk's, to challenge the Italian to a duel. Baron von Popper pretended not to hear and made himself scarce until the storm had passed. It blew over quickly enough for Jeritza to forget to mention the incident in her autobiography; in Gigli's, by contrast, it figures as one of the most cataclysmic and bewildering events of his life.

Temperament tends to manifest itself long before a singer ever faces an audience. Indeed, one of the most frequent points of conflict and upheaval is the delicate negotiation of the terms and conditions of performance.

The pecuniary ambitions of leading singers are the stuff of legends and accountants' dreams. Vocalists vie with each other and with concert managers to obtain the highest fee ever awarded for a single performance, only to see their record shattered a few nights later by a more insistent rival. Feodor Chaliapin, the mighty Russian bass, viewed his exorbitant emoluments as recognition of his unique gift. He once walked off in the middle of *Mefistofele* at Covent Garden after a disagreement with the conductor over the tempo. If the management wanted a first-class bass who would simply follow the conductor's beat, he said, they could find one for £40 a night; there was no need to hire a Chaliapin at £400.

Adelina Patti, immortalized as 'Sweet Adeline' in the popular song, was another who set great stock by high wages. Patti demanded cash payment in full before her foot would touch boards. The hapless Colonel Mapleson, touring America with her in the 1880s, found himself one night with only £800 of the £1,000 that was her due. Her agent refused to accept a lower payment and cancelled the contract for the entire tour. While Mapleson was consoling himself that he had at least saved the £800, the agent returned. Patti, he said, was too fond of the impresario to break the engagement. If the £800 was handed over she would dress in preparation for an appearance that night; but she must have the rest before she went on.

Mapleson gave him what cash he had and the agent returned a short while later for more.

By this time an extra sum of £160 had come in. I handed it to my benevolent friend, and begged him to carry it without delay to the obliging prima donna, who, having received £960, might, I thought, be induced to complete her toilette pending the arrival of the £40 balance.

Nor was I altogether wrong in my hopeful anticipations. With a beaming face he came back and communicated to me the joyful intelligence that Mdme Patti had got one shoe on. 'Send her the £40,' he added, 'and she will put on the other.' Ultimately the other shoe was got on; but not until the last £40 had been paid. Then Mdme Patti, her face radiant with benignant smiles, went on to the stage.

After deducting Patti's fees and his other expenses, the impresario calculated that he was left with a profit of £5 or £6, about half of one per cent of what he paid the singer. The tour went on to Washington, with *Semiramide*, in which a penny-pinching opera lover calculated that Patti was being paid 42.63 cents per night for every note she sang — 7.1 cents per note more than Rossini earned for composing the opera.

The Washington performance was delayed for one night by another principal point of contention with singers: a sudden and inexplicable sickness of the throat. Patti, to her credit, both moral and pecuniary, was not a capricious or frequent canceller. Chaliapin, on the other hand, six foot four inches of virile health, broke the hearts and banks of a succession of managers with his spontaneous withdrawals. As proof of his desperate condition, he would whip out a laryngoscope and don the dying look of the great tragedian that he was. Sometimes he let himself be cajoled out of his recalcitrance. Once, he was terrorized out of it.

In my room I was suddenly confronted by a long, bony lady wearing spectacles, with frowning eyebrows, and a turned-down mouth. Pointing her finger at me, she said something in English. I gathered she wanted to know if I was Chaliapin and I replied in the affirmative, apologizing in my best Russian for appearing in a dressing-gown. With eloquent gestures she then bade me to lie down on the bed. I did so, and to my horror saw her removing instruments from her doctor's bag.

She ordered me to go to bed, and then to my further alarm I saw that I was to have a colonic *lavage*. This scared me and I yelled for the valet, who spoke French. He explained that the lady was a doctor who would cure me within twenty-four hours. I asked him to convey my respects to her, but that I was not requiring her services. In spite of this she insisted that I should go to bed. The instrument for *lavage* hung in the air; I pleaded with her to go away.

'I will sing. I will sing! Just go away. Please.' And she went. The scene made me laugh, and in fact calmed me down a little. Although that night I was feeling exhausted, I sang well.

More drastic treatment still was required to induce Pasquale Brignoli, a splendid Italian tenor on tour in the Americas, to fulfil his obligations to the opera-loving public of Havana, in 1857. Smitten with a sudden sickness, he was attended by a Spanish military doctor.

After having felt Brignoli's pulse, looked into his throat and examined his eyes, the doctor most solemnly declared, with a serious shake of his head, 'really some precursory symptoms' of yellow fever, but that by employing 200 leeches immediately on the shoulders of the patient the great evil may be averted.

'Mama mia!' screamed Brignoli, with his clear, beautiful, tenor voice, reaching with ease on that occasion the high B, '200 leeches. You are a fool, but not a doctor! I am perfectly well.'

'No, hijo mio,' replied the doctor, 'you are sick and cannot sing tonight.'

'Clear out,' vociferated Brignoli, 'I will show you whether and how I can sing this evening.'

And he did sing better than ever.

Colonel Mapleson had a casebook of strategies for dealing with hypochondriacs. He would humour them, cajole them, plead with them, connive against them, even spy on them. Tipped off that a malingering soprano had just ordered lobsters and roast duck for dinner, he charged into her rooms behind the waiter like an avenging angel and commanded her to eat, digest, dress and sing.

When his principal tenor Antonio Giuglini, to recover from an alleged ailment, took to the invigorating sea air of Brighton 'accompanied by a certain notorious lady', the impresario replaced him with an inferior substitute and prompted a tame journalist to praise the surrogate. Armed with the relevant newspaper, he travelled to Brighton to assure

Giuglini that he could now enjoy a prolonged rest. The tenor caught the next connection back to London.

In the very last resort, the armed forces might be called out to tackle recalcitrant singers. When a married singing duo named Gassier called off a concert in Cuba, claiming to have caught a cold but planning to go for a jaunt in the countryside, their manager turned to his friends in high places.

It may have been despotic, and certainly ungallant, but Mme and M. Gassier were arrested on the road by mounted soldiers and driven to the theatre where they were delivered to the police, who actually brought them on the stage. But, alas! there is a homely proverb which says: 'You can drive a horse to the water, but cannot make him drink,' and so you may take a hoarse singer to the stage, but cannot make him sing.

The orchestra struck up the introduction to the Gassiers' duet and the audience listened with bated breath, but no sound came from the singers apart from some sobs from the lady and a chuckle from her partner. The entire government of Cuba glared down at them from their boxes, but not a note emerged. The singers were fined $100 each, a tidy sum in 1857, but they made their point.

A hundred and one years later, almost to the day, Maria Callas, the most controversial singer in living memory, confronted the Italian government with comparable obduracy. After a triumphant first act in Bellini's *Norma* at the Rome Opera House, watched by President Gronchi and the Italian Cabinet, Callas refused to reappear after the interval. Nothing would induce her to continue; she had lost her voice, she said. The audience waited forty-five minutes, amid a torrent of whistles and cat-calls, then trooped unhappily home. Domestic casualties were heavy as spouses returned from the opera unexpectedly early to find guests in the marital bed. The President's chauffeur lost his job; instead of waiting all evening outside the opera house, he had been entertaining himself miles away when his master descended early.

The scandal dominated the front pages of all Italian newspapers, and many abroad. *The Times* reported:

Most people seem agreed that something unique in the history of Italian opera happened with the refusal of a soprano, appearing in the presence of the Head of State, to continue singing. Mme Callas has spent the day in her hotel being visited by doctors. Her husband claims they are agreed that she is suffering from inflammation of the vocal chords and bronchial complications.

Signore Latini, the new superintendent of the Opera . . . called for 'serene understanding' from the citizens of Rome.

His own serenity was shaken when he learned that Callas had made a late night appearance on television the night before her première. The government promised an official inquiry; three questions were asked in Parliament; there was talk of stripping Callas of a title she had lately received from the President, possibly also of some wealth. Callas, it was reported, condescended some days later to write a letter of apology to Signor Gronchi.

If the actions, or inaction, of a single singer could provoke political controversy, the rivalry between two could divide a nation. England in the 1720s was split into opposing camps by the contrasting attractions of two Italian leading ladies. It was a sideshow that engaged the principal political and social figures of the day and so diverted attention from the music they were supposed to sing that its composer, George Frideric Handel, went bankrupt.

Handel had been responsible for engaging both divas, though they sang for other composers as well. The dulcet-toned Francesca Cuzzoni arrived first, preceded by a reputation for glorious singing and inveterate mischief-making. To pre-empt trouble, the composer issued a premonitory warning: 'Madame, I am well aware that you are a veritable devil; but you must understand that I, I am Beelzebub, King of the devils.' Undaunted by this introduction, Cuzzoni refused to sing the air which Handel had written as her opening song. The composer seized her by the waist, carried her to the window and suspended her out of it until she started singing.

She was, without exaggeration, a veritable devil. A singularly ugly woman, she later married Sandoni, a London composer and harpsichord maker, but poisoned him on their return to Venice. The courts took an unusually harsh view of the matter and sentenced Cuzzoni to death. She was reprieved, imprisoned, released and banished. She tried singing in Germany, but her vocal chords had ossified and her success was limited. She returned to England where Handel, for old times' sake, gave her a part in *Messiah*. But she was soon back in trouble. In 1750, Horace Walpole wrote: 'Another celebrated Polly has been arrested for £30, even the old Cuzzoni. The Prince of Wales bailed her out — who will do the same for him?' Cuzzoni left London again and died destitute in Bologna.

She had reigned supreme in London for three years when Handel engaged Faustina Bordoni Hasse to sing beside her, probably with a view to deflating his troublesome star. Faustina was beautiful, sweet-natured, highly intelligent and as splendid a soprano as Cuzzoni: they could scarcely have been better matched as adversaries.

The two ladies first sang together — amicably and without incident — in *Alessandro* on 5 May 1726. By the morning of 6 May, there were few neutrals. Cuzzoni's faithfuls rallied behind Lady Pembroke, while a new party formed to support Faustina under Dorothy, Lady Burlington. The sopranos entered into the spirit of the conflict, tearing each other's hair out on one public occasion. However, they were contractually bound to sing together and England buzzed with anticipation whenever they appeared on the same stage. The last performance of the 1727 season was, according to the *London Journal*, the liveliest.

A great disturbance happened at the opera, occasioned by the partisans of the two celebrated rival ladies, Cuzzoni and Faustina. The contention at first was only carried on by hissing on one side, and clapping on the

Senesino and Cuzzoni

other; but proceeded, at length, to the melodious use of cat-calls, and other accompaniments, which manifested the zeal and politeness of that illustrious assembly. The Princess Caroline, Princess of Wales, was there, but neither her Royal Highness's presence, nor the laws of decorum, could restrain the glorious ardour of the combatants.

Genuine opera lovers who were caught up among the partisans were severely perplexed by the conflict of choice, but the satirists made the most of the situation:

> At Leicester Fields I give my vote
> For the fine-piped Cuzzoni;
> At Burlington's I change my note,
>   Faustina for my money.
> Atilio's music I despise,
> For none can please like Handel,
> But the disputes which hence arise,
>   I wish and hope may end well.

A one-act farce called *Rival Queans* was staged in the West End parodying the rivalry and morals of the singers and imputing that Handel was taking bribes from both:

Faustina lays flat Cuzzoni's nose with a sceptre, Cuzzoni breaks her head with a gilt leather crown: Handel, desirous to see the end of the battle, animates them with a kettle drum: a globe thrown at random hits the High Priest on the temples: he staggers off.

When Handel's company was forced into liquidation in the following year, its end was hastened by the phenomenal success of John Gay's *The Beggar's Opera*, which capitalized on the popularity of the queens' quarrel by staging fights between its sprightly heroines, Lucy and Polly. The fickle public, roused by the triumph of an English opera, poured scorn on its favourites of yesteryear:

> There's Madame Faustina Catso
> And the Madame Catsoni
> Likewise Signor Senesino
> Are tutti abandoni.
>
> Ha, ha, ha, ha! Do, re, mi, fa
> Are now but farce and folly
> We're ravished all with toll, loll, loll
> And pretty, pretty Polly!

While such passions of rivalry were unseemly to an English public, in Italy, where the great singers were nurtured, they were the very essence of opera. Rossini learned the ways of divas literally at his mother's knee. When he was ten years old, his mother, an opera singer, was summoned to Trieste to alternate in an opera part with Giuseppina Grassini, a local courtesan who was reputed to have consorted with Napoleon. Trieste formed into parties behind the two sopranos: traditionalists favoured Grassini, while younger opera-goers supported Madame Rossini. One night, hearing murmurs of discontent in the audience during her best aria, Grassini fell into a swoon and could not be revived to take further part in the performance. Her followers swore revenge on her rival. When Rossini's mother next appeared in the role, she was greeted by protracted whistling. Taking a leaf from her competitor's book, she promptly fainted. But the Grassinists were shamed into silence a moment later when her small son rushed onto the stage to help her, looking up now and then to glare a tearful reproach at his mother's tormentors.

Patti, too, received early training from her mother. That lady, a performer of variable distinction, discovering that another soprano had shaved her eyebrows and replaced them with fashionable falsies, proceeded to stare fixedly at her rival's right eye. 'What's the matter?' whispered the other vocalist at a moment when neither was singing. 'Your right eyebrow has fallen off,' hissed Patti's mother. The woman immediately stripped off her left eyebrow supposedly to conform, and sang the rest of the opera with only one eyebrow, to the increasing amusement of the audience.

Dame Nellie Melba, Australia's finest export, was another who would countenance no rivals, particularly once her voice declined with age. At Covent Garden she was the only diva in its history to have exclusive use of a dressing-room, from which not even Sir Thomas Beecham managed to dislodge her. Defeated by an obduracy that exceeded his own, Sir Thomas preserved for Melba a savagely equivocal eulogy. She was, he said, 'a singer who had nearly all the attributes inseparable from great artistry.'

Singing in *La Bohème* with a young Austrian, Fritzi Scheff, Melba bided her jealousy for the one point in Puccini's opera where her rival had to stretch to reach a high B natural. As Scheff summoned her vocal resources to defy glottal gravity, the celestial note to which she aspired was emitted loud and clear from the wings. Melba had helped out. When the curtain fell, the interval was unusually prolonged. The manager emerged pale and dishevelled, with the announcement that the opera could not continue 'owing to Madame Scheff's sudden indisposition'. Madame Melba, however, had kindly agreed to sing the mad scene from *Lucia* instead. The manager had spent the previous half hour physically

The young Melba

restraining Mmes Melba and Scheff from scratching each other's eyes out.

Melba also engaged the stately English contralto, Dame Clara Butt, in the splatter of a mud-slinging war when, on the eve of Butt's tour to her native Australia, she counselled: 'Sing 'em muck; it's all they can understand.' Discovering her advice to be disingenuous, Butt turned the tables on Melba by disclosing to outraged Australian journalists the nature and origin of the tip she had received. The 'sing 'em muck' slur still tarnishes Melba's reputation in her homeland, half a century after her death.

While few of her fellow divas dared challenge the Australian's supremacy, the peerless Italian tenor Enrico Caruso was under no such inhibition. A natural prankster, he resented Melba's high and mighty ways:

Never shall I forget one night at Monte Carlo, before an immense audience 'thick' with Grand Dukes and Princesses and Marchesas, how I was suddenly startled in the middle of the death scene by a strange squeaking noise which seemed to come from Caruso as he bent over me. I went on singing, but I could not help wondering at the time if Caruso was ill, for his face was drawn and solemn, and every time he bent down there was this same extraordinary noise of squeaking. And then with a gulp which almost made me forget my part, I realized that he had a little rubber toy in his hand, which at the most pathetic phrases he was pressing in my ear. You know how difficult it is to stop laughing when you are supposed to be solemn; but when you are supposed to be dying the temptation is almost too much to be borne.

In another production of *La Bohème*, Caruso, while singing 'Your tiny hand is frozen' one night, slipped a thin, hot sausage into Melba's palm. When she dropped it in horror he whispered, 'Whassa matter? Engleesh lady no lika da sausage?'

While prima donnas fought each other for supremacy, their male counterparts took up arms in defence of their vocal tribe. Though sopranos and altos happily co-exist, no love is lost between the tenor and the baritone or bass, who are regularly called upon in opera to fight each other for a lady's favour. The giant Chaliapin, for example, could not abide tenors. Finding himself in Gounod's *Faust* faced by a particularly tiny tenor who barely reached his chest, Chaliapin picked the little fellow up bodily in the Garden Scene and stood him on a bench so that Faust could be seen to face Mephistopheles on level terms. Such seeming equality, though, could not be tolerated for long. Minutes later, he pulled Faust down from his perch and dragged the terrified tenor squeaking around the stage until his exit line set him free.

Never was Chaliapin more affronted than when it was reported that his nose had been broken in rehearsal by a tenor. The incident occurred during a run-through of *Boris Godunov* while Chaliapin was demonstrating too realistically how violent the mad Tsar had become in the opera. It was not Chaliapin, he cabled furiously to American newspapers, whose nose was broken. If it had been, he declared, the news would have been overtaken by the announcement of a tenor's funeral.

Chaliapin's pride was reflected at the upper end of the scale by Mapleson's tenor Ravelli, who detested baritones. Rehearsing an ephemeral opera, *The Renegade*, he was mortally offended to discover that it committed a monstrous social injustice.

In the second act the tenor and baritone fight a duel. In this there was no novelty. But instead of the tenor killing the baritone, the baritone puts the tenor to death, and this struck Signor Ravelli as far too new. He appealed to operatic traditions and asked in an excited manner whether such a thing was heard of before. 'No!' he exclaimed, answering with vigour his own question; and he added that though he was quite ready to take part in the duel, he would do so on condition that not he but his antagonist should be slain. It was useless to explain to him that in the story upon which the opera was based the character represented by the tenor perished, while the baritone lived on. This, he said, was just what he complained of. 'Why,' he indignantly demanded, 'should the tenor's part in the opera be thus cut short?'

It was impossible to get the infatuated man to hear reason. He cried, screamed, uttered oaths, and at one time threatened to kill with his dagger, not only his natural enemy, the baritone, but everyone around him. 'I will kill them all!' he shrieked. After a time, by humouring him and agreeing with him that in a well-ordered operatic duel the tenor ought, of course, to kill the baritone, I at last contrived to make him understand that there were exceptions to all rules. It was settled then that Ravelli was to be killed. But what, he wished to know, was to be done with his body after death? The proper thing would be, he said, for six attendants to enter, raise the corpse, and carry it solemnly away to a place of repose.

The script, however, called for the dead tenor to lie prone on stage for ten minutes while the bereaved soprano bewailed his passing. This was altogether too much for Ravelli. He could not agree to lie in an undignified position with some woman bawling over him, while a homicidal baritone gloated. Either he was given a funeral with full tenorial honours, he proclaimed, or he would not sing, let alone die. To save the production, Mapleson acquiesced to his demand during rehearsals, in which Ravelli was ceremoniously borne from the stage by undertakers within moments of his passing.

On the night of performance Ravelli was left recumbent on the stage. He must have thought more than once, as he lay writhing with shame and anger on the boards, of rising and rushing off. But he feared too much the laughter and derision of the public, and he had to remain passive while the orchestral introduction was being played, and while the prima donna's soliloquy was being sung. Many of us thought the strain would be too much for him, and that he would go raving mad. But when he found himself once more a free agent behind the scenes he stabbed no one, struck no one, and, strange to say, seemed perfectly quiet. The humiliation to which he had been subjected had somehow calmed him down.

Melba was another who would not die easily. When forced to expire, she insisted on dying in comfort. She had special mattresses and cushions put into her stage coffins and, rather than swooning fatally to the boards, would climb gracefully into her place of last repose, to sing and regally be sung her eulogies.

If singers' conflicts do not end with death, they have on occasion begun before birth. Ructions erupted at the Royal Opera House, Madrid, on 10 February 1843, when the heroine failed to appear for the third act of Bellini's *Norma*. During the interval, she had entered the second stage of labour and, while the audience raged, was preparing to give birth — attended by her tenor husband — to a baby girl, whom they named Adelina Patti. If opera lovers were disappointed that night, there was generous compensation in store for them when the involuntary cause of disruption emitted her first musical cries some years later.

When temperaments were aroused as much by sexual frictions as by professional jealousies, the consequences could be more violent still. The scandal generated by Adelina Patti's second marriage pursued the couple on and off stage halfway across Europe. She and the tenor Ernesto Nicolini were married to their first partners when they began a romance and eventually married. The original Signora Nicolini, however, left with five bambini, refused to come to terms with her loss and followed the lovers from venue to venue, creating scenes wherever she could gather an audience. She finally cornered Ernesto in Italy where she engaged several of her relatives to throw him down a flight of stairs.

Less comically, the German soprano Gertrud Bindernagel was shot dead in 1932 at the Charlottenburg Opera House in Berlin (where she had sung Brünnhilde in Wagner's *Siegfried*) by her husband, maddened by rumours of her infidelity. A similar fate befell the Bulgarian tenor Trajan Grozavescu, who was shot dead by his neglected wife at a Vienna railway station in 1927, just as he was leaving to make a glittering début in Berlin.

A suspicious spouse, according to Wagner, was responsible for wrecking the première of his second opera, appropriately if wishfully entitled *The Ban on Love* (*Das Liebesverbot*), and based on Shakespeare's *Measure for Measure*.

I was still hoping for an increase in the audience, when suddenly the most incredible commotion occurred behind the scenes. Herr Pollert, the husband of my prima donna (who was acting Isabella), was assaulting Schreiber, the second tenor, a very young and handsome man taking the part of Claudio and against whom the injured husband had for some time been nursing a secret rancour born of jealousy. It appeared that the singer's husband, who had surveyed the theatre from behind the drop-scene with me, had decided that the longed-for hour was at hand when, without injuring the operatic enterprise, he could wreak vengeance on his wife's lover. Claudio was so severely used by him that the unfortunate fellow had to seek refuge in the dressing-room, his face covered with blood. Isabella was told of this, and rushed despairingly to her raging spouse, only to be so soundly cuffed by him that she went into convulsions. The confusion that ensued amongst the company soon knew no bounds: they took sides in the quarrel, and little was wanting for it to turn into a general fight.

Though the fiasco brought a summary end to Wagner's career as conductor and composer in Magdeburg, it taught him no lessons. Before leaving the town, he married an actress, Minna Planer, whose infidelities exercised his emotions greatly in their years together.

A reputation for sexual rapaciousness and mayhem attaches itself, often unjustly, to many singers. It could well stem from the extra-ordinarily combative amours of the very first prima donna in France, Mademoiselle de Maupin. 'She was equally fond of both sexes, fought and loved like a man, and resisted and fell like a woman,' gossips the English musical historian Charles Burney with ill-concealed delight. La Maupin married young, but soon ran away

with a fencing-master, of whom she learned the small-sword, and became an excellent fencer, which was afterwards a useful qualification. The lovers first retreated from persecution to Marseilles; but necessity soon obliged them to solicit employment there, at the opera; and, as both had by nature good voices, they were received without difficulty. But soon after this she was seized with a passion for a young person of her own sex, whom she seduced, but the object of her whimsical affection being pursued by her friends and taken, was thrown into a convent at Avignon, where the Maupin soon followed her; and having presented herself as a novice, obtained admission. Some time after, she set fire to the convent, and, availing herself of the confusion she had occasioned, carried off her favourite. But being pursued and taken, she was condemned to the flames for contumacy; a sentence, however, which was not executed, as the young Marseillaise was found, and restored to her friends.

She then went to Paris, and made her first appearance on the opera stage in 1695, when she performed the part of Pallas, in *Cadmus*, with the greatest success.

Content with this satisfactory launch to her career, she looked around for further conflict.

Dumeni, the singer, having affronted her, she put on men's cloaths, watched for him in the Place des Victoires, and insisted on his drawing his sword and fighting her, which he refusing, she caned him and took from him his watch and snuff-box. Next day Dumeni having boasted at the opera-house, that he had defended himself against three men who attempted to rob him, she related the whole story, and produced his watch and snuff-box in proof of her having caned him for his cowardice. Thevenard was nearly treated in the same manner, and had no other way of escaping her chastisement, than by publicly asking her pardon, after hiding himself at the Palais Royal during three weeks.

At a ball given by Monsieur, the brother of Louis XIV, she again put on men's cloaths, and having behaved impertinently to a lady, three of her friends, supposing the Maupin to be a man, called her out. She might easily have avoided the combat by discovering her sex, but she instantly drew, and killed them all three. Afterwards, returning very cooly to the ball, she told the story to Monsieur, who obtained her pardon. After other adventures, she went to Brussels, and there became the mistress of the Elector of Bavaria.

After which, she did little more of musical interest. Suddenly remembering that she had discarded a husband in Provence, she returned to him and spent her last years 'in a very pious manner' in his embrace, dying young but fulfilled at thirty-four.

La Maupin's record for riotous conduct has often been challenged by her successors but never, so far as can be ascertained, matched. It was she who established for all time that the private life of the prima donna was to be inseparable from her public role and was itself to be a legitimate cause of musical conflict.

The statuesque soprano Luisa Tetrazzini carried her example into our own century. Tetrazzini would alarm her managers with the alacrity with which she changed partners and the storms her dalliances created. Her American impresario Sol Hurok would be summoned to Detroit one day to defuse a romantic situation between the lady and her pianist, only to find when he arrived that it was now the 'cellist who was at the heart of the trouble. She died at the age of sixty-eight, tranquil, single and poor, having squandered the five million dollars she earned on a succession of expensive consorts.

Tetrazzini was reckless in her choice of husbands and had little pleasure from her spouses, but she took evident delight in devising an operatic ending for one of her marriages.

Imagine a gala night at the end of a brilliant opera season. Many floral tributes were taken to the apartment of the leading star, who was giving a supper party. In the course of the evening she succeeded in encouraging her husband, the conductor, to drink until he was so overcome that he fell asleep. Whereupon she and her lover, a handsome

Tetrazinni by Caruso

basso, laid him stretched out on the floor, surrounded him with masses of flowers, and, like La Tosca after bumping off Scarpia, placed a lighted candle at each end of him and a crucifix on his breast. They then eloped together.

To Tetrazzini, as to many of music's combatants, it was opera, more than any other medium, that offered the ideal setting for conflict.

CHAPTER FIVE

STAGED BATTLES

A composer's formula for operatic peace:

> Before he actually starts writing the music, the composer should call on all female singers in the company and offer to include anything they might care to have, such as arias without bass in the accompaniment, with the violins accompanying in unison, etc.

In opera, all is illusion. What might appear to be a prudent tip to a young composer about to encounter his first troublesome singers is in reality a subtle blow aimed by one composer at another. The Venetian composer Benedetto Marcello, author of this advice, resented the way in which Antonio Vivaldi managed to mass-produce new operas (he wrote forty-four and staged them in relative tranquillity). His vexation was intensified by the grievances borne against Vivaldi by a singer, Rosanna Scalfi, with whom Marcello was infatuated. Between them they concocted this savagely entertaining satire on operatic manners:

> The composer should lend his services to the impresario for very little, mindful of the thousands of *scudi* that must be paid to famous singers. He should content himself with less pay than the least of them, though he should not bow to the injustice of receiving less than the theatre bear, or the stage auxiliaries.

The lot of the composer and conductor in opera, it would seem, is not an easy one. He is faced with a larger and more multifarious assembly of musicians and auxiliaries than in any other musical medium, as well as with a dramatic theme which lends its own exaggerations to any passions that may be stirred. The opera, to its creator and director, is a minefield in which he can tread only too easily on the exposed sensibilities of fellow-composers, musicians in the orchestra, members of the chorus, scene-shifters, dressing-room attendants and, first and foremost, his singers.

Few had the temerity of Handel to seize a belle by the haunches and swing her from a window, although Thomas Arne, composer of *Rule Britannia* and much that is less memorable, could be equally forthright.

> When one night Mrs Clive having undertaken a song in which she was out of time as well as tune; at a hitch, she calls out aloud to the band, 'Why don't the fellows mind what they are about?' At the end of the act Arne went up stairs in the name of the whole band to remonstrate against her insolence, when the only satisfaction he obtained, was a

slap on the face. In return, he literally turned her over his knee and gave her such a manual flagellation as she probably had not received since she quitted the nursery; but as a proof that she had made a good defence, he came back without his wig, all over blood from her scratches, & his long point ruffles torn & dangling over his nails.

Gustav Mahler was another who took a mauling from his singers who, when they could not provoke him musically, taunted the chaste, intense young conductor with their sexuality. A singer in Laibach (now Ljubljana), whom he reproved for loose morals, responded by jumping onto his piano and slapping her bare thighs at him. Another, in Vienna, came to rehearsal with her dress slit on both sides up to her waist. A Hamburg soprano, whose advances he resisted, started a rumour that he was homosexual; others spread the story that he seduced young girls. He had to contend with trouble from male singers as well. In Budapest, two baritones challenged him to a duel after he ordered them to stop inserting improper innuendos in their dialogue. Mahler averted a fight by persuading a friendly newspaper to ridicule the mutinous singers.

Handel himself would sometimes prefer farce to force. When a singer in a tantrum threatened to jump on the composer's harpsichord and smash it to bits, he responded disarmingly: 'Let me know when you will do that and I will advertise it. For I am sure more people will come to see you jump than to hear you sing.'

The use of wit to deflate singers inflated by operatic pretensions was perfected by Sir Thomas Beecham who, like Handel, allowed his enthusiasm for opera to propel him into bankruptcy. When a wayward soprano, unable to keep pace with the life-and-death developments in Massenet's *Don Quixote*, complained that she was left stranded by Chaliapin dying too soon, Sir Thomas crushed her with a drawled: 'Madam, you are gravely in error. No operatic artist has ever died too soon.' Saddled with an Italian tenor who persisted in extending unnaturally the last note but one in his farewell in Wagner's *Lohengrin*, Beecham one night pulled out his watch, turned to the audience and conspicuously timed the singer. The last note never sounded, its predecessor catching in a startled throat. The singer resigned next day on discovering, on a crowded railway platform, that pinned to the back of his coat was a large placard announcing, 'I AM A TENOR'.

The method favoured by Arturo Toscanini for keeping singers in order was to throw tantrums wilder than any they could match. The Italian maestro terrorized a clutch of opera companies into obedient excellence and inspired fear in men and women twice his modest size. He would flail about, scream and rant, punctuating musical directions with epithets from the gutters of his native Parma.

Toscanini's rage was his hallmark, seemingly a force beyond his

Sir Thomas Beecham

control. When a corpulent and complacent tenor asked the conductor if he wanted *Lucia di Lammermoor* sung in the old way or the new, Toscanini screamed: 'I know only one *Lucia*. The one written by Donizetti,' and abandoned the production rather than stage it with a singer of questionable dedication. His replacement by an inferior conductor caused a riot in the theatre in Bergamo during the opera, when supporters and opponents of Toscanini lifted out rows of seats and hurled them at each other.

During a performance of *Otello* a small bomb went off backstage, causing fright and damage but no injuries. Toscanini, with great presence of mind, struck up the National Anthem to restore order among the panic-stricken audience. The culprit was never found, but suspicion fell on several artists whom the conductor had insulted and dismissed.

Toscanini's extra-mural relations with singers were another cause of operatic conflict. One of his romances had an outcome so prominent that it succeeded in wrecking an opera in which he was not even involved. In fact, he was half a world away at the time. In 1904, he had stormed out of La Scala, Milan, in mid-performance after sections of the audience barracked him for refusing to allow an aria to be encored. Still bleeding from cuts caused by charging through a window in his rage, he left next day to conduct in Buenos Aires. His sudden departure meant that he missed the première at La Scala of the much-awaited new work by Italy's greatest living opera composer. Toscanini had seen the new score and pronounced it too long and unwieldy. Others had reservations about the plot, which dealt with a tragic liaison between an American naval lieutenant and a Japanese geisha girl, a far-flung departure from the normal count-meets-girl theme of Italian librettos. However, it was based on a popular Broadway play and the composer's reputation was such that success seemed guaranteed. Preparations went wonderfully, the whole orchestra rising to cheer the composer at the end of the dress rehearsal and he, so excited by their enthusiasm, abandoned caution and invited his entire extended family to the première.

The performance, though, was a disaster from the overture onwards. Rival composers had planted disrupters in the audience who were soon aided by conservative opera-goers who found the Oriental plot too exotic. In the best Italian tradition, they submitted each new tune to instant analysis: 'Ah, that is from *Bohème*! Boo, that is from *Tosca*!', demonstrating to the distraught Giacomo Puccini how familiar they were with his work.

Worse was to come in the second act. As *Madam Butterfly*, played by Rosina Storchio, sang one of her loveliest arias, a slight breeze made her kimono billow out in front of her. 'She's pregnant!' a disgruntled opera-goer called out. Others in the audience digested this revelation, drew the inevitable conclusion and began to shout, 'Il bambino di Toscanini!', showering the absent conductor with ironic congratulations. Storchio, poor girl, collapsed in hysterics.

Puccini withdrew the opera after that single performance. When he staged a revised version away from Milan, to tumultuous acclaim, Storchio was no longer available for the leading role. She had joined Toscanini to sing the Argentine première of *Butterfly* under her lover's baton. Puccini wrote to her in farewell: 'And so my butterfly, the lovesick little maiden, would leave me . . .'

Puccini's enemies, however, would not go away. One of the few comic moments in the première had come when Pietro Mascagni, composer of *Cavalleria Rusticana*, jumped on stage and appealed to the audience

Puccini by Caruso

with tears running down his cheeks to give the work a fair hearing. 'No one,' observed Giulio Gatti-Casazza, manager of La Scala, 'was moved by this great grief.'

Opera has given composers their most fertile field of conflict with one another. Puccini's rivals had been practising sabotage on his premières for some years. When *Tosca* was about to be staged in Rome in 1900, they picked on the engagement of a stage designer from La Scala, calling

82

it a slur on Roman competence. Flames of civic pride were fanned as the day of the première approached and several singers received anonymous threats of violence. A senior police officer visited the conductor in his dressing-room just before the performance to advise him how to proceed if a bomb was thrown (Toscanini's conduct was by now enshrined in police rules: he was told to conduct the National Anthem). The conductor, a timid man who had seen people killed in one audience by an anarchist's bomb, ventured upon his task with trepidation. At the first sound of a disturbance, he ordered the curtain down and dashed backstage to safety. The opera was resumed peacefully only when the noise he had heard was proved to his satisfaction to have been the arrival of a party of latecomers.

The contest between composers had been even keener when they had to fight one another for royal approval. Capricious courtiers would often promote antagonism between composers, much as they would between cockerels, and it was not always the better musician who won. In Vienna in 1786, however, the Royal prerogative for once made the right musical choice, discarding the claims of two opera composers, Rigini and Salieri, in favour of those of a genius, Mozart.

The contest raised much discord, and parties were formed. The characters of the three men were all very different. Mozart was as touchy as gun-powder, and swore he would put the score of his opera into the fire if it was not produced first; his claim was backed by a strong party: on the contrary, Rigini was working like a mole in the dark to get precedence. The third candidate was Maestro di Cappella to the court, a clever shrewd man, possessed of what Bacon called, crooked wisdom; and his claims were backed by three of the principal performers.

Every one of the opera company took part in the contest. I alone was a stickler for Mozart, and naturally enough, for he had a claim on my warmest wishes, from my adoration of his powerful genius, and the debt of gratitude I owed him, for many personal favours.

The mighty contest was put an end to by His Majesty issuing a mandate for Mozart's *Marriage of Figaro*, to be instantly put into rehearsal; and none more than Michael O'Kelly, enjoyed the little great man's triumph over his rivals.

Kelly, an English singer, was rewarded for his loyalty with two parts in the première of *Figaro* and a place in musical history. The opera, however, received only nine performances and Salieri's star was soon in the ascendant again with both monarchy and audiences. He alone recognized Mozart's superior talent and campaigned tirelessly to prevent his rival achieving another such victory. When Mozart died, young and suddenly, it was natural that suspicion should fall on Salieri.

Audiences were as fallible as royalty in judging the merits of rival opera composers. Offered a choice in the 1720s between the inspired Italian operas of George Frideric Handel and the competent ones of Giovanni Battista Bononcini, sung by the same performers, the London public could not tell gold from glitter.

> Some say, compared to Bononcini,
> That Mein Herr Handel's but a ninny; [ran a popular rhyme]
> Others aver that to him Handel
> Is scarcely fit to hold a candle.
> Strange all this difference should be
> 'Twixt Tweedledum and Tweedledee.

Only when the Italian fled home in disgrace (having been caught in an act of plagiarism) did genius gain recognition.

Handel's relations with other composers were not eased by having to perform their works. As a young man, Handel had collaborated quite peaceably with another itinerant opera composer, Johann Mattheson, while travelling together across northern Germany. Until one December night in Hamburg, in 1704, when Handel was playing the harpsichord in *Cleopatra*, an opera by Mattheson:

> I as composer directed the performance and also sang the part of Antony, who has to die a good half-hour before the end of the opera. I had been accustomed after finishing my part to go into the orchestra and accompany the remaining scenes, and this is a thing which incontestably the composer can do better than any one else. However, on this occasion Handel refused to give up his place. On this account we were incited by some who were present to engage in a duel in the open market-place, after the performance was over, before a crowd of spectators — a piece of folly which might have turned out disastrously for both of us, had not my blade splintered by God's grace upon a broad metal button on Handel's coat.

A younger compatriot, Christoph Willibald von Gluck ('He knows no more of counterpoint than my cook,' sniffed Handel), unwilling to compete with Handel in London, decided to seek his fortune in Paris by launching an attack on the Italian operas which had dominated French music for a century. 'It is all very fine, but it doesn't draw blood,' he declared and offered more meaty Teutonic fare, sung in French. Paris, having sampled his wares, arranged to pit the newcomer against the best exponent of the Italian style, a composer of some 130 operas, Niccolò Piccinni.

This admirable composer, the delight and pride of Naples as Gluck (was) of Vienna, had no sooner erected his standard in France than all the friends of Italian Music, of Rousseau's doctrines, enlisted at his service. A furious war broke out, all Paris was on the *Qui vive?* No door was opened to a visitor without this question being asked previous to his admission: *Monsieur, êtes vous Picciniste ou Gluckiste?*

wrote Burney, disapprovingly, for the dispute 'seems to me to have soured and diminished the pleasure arising from Music'.

So far as the French were concerned, however, the conflict *was* the pleasure. Both composers were invited to write an opera in French on Euripides's fable of *Iphigenia in Tauris*, each having been assured that his would be produced first. Piccinni laboured under the distinct disadvantage of knowing no more French than was necessary to order a cab to the Opera. He had completed two acts when he learned that Gluck's opera was finished and already in rehearsal. Piccinni's pleas for his unfinished opera fell on deaf ears. He had no choice but to retreat to Naples, a sadder and wiser composer.

One reason that the French were so attached to Italian opera was that its composers provided constant fodder for salon gossip. Few, though, outdid the scandalous exploits of one of the earliest musical immigrants, Giovanni Battista Lulli, who entered the service of Louis XIV in 1653, promptly changing his name to Jean-Baptiste Lully. He quickly established himself as the Sun King's favourite composer, but his private pastimes ensured that his position was never secure. A compulsive homosexual, Lully was forced to conceal his penchant from his prudish King, but rival composers would diligently keep the monarch informed of the latest pecadilloes of the royal minstrel. To counter their whispering, Lully married an attractive and well-born girl and, when the effectiveness of that ruse waned, took an equally attractive mistress of high repute. To no great avail, however. One of his page boys was arrested and confessed to the pleasures he and his fellows enjoyed with Lully. The composer prudently stayed away from court until the ensuing graffiti on the walls of Paris faded. Louis liked his music too much to banish Lully forever, but his exclusive tenure was eventually contested by other composers.

National passions served only to inflame operatic conflicts between composers. As the pendulum swung from French to Italian musical domination and back, there erupted in Paris in 1752 what became known as the *Guerre des Bouffons*, the war of the comedians — a pamphleteering battle between proponents of the two national styles of music. As one of the few musical conflicts which has been accorded military nomenclature (though it produced no casualties), it deserves some attention.

It began with a row over an insipid opera by a lately deceased Frenchman, André-Cardinal Destouches. The opera's paucity resulted in an invitation from disaffected music lovers to a troupe of Italian *bouffons*, who delighted at least half the town, including the Queen, with a comic opera by Pergolesi. The King, however, together with Madame de Pompadour and the nobility, staunchly defended the virtues of traditional French opera.

Innumerable pamphlets were written on both sides, and among the rest, the celebrated *Lettre sur la Musique Française*, by Rousseau. There was too much good sense, taste, and reason in this letter for it to be read with indifference; it was abused, but never answered. The author was burnt in effigy at the Opera-house door.

The philosopher, Jean-Jacques Rousseau, had actually written a serious theoretical analysis of the two schools of music, abandoning scholastic impartiality only in the final paragraph:

I think I have shown that there is neither measure nor melody in French music, because the language is not capable of them; that French singing is a continual squalling, insupportable to the unprejudiced ear . . . From this I conclude that the French have no music and cannot have any; or that if they ever have, it will be much the worse for them.

Perhaps in that warning he foresaw the disorders that would arise from the works of Berlioz, Debussy, Satie and Les Six. Nevertheless, Rousseau's cosmopolitanism could not prevail over French chauvinism and the Italians and their music were driven out. For a while.

Once they have applauded a foreign-born composer's works, as they did Gluck's, the French are only too happy to claim him as their own. Giacomo Meyerbeer, son of a Berlin banker, experienced little resistance and became, together with the Frenchman, Jacques Fromental Halévy, the most popular French opera composer of the post-Napoleonic period. They were both to be eclipsed by Jacques Offenbach, originator of the quintessentially French can-can, whose thick German accent did not prevent him from earning the title of 'the Mozart of the Champs Elysées'.

Yet one foreign operatic genius was never made welcome in Paris. Richard Wagner spent three years in the French capital in dire poverty, failing to get any of his works performed although using the time to compose his first mature operas, *Rienzi* and *The Flying Dutchman*. Two decades later in 1860, while banned in Germany because of his revilutionary activities, he returned to Paris to conduct three concerts. In the following year he allowed Paris to stage his *Tannhäuser*, but the opera fell into the hands of a weak conductor, a recalcitrant tenor and an obese Venus. If these were not sufficient to ensure disaster, the production coincided with an outbreak of anti-German feeling which centred on hostility to the influence of Princess Metternich, Wagner's sponsor at the court of Napoleon III. Wagner tried to ingratiate himself by allowing the opera to be sung in French, and even inserted a ballet in Act Two to satisfy the local convention, but it did him little good.

The Emperor Louis Napoleon and the Empress Eugénie were present on the first night, and the opera was received in cold, significant silence.

On the second night the audience, from the second act onward, made a great row, fighting among themselves and disturbing the singers.

On the third night there was a terrific noise, and no member of the audience could hear a note of the music. The one success of the opera was the appearance of the sporting dogs, which the Emperor had specially lent from the royal kennels.

The page who had to lead the dogs on the stage towards the end of the first act told me recently that the audience cheered them and called them before the curtain, shouting, 'Bravo les chiens!' 'Bis les chiens! on vous rappelle!'

Neither the dogs, nor Wagner, returned. He left France in a fury, blaming his failures on the 'bastard nature' of French taste, which spurned him for two other Germans, Jews at that, Meyerbeer and Offenbach. When the latter's work was preferred to his *Tristan and Isolde* in Vienna in 1863 (thanks to a crafty manoeuvre by Hanslick), Wagner's venom knew no bounds. 'Offenbach,' he declared, 'possesses the warmth that Daniel Auber lacks; but it is the warmth of the dungheap. All Europe is wallowing in it.'

A personal duel between Offenbach and Wagner ensued, Offenbach jabbing with razor-sharp jibes, Wagner parrying with blunt and heavy insults. An unverified story has it that Wagner sent his rival a copy of his offensive *Judaism in Music*. Offenbach returned it with the comment that he should stick to writing music. When Wagner sent him the score of *The Mastersingers*, Offenbach responded that he should stick to essay-writing.

Offenbach sprinkled his operettas liberally with parodies on Wagnerian themes which Paris audiences recognized and roared at. Wagner hated them and the composer all the more. In 1871, while Paris starved under siege, Wagner anonymously published a satirical play on the French

87

defeat by the Prussian armies. In it Wagner singled out Offenbach for derision as a fiddler who played while Paris burned:

> Crack! Crack! Crack-crack-crack
> Oh the splendid Jack von Offenback!

A Capitulation, as he called it, was in such infantile bad taste that no theatre, even in victorious Berlin, would touch it. He brought forth another sample of ponderous vulgarity when Vienna's Ring Theatre caught fire during a performance of Offenbach's *Tales of Hoffman*, causing the death of 384 members of the audience:

> When coal miners are buried alive, I am filled with disgust at a society which obtains its heating fuel in such a manner. But I am scarcely moved when members of a crowd perish while listening to an Offenbach operetta, which contains not one iota of moral worth.

Forty years after *Tannhäuser*, a French composer, while adopting Wagner's use of lush orchestrations to sustain dramatic action, tried to avoid sensationalism by toning down the more lurid scenes of love, hate and murder in his opera. But *Pelleas and Melisande* was dogged by scandal nonetheless. While Claude Debussy was putting the finishing touches to his score, he was introduced to a striking young Scots singer. He heard Mary Garden sing only a few bars to recognize her as Melisande, overlooking the fact that he had already promised the part to an established singer, Georgette Leblanc, who also happened to be the established paramour of his librettist, Maurice Maeterlinck.

Debussy was actually rehearsing Leblanc as Melisande when Maeterlinck read in a newspaper that he had engaged Garden. Incensed at the rejection of his mistress, the librettist tried to obtain a court order to stop the opera. Denied legal redress, he seized his cane and announced that he would 'give Debussy a drubbing'. Leblanc clung, she says, to his coat-tails and begged him to desist, but the impassioned lover leapt through a first-floor window and made for Debussy's home. According to Maeterlinck, Debussy, on seeing him at the door, promptly fainted. He was slowly restored with smelling salts, while the avenging poet, impotently waving his stick, was pushed aside by the ministering womenfolk.

He turned for sympathy to the Press, declaring in *Le Figaro* two weeks before the première:

> *Pelleas* has become an enemy alien to me. Banished from any control

over my work, I am compelled to hope that its failure will be resounding and prompt.

Newspapers and readers relished the mounting sensation, heaping fictitious incidents on true and avidly taking sides behind each of the protagonists. The first round of the contest, the public dress rehearsal, went convincingly to Debussy's opponents. Conservatives were perplexed by the intricate score and one old gentleman demanded in mid-performance to know when the orchestra would finish tuning up. A fake opera programme was sold in the street outside and spoof verses from it were chanted by sections of the audience. Mary Garden sang beautifully, but her accent grated on Parisian sensitivities and the Aberdonian inflexion of such momentous declarations as, 'Oh, je ne suis pas heureuse!', almost brought the roof down.

But at the première she and Debussy were triumphant. The composer had arranged that enough of his supporters, known as the Pelléastres, were given tickets. Garden won instant stardom; Leblanc lapsed into obscurity. Debussy's reputation was assured; Maeterlinck's, though he won the Nobel Prize for Literature, declined, and he never produced another work of the calibre of *Pelleas*.

Deprived of further discord between the collaborators, the newspapers turned on the delicate fabric of *Pelleas*'s score with a venom reserved for the truly original. 'The public is tired of hearing music which is not music,' one writer declared, somewhat confusingly. He attacked Debussy as a 'musical anarchist'; others accused him of 'a crazy pursuit of novelty'. An American critic complained that some of the effects in the strings had given him 'an involuntary start, as when the dentist touches the nerve of a sensitive tooth'.

Across the border in Germany, Richard Strauss observed the uproar with keen interest. Having shocked the musical world by scattering unresolved discords throughout his tone poems ('I employ cacophony to outrage people,' he boasted to Gustav Mahler), he now sought to scandalize it with an opera whose narrative would offend the strictest taboos. A French play provided his libretto, an adaptation of a New Testament passage by a cynical English dramatist, who had recently died after enduring imprisonment for homosexuality. Oscar Wilde's lurid treatment of *Salome*, redolent with sacrilege, eroticism and overt necrophilia, was set by Strauss to sensationally sensual music. Its *Dance of the Seven Veils* was more daring than the gyrations permitted at the most risqué Paris cabaret, the rapacious kiss bestowed by Salome on the mouth of the beheaded John the Baptist was beyond anything censors had dared to imagine. Dumbfounded, they let it remain.

Premièred at Dresden in 1905, *Salome* was declared obscene by a legion of Christian countries, the British and Austro-Hungarian Empires

Richard Strauss in Salome

righteously at their head. It enjoyed an extraordinary success in Germany and two years later reached the United States, where its première provoked the headline: 4000 SURVIVE THE MOST APPALLING TRAGEDY EVER SHOWN ON THE MIMIC STAGE.

Among the most appalled was a doctor, who wrote to the *New York Times*:

> I am a man of middle life who has devoted upwards of twenty years to the practice of a profession that necessitates a daily intimacy with degenerates. I say after deliberation that *Salome* is a detailed and explicit exposition of the most horrible, disgusting, revolting and unmentionable features of degeneracy that I have ever heard, read of, or imagined.

Next day, the paper published a rebuttal from another reader:

> I know a lady in Germany who has heard *Salome* 27 times and she likes it very much. It never did her any harm.

New York audiences were not exposed to further risk. After a single performance, the directors of the Metropolitan pronounced *Salome* 'objectionable and detrimental to the best interests of the Opera House' and took it off.

Not until 1910 was London allowed to see something of *Salome* and then only after Sir Thomas Beecham had personally pleaded its case with the Prime Minister, Herbert Asquith. Even so, Wilde's script had to be savagely rewritten to appease the Lord Chamberlain, overlord of the English stage. The names of several characters were changed to conceal their biblical eminence and the severed head of John the Baptist was outlawed altogether. The English Salome sang to an empty salver and blew her kiss to a phantom.

The Covent Garden première was purity itself until Salome forgot her new lines and began slipping into the foul original. Other singers followed suit. Beecham whipped up his orchestra into a frenzy to drown them, but many corrupting stanzas were audible above the din. Seeing the Lord Chamberlain descending upon him after the last curtain call, Beecham expected to be dragged off to the Tower. When all he heard was a murmur of congratulation, the conductor sardonically reproached his singers for not having made themselves sufficiently distinct. The editor of *Punch* found the evening so entertaining that he clamoured for another opera 'in which Messrs Strauss and Censor shall have again collaborated'.

Strauss attained his objective of shocking audiences with *Salome*, but the powers of propriety were still strong enough to restrict those he could reach. After the suppression of his next opera, *Elektra*, whose Sophoclean theme of incest offended a more abiding bourgeois sensibility than anything in *Salome*, Strauss was forced to return to safer ground. But when his comic opera *Der Rosenkavalier* promised to be his greatest success in 1910, Strauss tried to make it a condition of its performance that opera houses should also undertake regular productions of *Salome* and *Elektra*. To his disappointment even the Dresden Opera, which had given the world première of both without demur, refused to be committed to further performances.

It was another eight years before *Salome* was admitted to the city that considered itself as the fount of modern opera. When it arrived there on 14 October 1918, the old order was crumbling and the last vestige of the Holy Roman Empire hovered on the brink of military defeat. *Salome* became the siren of a new era. A month after its première, the Empire collapsed. Strauss, by way of coincidence or reward, was appointed the first Director of the Vienna Opera under the Republic.

Once the dust had settled and the troops came home to their truncated country, Strauss was heard to remark that, whatever the régime or political situation, there would never be peace at the Opera. He had been confronted on arrival with a rebellion by the veteran singers, who got up a petition demanding that he agree to impossible terms or resign. He was to spend five turbulent and memorable years putting the Vienna Opera back on its feet.

Meanwhile, as soon as international armistices were signed and the curtain rose again, the Vienna claques reassembled for combat. The claques were as inseparable from opera as the singers who paid for their applause. Invented at the Paris Opera (*claquer*: to applaud for money), the idea spread to every large opera house. As well as lending encouragement to a particular singer, they were often hired to hiss his or her rival. Paris prided itself on the variety of claqueurs it could offer: there were *chauffeurs*, who would warm up the surrounding audience before the overture; *commissaires*, who intervened in conversations in the interval; *pleureurs*, who would weep when appropriate; and *bisseurs* who demanded encores. Vienna offered its clients musical specialization: there were claqueurs for Wagner, others who were expert in Mozart, others still who knew every suitable point for acclamation in Verdi. Whatever their individual finesse, their task was to orchestrate the reception of an opera, much as the conductor sought to co-ordinate its delivery.

Between the wars, the main Vienna claque was run by one Joseph Schostal, at times the most powerful man in the Opera House. The singers who were his clients were often his friends and he had been known to lend them money during rough periods in their careers. He imposed rigid discipline on his claqueurs, who were so conscious of the privilege of belonging to the principal claque that they would accept no payment and some would even pay the full price for their tickets. Standing in the gallery, they were opposed — sometimes physically — by a secondary claque, supporting lesser singers, led by a certain Otto Stieglitz.

Several conductors sought to ban the claques but none succeeded. When Clemens Krauss pronounced their abolition in the 1930s, it was widely rumoured that he continued to finance both principal claques out of his own pocket, for fear he would be received on the podium by complete silence. Only the Nazis, whose thugs took over the organization of operatic disruption by more brutal means, ultimately subdued the Vienna claques.

One of the strongest claques flourished at the Metropolitan Opera in New York, founded originally by the valet of an unappreciated Italian tenor. Subsequent singers who did not wish to hire its support found they had to pay the claque leader anyway to avoid barracking. Where more than one claque was engaged, the issue would have to be fought out in the pit, and often in the street outside, by the hired partisans. At one famous première at La Scala, Maria Callas was heckled and whistled by an opposing claque. Her supporters soon resisted, the police were called and two of the opposition were arrested. Callas triumphed again.

There was an additional element of unreliability about Italian claques, in a land where operatic appreciation is priced above gold. When a singer failed to give musical satisfaction, claque leaders were known to return their payment in the interval and conduct their forces against their presumptuous patron. Michael Kelly, Mozart's Irish tenor, relates that a singer called Poggi, arriving for his Rome début, secured the assurance of a distinguished Abbé that he would organize clerical acclaim in the audience. In return, Poggi fed, clothed and gave large sums of money to the co-operative priest. At the concert, the Abbé's voice was heard at the top of the chorus of *bravissimi* after the first song. But when Poggi's voice cracked in the second number, mutterings of disapproval were heard. When the third song proved even worse, the Abbé got up on his chair and exclaimed to loud cheers: 'Signor Poggi, I am the mouth of truth and thus declare that you are decidedly the worst singer that ever appeared in Rome! I also declare that you ought to be hooted off the stage for your impudence in imposing on my simple and credulous nature as you have done.'

Roman opera audiences, descendants of the mobs at the Coliseum, were notably alert to any attempt to impose on their simple and credulous natures. No musician, no matter how favoured or famous, was allowed to escape with a sound or gesture that implied pretension. Rossini, at the première of his *Barber of Seville* in 1815, found himself at the mercy of an audience which took instant exception to the brand new hazel-coloured jacket he was wearing, complete with bright gold buttons. Hoots of derision greeted this sartorial extravagance as its wearer sat himself at the harpsichord to direct the performance. The noise doubled in volume when the first singer made his sprightly entrance, tripped over a trap-door, fell head over heels, scratched his face and very nearly broke his nose. Blood flowed, and was loudly cheered. Every time the singer sang, he bled; every time he bled, the crowd roared. In the middle of the finale, a cat from the nearby Coliseum meandered onto the stage. Chased by Figaro, it jumped for safety into the ample bosom of a soprano who, fearing scratches, wriggled and leapt about to dislodge it. The audience, rising to a new star, egged the cat on with encouraging miaows and words of advice. It was subdued only at the point of an unsheathed sword as the opera stumbled to a confused close.

Rossini had barely managed to thank his singers before the audience set upon him physically, pelting the flamboyant jacket as its wearer fled. Pummelled and prone to self-pity, Rossini considered himself one of opera's most tragic victims and blamed maltreatment by audiences for his premature retirement. However, compared with other victims of the opera, he got off lightly.

The heightened passion of operatic drama, the extravagant artefacts used as props, the mass of musical and ancillary forces engaged, all conspire to make opera the most hazardous of musical occupations. It is no exaggeration that singers frequently take their lives into their throats simply by going on stage. The announcement of Melba's 1893 début at La Scala, for example, aroused such jealousy among the resident Italian divas and their followers that the young Australian received sacks full of poison-pen letters, threatening ingenious and painful retribution if she dared sing at La Scala. She became so alarmed that she refused to leave her hotel room or to touch food in case it was poisoned. Only the determination of her secretary persuaded her to emerge for one of the great triumphs of her life. With her first-night conquest of La Scala in *Lucia*, the threats ceased.

In Chicago, Melba narrowly avoided being shot at during a performance. A gunman dashed onto the stage during Gounod's *Romeo and Juliet* and pointed a revolver at the Polish tenor Jean de Reszke, but was overpowered by stage hands before he could shoot. Melba is said to have panicked and rushed around backstage screaming, somewhat improbably, that her voice was gone. De Reszke was unmoved and continued singing up at Juliet's window until she was calm enough to reappear.

Patti was almost murdered in San Francisco. As she returned for a curtain call, an anarchist threw a bomb on stage, which fortunately failed to explode. The would-be assassin departed in handcuffs explaining that he had intended to kill a banker sitting in a stage box, but would not have minded blowing up the singer because, 'she makes too much money, as well'.

On another occasion, when she was a young girl, a messenger left a pair of gloves at her house, with a note asking her to accept them, as the sender wished to call them the 'Patti gloves'. Her father thought they had a suspicious appearance and smell, so he took them to a chemist, who analysed them and found they had been steeped in a most deadly poison.

When only sixteen she was almost incinerated when the sleeve of her dress caught fire in the footlights. With remarkable presence of mind, Patti ripped the burning sleeve off at the shoulder and resumed her aria at the next downbeat.

Fire was a perpetual hazard in nineteenth-century opera. The French singer Emma Livry was fatally burned when her costume caught fire during the rehearsal of an Auber opera. On a Wagner evening in Budapest, Mahler watched his prompter's box shoot up in flames. To avert panic, he carried on conducting until the fire brigade arrived.

One of Mahler's singers, whose vanity exceeded his instinct for self-preservation, was permanently crippled by a steel safety curtain which descended on him when he outstayed his applause. The pride of a Viennese soprano, Marie Wilt, was so wounded by jokes about her broadening girth that she was driven to suicide by auto-defenstration. Most tragic of all was the death, at only twenty-eight, of Maria Malibran, a Spanish mezzo-contralto. Malibran simply burned herself out. She sang too often, attended too many balls and was too fond of energetic exercise. Thrown off her horse in Hyde Park, she concealed her concussion and sang that night at Covent Garden. After a short holiday, she went up to sing at the Manchester Festival in 1836, beset by piercing headaches and now also pregnant. Malibran was wildly applauded, but so was a rival singer for an aria which she ended on a long high B flat. Malibran, exhausted, insisted on returning to sing the same aria. 'If I sing again,' she told the conductor, 'it will kill me. But I must go on and annihilate her.' She did, but the exertion of the final note sent her into convulsions and she fell shrieking to the ground. Doctors were called but no treatment could be given without the approval of her husband, a Belgian violinist, Charles de Beriot, who was on stage playing a solo.

Ignoring urgent signals to come off, he stayed to play an encore. If his tardiness did not kill her, the eventual treatment did: she was bled with leeches and died two days later. So dramatic was her end that it formed the subject of an opera.

Singers were not the only performers to suffer the vicissitudes of opera. The fate of the animals — an ox, an elephant, several horses and a monkey — engaged for a balletic extravaganza by Luigi Manzotti, *Amor*, that La Scala saw fit to stage, is almost too awful to contemplate. The elephant, named Papus, gave trouble from the outset. When no vehicle was found large enough to convey him from the railway station to the Opera House, his trainer, after waiting for nightfall, put him on a leash and walked him through the Milan streets. On meeting his first omnibus, the beast panicked and charged into a ground floor flat where a caretaker and his family were having supper. The *carabinieri* arrived. Papus raised his trunk, the policemen cocked their pistols. Tragedy was averted only when the trainer convinced the cops that Papus was an artist at La Scala and consequently prone to pardonable outbursts of temperament.

At the dress rehearsal, Papus took exception to the chorus of warriors, priests and vestal virgins amassed for the 'great choreographic poem'. He charged, they fled. Some did not emerge from beneath the scenery until the next morning.

The ballet-opera *Amor* was a great success with the public until the night Pirri, the monkey, broke his chains and scampered into the audience. Unable to find a seat in the packed house, he scrambled from one row to the next, causing ever-greater havoc. The manager, Giulio Gatti-Casazza, called for a gun. By the time it arrived, the monkey had been subdued and the show closed down by the authorities. Elephant and ape were condemned to life in a travelling circus and the horses were sold at auction. But the saddest victim of the débâcle was the innocent ox. A few days after the closure, the following advertisement appeared round the corner from La Scala in a butcher's window:

MEAT OF THE FAMOUS OX OF THE BALLET *AMOR* SOLD HERE.

Any association with opera, however peripheral, entailed an element of risk. When Professors Eduard van der Nüll and August Siccard von Siccardsburg, two of the most esteemed architects in the Austro-Hungarian Empire, won the tender in 1860 to build the Vienna Opera House, they could not have foreseen that it would cost them their lives. The Opera was erected remarkably rapidly, in eight years (the modern Sydney Opera House took twice as long), but was bedevilled throughout by musical and political intrigues. The integrity of the architects was impugned and their musical disinterest loudly bewailed by operatic cliques. Everyone found something to condemn in their scheme. The building was almost sunk, literally, at the last moment by a malicious plot at the Ministry of Works to raise the level of the street outside by three feet. In August 1868, nine months before the opening, van der Null shot himself. Siccardsburg, his friend since childhood, had a heart attack on hearing the news and died two months later.

The Vienna Opera thus had blood on its conscience before it opened. Later, it drove its most inspired director, Gustav Mahler, to a premature death from a coronary condition exacerbated by operatic dissensions (he suffered at least one heart attack on the podium during rehearsal). Another director, Franz Ritter von Jauner, put a gun to his head in a moment of accumulated frustrations; a third, Karl Heinrich Strohm, appointed by the Nazis, went pitiably insane.

The construction of Richard Wagner's edifice at Bayreuth was similarly marred by publicized fatalities among its workmen and stagehands. By the time it was begun in 1872, Wagner's operas were alleged, not only by his enemies, to be the most hazardous in the entire repertoire. Their dangers were seen to be two-fold: the extraordinary contraptions that Wagner required to create his explicit visual effects on stage and the tremendous demands his music made on singers. Every death, and there were several, was greeted by his opponents as proof of Wagner's inherent malignity. Learning of a fatality in the orchestra during the first Bayreuth Festival, Johannes Brahms remarked drily, 'Ah, the first corpse.'

It was on his singers that morbid attention was most closely focused. Concern was expressed when Wagner's favourite tenor, Ludwig Schnorr von Carolsfeld, died of heart failure at the age of twenty-nine, shortly after creating the role of Tristan. Indiscreet as ever, Wagner wrote: 'For me he lived, for me he died.' The alarm spread when the soprano, Hedwig Reicher-Kindermann, died while touring as Brünnhilde; she was only thirty. Further ammunition was provided by the Viennese bass Emil Scaria, who went quite mad while singing in *Siegfried* and wandered around the stage muttering to his fellow-singers, 'What opera is this we are doing?'

Singing Wagner was deemed by many to be hazardous to the voice. Countless fine voices, it was said, had been ruined and vocalists were warned — not least by the composer himself — to approach his operatic roles with care. Irritated by the restrictions placed on his creativity by physical limitations of larynx and thorax, Wagner flirted briefly with artificial means to obtain the vocal effects he desired. While composing his last opera, *Parsifal*, he contemplated assigning the role of Klingsor to a male soprano, one whose boyish voice had been preserved into manhood by pre-pubescent castration. He was particularly impressed by one of the last such surviving castrati, Domenico Mustafa, a Roman relic of the most barbarous of musical practices. Had Wagner not relented, he might yet stand accused of perpetuating an ancient atrocity against the most sensitive of musical parts.

CHAPTER SIX

HOLY WAR

*G*ioacchino Rossini in luxurious retirement, fat, frivolous yet sometimes seeming restlessly unfulfilled, would gather friends and acolytes around him of an evening to reminisce about the trials and triumphs of his brief and brilliant career as a composer and conductor. His French circle of intimates would be plied with good food and drink and regaled with tales weird and wondrous from the Mediterranean cradle of opera, where the jealous lover, the secret marriage, the bartered bride and don juans (or giovannis) of all shapes and sizes were as common in everyday life as on the stage. Rossini had himself partaken vigorously of the fruits of passion and, as the spirit level in his decanters sunk lower in the candlelight, would spare no blushes by recounting encounters which substantiated operatic legends.

His Milanese admirer abandoned her splendid palace, her husband, her children, and her fortune, and early one morning plunged, as if from the clouds, into the little chamber of his lodging, which was any thing but elegant. The first moments were all tenderness, but scarce had the transports of their meeting subsided, when the door opened, and in rushed one of the most celebrated and most beautiful women of Bologna, (the Princess C . . .). A scene ensued which the comic pencil of Gay has already anticipated in the Beggar's Opera. The reckless Rossini laughed at the rival queens; sung them one of his own *buffa* songs; and then made his escape, leaving them gazing on each other in dumb amazement.

One evening, the composer confessed that he had come close in childhood to being permanently excluded from such scenes through qualifying as a castrato, a musical eunuch who paid the price of his virility to retain a soprano voice. 'Would you believe,' Rossini remarked with evident self-satisfaction, 'that I came within a hair's breadth of belonging to that famous corporation, or should I say, decorporation? As a child, I had a lovely voice and used it to earn a few *paoli* by singing in churches. One of my uncles, a barber by trade, convinced my father that there was a future income for us all — since most castrati lived in opulence — if my voice was not allowed to break. My brave mother would not consent at any price.'

'And you, Maestro?' chorused his tantalized friends. 'How did you feel about it?' 'I was quite proud of my voice' said Rossini blandly, '. . . as for my descendants . . .' 'Little you cared,' interjected the caustic Madame

Rossini in retirement

Rossini the second. 'Little,' her husband contemplated, 'no, that is too much. I didn't care at all.'

Such indifference to posterity was not shared by numberless thousands who were forced to undergo what Burney called, 'the inhuman practice of mutilating children in order to keep the voice in its adolescent state.' No one knows where or when the ugly operation was first performed for musical purposes although eunuchs had been provided since ancient times to stand guard over the chastity of noble ladies. The only certainty is that the introduction of castrati into music was a direct consequence of Church intervention, the result of a literal mediaeval interpretation of four words of St Paul (*mulier taceat in ecclesia*) which held that women were not to be allowed to sing in church.

Since the soprano voice was in great demand for masses and oratorios, an alternative and artificial source was required. Women having also been generally banned from the stage for their supposed lewdness (Shakespeare, for example, was forced to use men to play his female roles, occasioning pederastic ribaldry), a further niche opened for castrati in the theatrical art of opera. As demand for the services of castrati grew, so did their supply, and as more became available more operatic parts were composed for them. Many became wealthy international stars. To impoverished southern European families, overburdened with children, the castration of one or two sons offered a faint hope of financial salvation. Although no new operatic role was written for a castrato after 1829, boys continued to be emasculated for music in Italy and elsewhere until late in the last century.

While the church consistently condemned castration and promised excommunication to its practitioners, for some two hundred years every major church in Italy, including the chapels in the Vatican, employed castrati. The Vatican still had castrati in its chapel choir in 1902, when the first gramophone recording was made there. One of its engineers was dumbfounded when, after a short circuit in his equipment caused fire to break out, he was bowled over by a rush of portly gentlemen heading for the exit, all shrieking in the tones of schoolboys.

Castrati were created by three predominant methods. The first involved placing the child in a warm bath into which certain plant extracts had been poured and crushing his testes with the fingers to stunt their growth. Another method was to sever the vein that nourished the gonads. The third course was surgical castration whereby, having again put the boy into a warm bath, 'they pressed the Jugular Veins, which made the Party so stupid and insensible that he fell into a kind of Apoplexy and then the Action could be performed with scarce any Pain at all to the Patient.'

Many victims of these operations emerged — if they survived at all — doubly stricken, for the mutilation was often in vain. The boy would find himself robbed not only of his virility but, when his voice broke despite all, of any anticipated prospects of a musical career. Or he might become so fat that he would be laughed off the opera stage and be condemned to seek a meagre living singing in a provincial church.

Contrary to popular misconception, though, the sexual drive and capability of castrati were usually unimpaired. Carrying as they did a guarantee of contraception, many proved irresistible to women and enjoyed richly licentious lives. But the Church denied them its blessing if they sought to marry, or, contrarily, to enter the priesthood: for those sacred purposes they were not considered to be whole men. The more enterprising found brides in Protestant countries, where a man's credentials were not so scrupulously examined. One castrato, Giusto

102

Ferdinando Tenducci, became the talk of all Ireland in 1765 when he eloped with a girl from Limerick and married her in an Anglican ceremony at Cork. Her family, members of the landed gentry, were outraged and set out in pursuit of the couple, kidnapping the bride and imprisoning the despondent groom. Tenducci's friends raised bail and helped him stage a concert in Cork, but his irate in-laws disrupted the performance and he was forced to flee the town before morning. Captured again and thrown back in jail, he almost died of fever before his father-in-law relented. To the bride's further delight, her husband's situation turned out to be less clear-cut than it had appeared and she gave birth, amid general astonishment, to two fine children. Tenducci became director of the prestigious Handel Festivals at Westminster Abbey and lived in connubial bliss in London for more than twenty years.

Other castrati grew into quite lovely androgynous creatures, exciting the admiration of as discriminating a connoisseur as Giacomo Casanova:

> . . . the *castrato* who took the prima donna's role . . . in a well-made corset, had the waist of a nymph and, what was almost incredible, his breast was in no way inferior, in either form or beauty, to any woman's . . . you were madly in love before you realised it. To resist the temptation, or not to feel it, one would have had to be cold and earthbound as a German.

The French writer Montesquieu was similarly enraptured by

> . . . the most beautiful creatures I ever saw, who would have inspired the tastes of Gomorrah in people whose taste is least depraved in that respect. One young Englishman, believing that one of them was a woman, fell madly in love and was kept in that passion for more than a month.

Under the same misapprehension, the French sculptor Sarassin pursued a castrato so assiduously with his amorous attentions that a Cardinal, who was the singer's lover, had him assassinated. It was not, in short, for their voices alone that the castrati were sought after.

Whatever his sexual accomplishments, however, the castrato's real pride lay in his musical instrument. This was frequently shown off in singing contests. On one famous occasion in Rome in 1722, the outstanding castrato Carlo Broschi, better known as Farinelli, pitted his voice against the tone of a trumpet in the hands and mouth of one of the country's most accomplished players:

> After severally swelling out a note, in which each manifested the power of his lungs, and tried to rival the other in brilliancy and force,

they had both a swell and a shake together, by thirds, which was continued so long, while the audience eagerly waited the event, that both seemed to be exhausted; and, in fact, the trumpeter, wholly spent, gave it up, thinking, however, his antagonist as much tired as himself, and that it would be a drawn battle; when Farinelli, with a smile on his countenance, shewing he had only been sporting with him all this time, broke out all at once in the same breath, with fresh vigour, and not only swelled and shook the note, but ran the most rapid and difficult divisions, and was at last silenced only by the acclamations of the audience. From this period may be dated that superiority which he ever maintained over all his contemporaries.

He was brought to London by Handel's adversaries twelve years later and achieved unprecedented success with the nobility. 'One God, one Farinelli!' exclaimed a titled lady in rapture, a remark overheard by Hogarth and immortalized in *The Rake's Progress*. Handel was in despair as one after another of his best singers was publicly vanquished by Farinelli.

His singing entranced even a jealous rival like Senesino, who, when they first appeared together, burst into tears at the conclusion of Farinelli's first song, and, forgetful of all else, ran across the stage and threw himself into Farinelli's arms.

Emotional outbursts such as this were common among the eunuchs, who tended to compensate for the indignities they had suffered by extravagant gestures. Generally, though, their duels were resolved less amicably. Gaetano Majorano, known professionally as Caffarelli, returned to Venice to re-establish his supremacy there after defeat by Farinelli in London. Finding that he was to share an important church celebration with another castrato, Reginelli by name, he began the ceremony by loudly chanting some choice Venetian epithets at his rival. As the procession moved down the aisle he hit the other singer with a small stick he was carrying. Both were grabbed and disarmed by other musicians before Reginelli could respond, but Caffarelli craftily purloined from a player in the orchestra the bow of a double bass. As it descended on his head, Reginelli seized a piece of wood and returned measure for measure, the blows raining indiscriminately on each other and on nobility, priests and monks who struggled to separate the shrieking combatants. The castrati were hauled before the church court and charged with sacrilege. Caffarelli escaped a prison sentence thanks only to the intervention of the Spanish royal family who had engaged him to sing in Madrid.

It appears that Caffarelli was no lackey to royal masters, either. When

Louis XV of France sent him a gold snuff box, the singer told his envoy that he was accustomed to receive finer gifts. 'But His Majesty gives such boxes to Ambassadors,' the embarrassed Frenchman protested. 'Let him then ask the ambassadors to sing,' retorted Caffarelli. He was promptly expelled from France.

The wilful vanity of these unfortunates was renowned. Quadagni, another Venetian, having quarrelled with his impresario, proceeded to wreck a whole season of opera by singing as badly as he could. After five performances that were worse than a dilettante's, he was approached by a deputation of ticketholders who first requested, then commanded, him to do what he had been paid well for. To no avail:

> He howled instead of singing, stood stock still instead of acting. When the opera was finished, and Quadagni was about to get into his gondola, being still in his actor's dress, over which he had thrown a cloak, he was seized by four men in masks, who bandaged his eyes, and hurried him off into a boat. At last he found himself in a poorly furnished but clean room, with a bed in it. Two of the masked men remained with him. Some time after, two others came in, carrying a table, with a good supper on it. The hungry *castrato*, without more ado, sat down to eat, but one of his custodians called out:
>
> 'Hands off, sir! Unless you sing, not a morsel shall you have.'
>
> Quadagni refused. The mask ordered the table to be sent away, and then went off.
>
> This scene was repeated next day. Quadagni remained mute; the table and all the good things were shipped off again. So it went on for two whole days, but on the third day a perfectly irresistible soup was served up, and the fine gentleman, now at starvation-point, could hold out no longer.
>
> 'After all, I would rather sing than starve,' he exclaimed, and prepared to fall to.
>
> 'That is not enough, sir,' said the mask. 'If you do not sing — yes, and sing your *very best* — and *act* into the bargain, away goes the soup out of the door!'
>
> What was to be done? Quadagni submitted, and sang and acted as finely as if he were impelled by pure love of art.
>
> 'Bravo, bravissimo!' exclaimed all the masked critics, and clapped their hands vehemently.

Only after he had eaten his fill did the men in masks reveal their identities, introducing themselves as the chief executioner of Venice and his assistants, assigned by the Senate to the specific mission of taming a castrato.

So chastening was this confrontation, the Austrian composer Karl Ditters von Dittersdorf recorded, that

Quadagni returned home a sadder, wiser man, and from that hour he behaved more decently and modestly, which is saying a good deal for a castrato.

Ultimately, it was the behaviour of castrati rather than abhorrence of their means of creation that brought about their downfall. The eunuchs and their high ways became simply so unmanageable that composers eventually dispensed with their services. Rossini, who so narrowly avoided joining the castrati, was largely responsible for their abolition. Infuriated by the vocal callisthenics performed by a castrato in his second successful opera, *Aureliano in Palmira*, he determined that in future his singers would stick faithfully to the written notes, a discipline inconceivable to the preening eunuchs. Learning that the most progressive individual in Italian opera was boycotting castrati, other composers followed suit. Within a decade, all major composers had eliminated male soprano parts from new operas; the last to do so was Meyerbeer, whose *Crusader in Egypt* of 1824 has the distinction (one of few) of being the swansong of the castrato.

But their attraction has not faded entirely even today. A correspondent's letter in the November 1966 issue of the American monthly magazine *Stereo Review* proposed the revival of castrato singing in order to lend greater authenticity to the revival of Baroque opera.

'I definitely do not advocate force,' wrote this dedicated Californian music lover with all the benevolence of a Neapolitan barber,

> but if a young singer should possess a fine voice which he wishes to preserve, I can sympathize with no reason for discouraging him. Children in general are far more reasonable intelligent beings than most adults want to believe and a gifted child is a thorough pragmatist to whom nothing is more important than his talent.

For those children whose over-protective parents saved them from the knife, the alternative to castration was often dire poverty. Joseph Haydn, son of a simple wheelwright, was taken on as a choirboy at St Stephen's Cathedral in Vienna at the age of eight, displaying both a fine voice and a lively musical mind. The director of the choir school, acting in what he believed to be the best professional interests of his talented but impecunious scholarship pupil, wrote to Haydn senior recommending that his son be gelded for a prosperous singing career. The agrarian elder Haydn, unversed in urban manners, saddled a horse and rode into town. He burst into the choir school calling out, 'Sepperl, does anything hurt? Can you still walk?' and would not be pacified until he had verified his son's intactness.

Haydn sang in the choir until he was sixteen but, as soon as his voice broke, was summarily expelled. He spent the next eight years in extreme poverty, supporting himself by giving lessons and playing occasionally in an orchestra. Eventually, he came to the notice of the aristocratic circle which provided the patronage during most of the remainder of his long and prolific life. He never forgot the pangs of poverty (and remembered in his will the descendants of a lacemaker who lent him money in his time of direst need), but bore no grudge against the Church that had treated him so harshly, writing masses and oratorios with free and happy inspiration.

Unlike Haydn, the greatest of Italian opera composers, Giuseppe Verdi, pursued a lifelong conflict with the ecclesiastical authorities following an incident with an irascible priest when he was only seven years old. Serving as an acolyte in a village church, he was so entranced by the playing of the organ that he failed to hear the priest asking him to pass the holy water. A second request went similarly unheeded. The third was accompanied by a kick which sent the child flying down the altar steps onto the hard stone floor, knocking him insensible. As soon as he came round, the boy stood up and ran out of the church shouting, 'God blast you!'

Iis prayer was answered some dozen years later when lightning struck the church in a nearby village during Vespers, killing four congregants and two priests, one of whom was Verdi's assailant. The composer had meant to attend the fateful service but arrived late; he perceived both in his absence and in the retribution a divine justice.

By then Verdi was involved in further trouble with the clergy. He had lately returned home to Busseto, where the townsfolk who had sponsored his musical studies were keen to have him appointed church organist. The local priests, however, came forward with their own candidate, 'an organist almost below mediocrity but possessing the recommendations of two bishops'. Verdi's rival was appointed on the strength of his credentials and town and chapel went into battle array.

The Philarmonic Society, which loved and esteemed Verdi, whose remarkable merits they had been the first to find out, — this same Society, which for so many years had been in the habit of accompanying the music of the masses and hymns, lost its temper, went to the church, turned everything topsy-turvy, and carried off all the music belonging to it. This, in a district which previously had given to others an example of concord, was the signal of a civil war which lasted several years.

From this discord were engendered outrages, insults, satires, and strife of all kinds, which were the cause of imprisonments, persecutions, and other annoyances.

No sooner did he score his first success in opera, than Verdi became embroiled not only with the Church, but also with its powerful ally, the State. Both authorities took exception to his political views, which favoured the establishment of a free Italy, independent of Austria and the Vatican; both feared equally the demonstrations which tended to erupt when audiences recognized the political allusions with which his plots were peppered. He was subjected to close censorial scrutiny from the moment when Milan opera-goers recognized in the plight of the Hebrew slaves in the Babylon of *Nabucco* their own servitude under Austrian rule and roared out Verdi's choruses with patriotic vigour.

When he submitted *I Lombardi* in the following year, 1842, the Austrian censors went through it with the finest of toothcombs to eradicate any possible focus of political demonstration. Once they had savaged the score, the Archbishop of Milan objected that the opera contained processions, churches, a conversion and a baptism — all of which would be sacrilege in the hands of an unbelieving composer. He demanded the expunction of all scenes with a religious motif, threatening to write to the Emperor himself if he did not obtain satisfaction. Verdi refused to change another word or note. He was summoned to the police, but sent his collaborators instead. The Milanese police chief, fortunately, loved opera more than he did the Archbishop. He proposed a cosmetic change, the substitution of '*Salve Maria*' for '*Ave Maria*', in return for which he would assure the Church that it had nothing to fear. All alterations notwithstanding, the irrepressible Italians still found themes in the opera suitable for a raucous nationalist demonstration.

The political censors demurred again at *Ernani*, but the Church for once did not interfere, perhaps because the incumbent Pope, Pius IX, was flirting with the notion of posing as liberator of Italy. His tentative ambitions became public knowledge and were encouraged by Roman audiences when they found a rallying cry in Verdi's newest production.

Instead of singing '*A Carlo Quinto sia gloria e onor!*' (To Charles V glory and honour), they sang, '*A Pio Nono*' (To Pius IX)

> and naturally tricoloured banners and cockades replaced the Austro-Spanish cockades and banners in the act of the conspiracy. At each performance they had this scene repeated. One night a person in the costume of the National Guard, up in the gallery, with one leg over the balustrade, the piece having been already repeated, kept on shouting, 'Bis! Viva Italia! Viva Pio Nono!' Others joined in chorus, and the curtain rose for the third time. Still the fellow was not satisfied; he continued shouting, so that at last the public lost patience and hissed him. At that, redoubling his noise, and reaching the paroxysm of his patriotic fury, he took off his shako, and threw it into the pit; to his shako succeeded his tunic, then his waistcoat; the occupiers of the pit began to be nervous, fearing that he might throw himself over next;

Giuseppe Verdi

but he did worse than that: he drew his sword and hurled it with such violence, that it embedded itself in the stage, two steps from the footlights, in the midst of general alarm. At this moment an officer made his way to this madman, seized him, not without difficulty, and turned him out of the theatre.

Alarmed by the exuberance of his potential subjects, the Pope recoiled from his adventure and set about strengthening his traditional alliances with the prevailing monarchies. Independence-minded Italians, meanwhile, found themselves an alternative figurehead by adopting the name of their favourite composer as a symbol of their political allegiance. '*Viva VERDI!*' they would cry, exchanging many a wink with fellow-conspirators who understood that the slogan was to be interpreted as, '*Viva Vittorio Emannuele Re D'Italia!*' or 'Long Live Victor Emmanuel, King of Italy!'

The composer, though, was no monarchist. Commissioned in 1858 to write an opera for the royal theatres of Naples, he chose a French drama (previously set to music by Daniel Auber) that recreated the melodramatic events surrounding the assassination in 1792 of King Gustav III of Sweden. Aghast, the Duke in charge of the theatres put it to Verdi that regicide was not the most apt topic for a royal stage in an era of insurrection. When the composer refused to set his music to another libretto, the Duke sued him for two hundred thousand francs. The Neapolitan public rallied to the unassuming musician who, easily recognizable by his black beard and brooding air, could not leave his hotel in the city without being followed by a Pied Piper's trail of slogan-chanting libertarians. The Duke backed down and Verdi was allowed to leave Naples unfined, if also unperformed.

At this point he was approached by a well-known Italian middle-man, who suggested that the composer's old enemy, the Church, might prove more amenable to his opera than the temporal authorities. To emphasize the strength of his ecclesiastical connections, the impresario dropped a few names:

> 'I make the best of my way to Rome. I shall arrange with the censure, with the Cardinal-Governor, with St Peter if necessary. Within a week, my dear *maestro*, you shall have the libretto, with all the *visas* and all the *buono per la scena* possible.'

The Papal censors agreed that the killing of a monarch on a Roman stage, while not to be encouraged, was not altogether as unacceptable as, say, the uncovering of a feminine knee. Nevertheless, they were uneasy about granting dispensation to a murder that was both so recent and so European and insisted that the plot be transplanted elsewhere. *A Masked Ball* (*Un Ballo in Maschera*) duly received its Rome première in the guise of a fictitious attempt on the life of an English Governor of Boston in pre-

Revolutionary America. Subsequent presentations in more liberal climes and times have moved the action to Italy or Sweden, if only because leading singers refused to appear in the unflattering costumes of Puritan America. It was the last opera Verdi was to write for his own country for thirty years, the straw of Church and State interference had finally broken his resolve to contribute to national revival. Although he sat for five years (1860-5) as a deputy in the first Parliament of independent Italy, he composed his next operas for, respectively, St Petersburg, Paris and Cairo.

Disillusioned with the State, the composer began to make his peace with the Church. He married the soprano Giuseppina Strepponi, after living with her in flagrant sin for more than a decade. It is significant that his last composition, shortly after her death, was a religious work, the *Four Sacred Pieces*. His other devotional work, however, the mighty *Requiem*, conceived originally in memory of Rossini but dedicated to the nationalist poet Alessandro Manzoni, was unacceptable to the clergy. It was performed with enormous success in concert halls and opera houses, but was banned for years in many churches which could still not tolerate its complement of female soloists and choirs.

In all their many interventions in music, the ecclesiastical authorities have been most rigorous in the scrutiny to which they subjected music played in church. It might be argued that in this censorship they had some justification, but they often deprived themselves and their congregations of much that was sublime, if not wholly devout. The Council of Trent (1545-63), for example, recommended the exclusion from churches of music containing 'anything impious or lascivious', a resolution open to the most restrictive interpretation. Though the *Motu Proprio* of Pope Pius X in 1903 established a sensible set of principles to determine what music was suitable for church performance, it did not deter conservative clerics in the United States from banning masses and sacred songs by Gounod, Verdi, Cherubini and Rossini. The works of one Rev Carlo Rossini were, by way of contrast, overwhelmingly approved.

The Council of Trent also considered banning all polyphony from the Roman Catholic Church and replacing it with plainsong and chants, as many priests felt that modern sixteenth-century music had become too complicated for the public ear and was tainted by impure folk tunes. A total ban was averted, according to improbable legend, when the would-be reformer Pope Marcellus II, who reigned for a mere three weeks, was overwhelmed by the concise six-part *Missa Papae Marcelli* composed and dedicated to him by Giovanni Pierluigi da Palestrina (a crisis dramatic enough to inspire Hans Pfitzner's opera, *Palestrina*).

Palestrina, putative saviour of church music, was perennially in and out of the Vatican's favour. He was brought to Rome as a young man of twenty-five by Pope Julius III to train singers for the Sistine Chapel, only to be sacked by his successor, Paul IV, because he was found to have a wife. When that lady and her two sons were carried off by an epidemic, the distraught Palestrina contemplated entering the Church and becoming a priest. He was deflected by the rich widow of a fur merchant, who remarried him and set him up handsomely in commerce. By this time his relations with the Church had been further soured by his resignation from one choirmaster's post in protest against the meagre food rations accorded to his choirboys and from another in outrage against the outlawing of two of his masses. Palestrina died rich but uncelebrated, rueing the luck of his good friend Philip Neri, who, for lesser services to church music, was rewarded with no less than a sainthood. Saint Philip it was who, by staging sacred plays in the oratory of his church, invented the *oratorio*. The signal honour of his beatification indicates that there were enough sensitive music lovers in the Church to know a good thing when they heard it.

Sometimes, indeed, they found it so good that they attempted to keep it to themselves. One complex and beautiful *Miserere* in nine parts, composed to the text of Psalm LI by a priest, Gregorio Allegri, was agreed to be so outstandingly uplifting that the Vatican assumed exclusive ownership of the work, allowing it to be performed only within the Sistine Chapel. A thriving trade in pirate versions soon flourished around Christian Europe, but none of the alleged Allegris had the inspiration of the original and frustrated music lovers had to make a pilgrimage to Rome if they wanted to hear the famed Psalm. The Vatican monopoly was not broken, despite numerous attempts, for almost two centuries until a fourteen-year-old, one Wolfgang Amadeus Mozart, was taken by his father to Rome in 1770, heard the *Miserere* performed twice, and wrote out the entire score of interwoven voices from memory. When the Holy Fathers saw his clandestine manuscript, they must have deemed it a miracle.

So great was the attraction of devotional music that one unbelieving Englishman, an immortal poet, sold for five shillings the copyright to a collection of his verses to an unknown singing teacher who approached him with the offer of:

a considerable number of very beautiful Hebrew Melodies of undoubted antiquity, some of which are proved to have been sung by the Hebrews before the destruction of the Temple of Jerusalem. I am most anxious that the Poetry for them should be written by the first Poet of the present age.

Lord Byron, the poet in question, was tempted and fell. He wrote twenty-six poems for Isaac Nathan's Temple tunes, among them such reverential if irreligious stanzas as:

> She walks in beauty like the night
> Of cloudless climes and starry skies;
> And all that's best or dark and bright
> Meet in her aspect and her eyes;
> Thus mellow'd to that tender light
> Which heaven to gaudy day denies.

Having given the poems to Nathan, Byron defended the pretentious composer vigorously against a spate of attacks on his capabilities and on the authenticity of his music. What the priests of the Temple would have made of Nathan's music or Byron's words is neither here nor there, but both poet and composer derived profit, amusement and notoriety from the venture and harmed no one's beliefs.

A surfeit of music could not possibly damage an established faith. It was only when the roles were reversed and an established musician was exposed to an excess of religious zeal that misfortunes could arise. One of the most adored singers of all time, Jenny Lind, the Swedish Nightingale, had her musical career blighted and all but destroyed by the benevolent intervention of a fatherly Anglican prelate. Celebrated throughout Western Europe, she arrived in London in 1847, a serene but bewildered singer of twenty-seven unsullied years. Reports of her musical gifts had been so overwhelmingly laudatory, with *cognoscenti* from Felix Mendelssohn to Hans Christian Andersen vying with each other in their praise of her, that Queen Victoria, Prince Albert and most of the royal family turned out to hear her première in *Robert the Devil*, an opera by another admirer, Giacomo Meyerbeer. So impressive was she that Queen Victoria forgot her dignity for a rare moment and flung her own bouquet at Lind's feet. The aged Duke of Wellington, victor of Waterloo, became her most devoted fan, attending her every performance and calling out from his box when she made her first entrance, 'Good evening, Miss Lind, how are you tonight? All right, I hope?' He would trail behind her at parties and receptions, leaping forward to retrieve a fallen glove or shawl like, in the words of a half-jealous Frederic Chopin, 'an old faithful dog'.

But Lind was made uneasy by over-adulation. Prim by nature, she was revolted by the loose morals of other singers who, in her native Sweden, gave of their favours on a scale that was lavish even by prevailing operatic standards in France and Germany. She also resented the indecency of some of the operas in which she acted and was embarrassed by the frequent immodesty of her stage dress. She was therefore ripe for redemption when, on her first tour of the English provinces in 1850, the reverend Bishop of Norwich, Dr Stanley, proposed that she retire from the stage and devote her God-given gifts to Him who bestowed them by singing in future only for the Church. Lind seized upon his suggestion as her salvation but, upright soul that she was, insisted on fulfilling all her contractual obligations to opera impresarios before she ceased forever to sin.

Magical though her voice remained, her new repertory of sacred music failed to attract large audiences. She was soon forced to introduce operatic arias into her programmes, but would not betray by the flutter of a hand any theatrical emotion while delivering them. Yet she still had enough drawing power to attract the greatest of American showmen, the circus promoter Phineas T. Barnum, otherwise known as the King of Humbug, to engage her for a razzamatazz tour of the United States. His gimmickry and her golden voice combined to produce a phenomenal nationwide Lind hysteria, but subsequent tours were less successful as the Nightingale absolutely refused to sing any opera. Jenny Lind is remembered only as a great singer, her magnificent performances in opera virtually forgotten — and that is probably how she would have wished it. She spent her later life in England, was buried at Malvern and became the first woman to be commemorated in the Poet's Corner of Westminster Abbey, where her plaque, beneath Handel's statue, bears a declaration from his *Messiah*: 'I know that my Redeemer liveth.'

It is at the death, where its patronage and gift of absolution are so powerful, that ecclesiastical involvement in musicians' affairs has shown itself at its most malign. Jenny Lind may have been rewarded by Anglicanism for her purity, Philip Neri by Roman Catholicism for his oratory, but many other musicians equally worthy were humiliated in their last days because of real or imagined acts of unbelief. Antonio Vivaldi, the best-known of composer-priests and probably the most prolific, was driven from his native Venice by intra-church squabbles and died indigent in Vienna. He was given a pauper's funeral and an unmarked grave, the invaluable manuscripts he left behind being hawked for pfennigs in the streets. Not until the middle of the present century was his reputation restored and many of his lost scores excavated from monastic libraries.

Other composers were made to suffer for more provable mortal transgressions. The irredeemably hedonic Jean-Baptiste Lully, dying in prolonged agony from gangrene, agreed to see a confessor to please his devout wife and his concerned king, Louis XIV. They searched far and wide for a cloistered monk who had heard no hint of Lully's debauches and finally lighted on a remote curé who consented unwittingly to hear what must have been one of the most titillating confessions in Church history. He was about to give absolution for these multifarious sins, when it occurred to him to ask if Lully was working on a new opera. Learning that he was, the priest said he could not accept the sincerity of his repentance unless he renounced the sinful theatre altogether and destroyed the new work. Forced to choose between posterity in this world and a place in the next, Lully wavered for a moment, then pointed to a drawer in which the unfinished score of *Achilles and Polyxene* resided. With righteous zeal the priest burned the manuscript, then gave the composer Extreme Unction.

Later, one of the young princes came from Versailles to visit the dying man and was horrified to discover that he had sacrificed good music for the sake of his soul. 'Hush, hush,' the expiring Lully consoled him, 'I have another copy.' While waiting to breathe his last, he called for paper and composed a five-part canon on the words *Il faut mourir, pêcheur, il faut mourir* (something on the lines of 'When you've got to go, you've got to go'). His final deed on earth, however, was an act of genuine piety: calling for his will, he reinserted and forgave his reprobate eldest son whom he had earlier disinherited. Lully may have been no saint, but he was a man of mercy.

The death, in Nice in May 1840, of the uniquely prestidigitatious violinist Niccolò Paganini, lonelier in his last moments than Lully and more obstinately unrepentant, gave his enemies among the priesthood an opportunity for vengeance. Throughout his fifty-six celebrated years, Paganini's unprecedented skills on the violin had so baffled audiences that they devised ever more fanciful explanations of their origin. One of the most prevalent stories was that, having been convicted of murdering a rival violinist, Paganini had spent years in a dungeon perfecting his technique. Another more pernicious slander, and one which gained credence among churchmen who resented the fiddler's open disrespect for their cloth, was that he owed his gifts to the forces of darkness.

A still more ridiculous report tested the credulity of some enthusiasts. I had played the variations entitled 'Le Streghe' (the Witches), and they produced some effect. One individual, who was represented to me as of a sallow complexion, melancholy air, and bright eye, affirmed that he saw nothing surprising in my performance, for he had distinctly seen, while I was playing my variations, the devil at my elbow directing my aim and guiding my bow. My resemblance to him was a proof of my origin. He was clothed in red — had horns on his head — and carried his tail between his legs.

Paganini strove in vain to disprove the libels. He had some success in discrediting the allegations of homicide.

Paganini

I deem it a duty to communicate to you an anecdote, which gave rise to the injurious reports propagated against me. A violinist, of the name of Duranowski, who was at Milan in 1798, connected himself with two persons of disreputable character, and was induced to accompany them to a village, where they purposed assassinating the priest, who was reported to be very rich. Fortunately, the heart of one failed him at the moment of the dreadful deed, and he immediately denounced his accomplices. The gendarmerie soon arrived on the spot, and took Duranowski and his companion prisoners at the moment they arrived at the priest's house. They were condemned to the galleys for twenty years, and thrown into a dungeon; but General Menou, after he became Governor of Milan, restored Duranowski to liberty, after two years' detention. Will you credit it? — upon this groundwork they have constructed my history. It was necessary that the violinist should end in *i*, it was Paganini; the assassination became that of my mistress or my rival; and I it was who was sent to prison, — with this exception, that I was to discover there a new school for the Violin: the irons were not adjudged against me, in order that my arms might be at perfect liberty. Since these reports are persisted in, against all probability, I must necessarily bear them with resignation. One hope remains: it is, that after my death, calumny will abandon its prey, and that those who have so cruelly avenged my triumphs, will leave my ashes at rest.

But they would not leave him be. His death, though reported to have been tranquil, served only to resurrect the supernatural allegations.

At this solemn hour, he seemed desirous to return to Nature all the soft sensations which he was then possessed of; stretching forth his hands towards his enchanted Violin — to the faithful companion of his travels — to the magician which had robbed care of its stings — he sent to heaven, with its last sounds, the last sigh of a life which had been all melody.

When the news reached Nice, crowds gathered to file past the bier. The bells had begun to toll to announce the death of a great man when they were suddenly quelled by order of the Archbishop, who announced that, since Paganini had not confessed before his death, he would be denied burial. While his friends petitioned the Pope for permission to inter the corpse, the Archbishop talked of seizing the body, exorcizing it and throwing it into a torrent. The corpse was moved to a hospital where it was embalmed, then deposited at several temporary addresses to await the judgement of the Church. Two Papal commissions were convened to consider Paganini's worthiness for burial. Witnesses were called to Rome from all over Europe while the body mouldered. An appeal for dispensation to the Archbishop of Genoa, the violinist's birthplace, to which he had bequeathed his beloved Guarneri, was rejected; the Protestants of Genoa also refused to accept his remains. The coffin was removed from Nice one night by boat after complaints that strange noises and music had been heard from within. It was to sail the high seas for months on end.

Not until 1845, five years after he died, were Paganini's remains granted a private burial without religious ceremony by the compassionate Bishop of Parma. Eight years later, a rudimentary service was pronounced over his grave. Another quarter of a century passed until Rome called a halt to the vendetta and authorized his re-burial in consecrated earth; a small funeral procession was staged at Parma. Finally, in the 1890s, his illegitimate son and heir, the Baron Achillino Paganini, was permitted to erect a tombstone over his father's grave, reading: 'Niccolò Paganini, who drew from the violin divine music.'

Even then the slanders persisted. In 1925, many of the fabrications were incorporated into the operetta *Paganini* by Franz Lehár. A decade later, almost a century after his death, the exiled Russian composer Sergei Rachmaninov wrote to the choreographer Mikhail Fokine:

About my Rhapsody, why not resurrect the legend about Paganini, who, for perfection in his art and for a woman, sold his soul to an evil spirit?

Borrowing one of Paganini's own tunes, Rachmaninov created from the violinist's agony one of Fokine's greatest successes and his own most abidingly popular work.

Rachmaninov was no stranger to religious difficulties himself, but of an opposite nature. A devout Christian, he left his native Russia a year after the Bolshevik Revolution. For a while he was viewed with ambivalence by the Moscow authorities, who were endeavouring not to outlaw the more famous of their artistic exiles but he disgraced himself with the Kremlin in 1931 by signing a letter to the *New York Times* disparaging the Soviet Government. The contortionists of the Soviet Press alighted on a performance at the Moscow Conservatory of his choral symphony, *The Bells*. Ignoring the secular nature of the work, which is based on a poem by Edgar Allan Poe, the Party hacks launched into an attack on the composer's religious beliefs:

The sound of bells, a liturgy, the devil knows what, the fear of elemental upheaval, everything in perfect harmony with that régime which had rotted away long before the October Revolution . . . composed by Rachmaninov, a violent enemy of Soviet Russia . . .

It was the prelude to his formal excommunication, a sanction which had already estranged such outstanding Russians as Stravinsky and Chaliapin and which still descends periodically on artists and musicians who dare to question the more repressive of the Kremlin's musical dictates.

As the Soviet Union's acts of excommunication suggest, interference on religious grounds in musical affairs is neither a thing of the past nor a practice confined solely to Christianity. The most sweeping recent attack by a prelate on music originated from a Moslem holy man and was expressed in a metaphor curiously reminiscent of Karl Marx's aphorism on religion. In a Ramadan speech on 23 July 1979, the religious leader of republican Iran, Ayatollah Khomeini, proclaimed:

Music is no different from opium. Music affects the human mind in a way that makes people think of nothing but music and sensual matters. Opium produces one kind of sensitivity and lack of energy, music another kind. A young person who spends most of his time with music is distracted from the serious and important affairs of life; he can get used to it in the same way as he can to drugs. Music is a treason to the country, a treason to our youth, and we should cut out all this music and replace it with something instructive.

Khomeini was re-introducing the strict traditions of Shi'ite Islam which had proscribed musical activities in Iran between the sixteenth and nineteenth centuries. Whatever the undoubted evils of his régime, the Shah whom he deposed had done much to foster musical culture, sponsoring orchestral and ballet companies and building an opera house in the capital. Western musicians were imported for regular concerts and recitals, often performing together with aspiring Iranian artists. The annual Shiraz Arts Festival was a lively affair which ventured less nervously than many European organizations into the avant-garde. A performance by the electronic experimentalist Karlheinz Stockhausen so captivated the town of Shiraz that its bazaar, which was enlivened by the hammering and banging of metal workers, was popularly redesignated 'Stockhausen Street'.

With the advent of Islamic fundamentalism, however, artistic progress was damned as Western decadence. A year after Khomeini's opium edict, the Society for the Prevention of Sin (long may its sanctimonious hands be full) banned the playing of music in all public places, including shops and restaurants. Singing, in particular, whether male or female, Iranian or foreign, was declared 'vulgar'. Those few musicians who had remained in Iran in the hope of soothing the savage breasts of its new rulers must have known their cause was lost. Those who could, packed their instruments and scores and joined their colleagues in exile.

CHAPTER SEVEN

RETREATS, ROUTS AND RETRENCHMENTS

*Stravinsky,
self portrait
in exile (1962)*

*M*usic owes more to geography than meets the ear. National and regional feelings have motivated the works of many composers — not just the overtly patriotic and revolutionary such as Chopin, Smetana and Verdi. Haydn wove German folk-tunes into his symphonies and quartets, Liszt incorporated Hungarian melodies, Grieg sought to personify Norway in his works, Sibelius Finland, Vaughan Williams England, Charles Ives New England and Villa Lobos captured the rhythms of Brazil. Often as not, the 'national' sound of their music was unintentional: try as a composer might to create a work that transcended time and place, the sounds of his native environment and heritage would surge to the fore. To lose touch with those elements could entail a total loss of creativity. Consequently, to the musician — far more than to most artists or writers who are able to draw descriptively on a new surrounding — the threat of exile is one of the worst fates imaginable.

Nonetheless, confronted with insupportable conditions at home, many musicians have been forced to retreat, regroup and live to fight another day. Often they have had to depart with a rampant mob or angry government at their heels. Some have not got far. The Italian composer and virtuoso violinist Giuseppe Tartini fled his native Padua in 1713, when the authorities found out that he had illicitly courted and wedded a girl pupil. Arriving at Assisi with pursuers not far behind, Tartini scaled the walls of the Franciscan monastery and joined its holy fraternity.

If he lost his inspiration in hermetic exile, it was soon restored by a most unlikely agent. Asleep one night in his cell, Tartini was visited by the Devil, who offered to play for him any music the composer chose. 'Let's hear something of yours,' said Tartini, whose tastes were catholic. Satan seized a violin and played a sonata so wondrous that the composer awoke with a start and dashed to his own instrument in the hope of recapturing it. All he could repeat was a faint resemblance of the diabolical recital, but the resultant *Devil's Trill* sonata survives to test the faculties of virtuosi nearly three centuries later.

The revelation shocked Tartini out of the paralysis of exile. He launched a pioneering study of the science of acoustics, invented a new bow for the violin and, in response to requests from his fellow monks emerged to give an occasional recital in their chapel, though hidden from the audience behind a curtain. His playing drew crowds from miles around; within two years he was identified by his virtuosity as the fugitive fiddler from Padua. Impressed by his celebrity, his home town finally granted Tartini a pardon and invited him back to rejoin his wife and establish a violin school.

Other musicians have resorted to flight as their only solution to a crisis of mounting debt. Where in our own enlightened era they might happily have stayed put and declared bankruptcy, in times when property was valued more highly the sole alternative to flight was to be thrown into a common jail until the debts were settled. This severity cost Europe the services of, among others, its finest librettist, Lorenzo da Ponte, collaborator with Mozart in *The Marriage of Figaro, Don Giovanni* and *Cosi fan tutte.* Having been banned from Vienna and from his native Venice by a new Emperor, Da Ponte set out to make a living in England. He wrote operas and ran a bookshop, the like of which 'London had not seen, and I dare say will never again see', containing as it did '15,000 volumes in choice works, both ancient and modern, among which were a considerable number of rare books, classics in first editions'. However, he incurred heavy debts and, worse, underwrote financial obligations for his friends. After being snatched from his wife's bed on their wedding anniversary, for a spell in a debtor's prison, Da Ponte withdrew tactically when credit notes again started raining down on him for payment. With his family he fled to America where he languished incognito for some twenty years until, in his seventies, he was recognized by a fellow browser in a New York bookshop and was helped to start a new career as Professor of Italian at Columbia University (1826-37) and founder of the Italian Opera House in New York.

Another musician pushed into a colonial exile by debts and a change of régime was the presumptuous Hebrew melodist, Isaac Nathan. After his patron Lord Byron had died fighting in the corner of a foreign feud that he believed was forever England's, Nathan continued to enjoy fame as the collaborator of the writer martyred for neo-Hellenism. As gallant as the poet, he is reported to have fought a pistol duel over a lady's honour in 1829, sustaining a painful flesh wound in the right arm. Six years later, *The Times* noted that:

Isaac Nathan, a composer of several Hebrew melodies, was indicted for committing an assault on Hercules Langford, commonly called Lord Langford.

Nathan had testified on behalf of Lady Langford, who was taking action against her husband for his flagrant infidelities. Langford called Nathan a liar; the composer hit him. In court he pleaded guilty to assault but 'under circumstances of great provocation'; he was acquitted by the jury and his public standing rose still further.

While his combativeness and his music kept him in the public eye, Nathan was also carrying out certain secret and delicate political missions for members of the royal family, to whom he had been appointed music teacher. Letters from King William IV acknowledged the value of his services, though their nature was, for reasons of confidentiality, never specified. Speculation involves Nathan in political espionage in France, covering up Watergate-style for the misdeeds of the son of the Duke of Sussex and, most probably, conducting shuttle diplomacy to ensure that the popular and troublesome Queen Caroline continued to reside peacefully far away from where she could embarrass her relatives royal. Whatever the nature of his endeavours, his expenses seem to have gone unpaid. After William IV died, the composer submitted his bill together with the late monarch's authority for payment. The Civil Service, in time-honoured fashion, elected to do nothing about the unsavoury matter in the hope that it would go away. Nathan applied directly to the Prime Minister, Lord Melbourne, who, in time-honoured fashion, set up a Commission to look into the problem in the hope it would go away. Desperate and increasingly harassed by his creditors, the composer stated his case for all to read in *The Sunday Times* and threatened to display his royal correspondence at every bank in the country until he was paid. Melbourne, though, was unmoved. Eventually the problematic musician did go away, his secrecy unbroken, to a city that bore the name of the recalcitrant Prime Minister.

His destination, until lately a convict colony, did not promise a comfortable repose for a man who had mixed in the most refined circles, but Nathan was nothing if not resourceful. He demonstrated his flair for publicity from the moment he landed in Australia, declaring himself to be descended from the Lion of Judah and the Kings of Poland. These credentials attracted audiences to several concerts in Melbourne, from where he proceeded to Sydney to found an opera company. His *Don John of Austria* was the first opera to be composed and performed in Australia and earned him, in sum with other contributions, the title of 'Father of Australian Music'. Among his descendants is the distinguished conductor, Sir Charles Mackerras.

Paradoxically, Frederic Chopin, the most famous of musical exiles, was self-exiled rather than compelled to leave his home. The pianist, whose romantically pale visage and yearning eyes were to become symbols of a Poland crushed beneath the paw of the Russian bear, found himself in Vienna trying to obtain concert engagements when the 1830 Polish uprising against the Russians broke out. Chopin's companion sped back to Warsaw to join the fray, but persuaded the young composer to stay abroad and fight for the cause with his music. When the rebellion was put down early in the following year, Chopin was in Stuttgart waiting for a train that was to take him to a lifetime's exile in France. It is said that he sat down that night and composed his famous *Revolutionary étude* in C minor (opus 10, no 12) — an innocuously-termed 'study', which was to become an inflammatory liberationist slogan.

It was in France that he won fame as a pianist and composed many of his best-known works. Son of a Lorraine-born wheelwright, it would have been easy for Chopin to immerse himself in the life of his paternal homeland, yet his emotions remained with Poland and his music was dedicated to its redemption. When he died in 1849 of tuberculosis, plague of poor refugees, four months short of his fortieth birthday, his last wish was that his heart be taken for burial in Warsaw.

Chopin's ambition to return to his country as a free citizen was fulfilled seventy years later by another pianist-composer, who had similarly yoked his music to the cause of Polish nationhood. Ignacy Jan Paderewski, the most adulated of keyboard artists, around whose concert platforms swooned the cream of American girlhood, spent his prime touring four continents with Chopin's and his own nationalistic compositions, often donating his concert fees to patriotic causes. He won support from other Polish musicians in exile. In Berlin, Karol Szymanowski and three fellow composers formed a Young Poland in Music society which achieved the propaganda coup of convincing the mighty Berlin Philarmonic Orchestra to play its works. Likewise, the pianist Arthur Rubinstein carried his impassioned recitals of Chopin's most stirring pieces into the very heartlands of tyrant Russia.

During the First World War, Paderewski campaigned indefatigably for the Polish cause. He was rewarded at its end by being appointed the first Prime Minister and Foreign Minister of independent Poland. In these capacities he attended the Versailles Conference (provoking Georges Clemenceau, Premier of France, to exclaim: 'So you are Paderewski the famous pianist? My word, what a comedown!') where he obtained, according to one participant, more for Poland by virtue of his international renown as a musician than any politician could have won. He lacked political skills though, and resigned from government after only a year at the first murmurs of disaffection with his policies. He spent most of the rest of his life abroad, but responded generously to regular calls from Warsaw to give concerts in one national interest or another. Sadly, Paderewski lived to see Poland lose its freedom again; he died in New York in 1941, while urging Americans to help overthrow German tyranny in his country, an exile once more.

While the Polish expatriates used music as an extra-terrestial political weapon, Richard Wagner sought to harness it to the chariot of domestic rebellion. For this ambition he paid a penalty of twelve years' enforced exile from Germany and two decades of wandering in the musical desert. While Wagner's credentials as a musical revolutionary are second to none, his motives for becoming a republican agitator owe less to idealism than to self-interest. In 1848, Wagner had passed five years of a lifetime contract as conductor at the Royal Opera House in Dresden and the prospect of wasting the rest of his working life on the capital of the tiny Kingdom of Saxony did not lie easily on his ambitious spirit. He had become something of a local hero by repatriating from London the remains of the town's most distinguished musical son, Carl Maria von Weber, composer of *The Freeshooter* (*Der Freischütz*) and *Euryanthe*, and by acknowledging a considerable Weberian influence on his own *Rienzi* and *The Flying Dutchman*. But success in provincial Dresden was not the acclaim Wagner was seeking. He needed to conquer the minds of men in the great centres of civilization — Vienna, Paris, Berlin — whose obdurate denial of his genius made the homely affection of Dresden cloy all the more.

His ambitions far outstripped his means. Trying to get his operas staged, he was perennially in debt and in dread of creditors. When the first signs of republican revolution that were sweeping Europe reached sleepy Dresden, Wagner, sensing a prospect of change, published an anonymous newspaper article calling on the monarchy to shed some of its privileges. When this outburst was benignly ignored, he summoned a public meeting of three thousand people to inveigh against 'the sycophants at the Royal Court'. Concurrently, he presented those same sycophants with a proposal for reorganizing the court theatre which would have brought most of artistic Dresden under his own command. The authorities could not overlook such presumption and rapped the upstart conductor sharply over the knuckles by refusing him permission to perform *Rienzi*.

Events began to move quickly. The pianist-composer Franz Liszt rode into town with inflammatory news of the revolution in Vienna. Wagner's assistant conductor, August Röckel, was arrested for distributing a tract calling on the Saxon army to mutiny. Röckel was released on bail but, having lost his job, devoted his energies to growing a beard and establishing a revolutionary newspaper. Wagner became a regular contributor, his republican fervour growing in intensity when the authorities, by way of retribution, cancelled the première of his *Lohengrin*. Sensing trouble in Saxony, revolutionaries who had been vanquished in other cities began to converge on Dresden. A new friend entered Wagner's life in the form of the Russian anarchist Mikhail Bakunin, whose philosophy of the total destruction of established society intrigued the ultra-radical composer. Bakunin's ideas extended even to the music of the revolution. 'He advised me,' Wagner wrote, 'to set but one text: the tenor should sing, "Off with his head," the soprano, "String him up," and the bass "Fire! Fire!"'

When revolution finally broke out, Bakunin leapt to the barricades with Wagner in close attendance. Röckel having fled when the first shots were fired, Wagner took over his presses and printed in the largest type he could find the proclamation, 'Are you with us, against the foreign troops?' This slogan was plastered on the outside of the barricades, appealing to the local troops who had been joined by Prussian reinforcements.

The first act of the Dresden revolt was to set fire to the old opera house, Wagner's place of work, where he had conducted at its very last concert Beethoven's symphony of goodwill to all mankind, the choral Ninth. As he watched the theatre burn, one of the incendiaries passed Wagner shouting, 'There, Herr Kapellmeister, it has been sparked off nicely by your *beautiful spark of the Gods*!' (*Freude, Schöner Götterfunke*, the chorus's opening line in the symphony). Wagner admits to having enjoyed the blaze; the building, he says, was ugly and worthy of demolition. Indeed he was having such a good time that only a fearful appeal from his wife, Minna, persuaded him to leave. He went home, took her to safety to his sister in Chemnitz (now Karl-Marx-Stadt) and returned to rejoin his comrades. But when he got back he found the revolution almost over and Bakunin on the point of flight. In the confusion, Wagner lost sight of the anarchist; it was as well for him that he did, since Bakunin was arrested while the composer made good his escape.

He fled to Weimar, home of his friend Liszt, dishevelled but unbloodied and, behaving as though nothing had happened, proceeded to discuss a scheduled performance of *Tannhäuser*. It was only when a Saxon warrant arrived for his arrest on a charge of high treason that Wagner was made to appreciate that playing with fire inside the opera house was not the same as setting fire to it and that his flirtation with revolution would have severe consequences. Wagner was now a fugitive from justice in all territories of the confederation of German states; the Austro-Hungarian Empire, in monarchic solidarity, declared him a prohibited immigrant.

Liszt, the truest of friends, kept Wagner in hiding at Weimar at the risk of his own liberty and livelihood. He secured a forged passport, gave the fugitive money and sent him to friends in Paris. It was the beginning of Wagner's two decades of homeless wandering. An attempt to settle in Italy was thwarted by the Austrians; a stay in Bordeaux was abruptly ended by the police at the behest of a jealous husband; another cuckolded husband eased him out of Zurich by giving him enough money to live in Paris; but he quit France again in disgrace after the débâcle of *Tannhäuser*. It was not until 1861 that an amnesty allowed him back into Germany (though not into Saxony), and not for another three years that he found a haven, when King Ludwig II of Bavaria, an operamanic aesthete, paid off his financial debts and invited him to settle in Munich.

Even then, Wagner's wanderings were not over. Having incurred the enmity of some members of the Bavarian Cabinet, Wagner asked his patron to sack them. The politicians hit back with a press campaign against the King's musical Rasputin. Ludwig reluctantly asked Wagner to leave for a while and the composer returned to Switzerland, to Villa Triebschen on the shores of Lake Geneva. There he was joined by Cosima, daughter of Liszt and wife of his friend Hans von Bülow. Having assured Ludwig of the propriety of their relationship, Wagner's new-found support from the King almost foundered when evidence of the adulterous liaison became apparent in a succession of illegitimate births. Although Bavaria continued to stage Wagner's works and he was allowed to establish a permanent home and theatre at Bayreuth, Ludwig was so mortified by the carnal deception that he refused to see his favourite composer for eight years.

These years of exile were the most turbulent of Wagner's life, but also the most productive. His temperament thrived on upheavals and he created during his sojourns both the great mythological trilogy *The Ring of the Nibelungen* and the historio-satirical *The Mastersingers of Nuremburg*. It was as though the restlessness that had made him rebel against the undemanding applause of Dresden had been assuaged by violent action and nervous wandering, leaving him with the inner peace through which to create his masterpiece.

By a quirk of history, his granddaughter Friedelind Wagner found herself similarly forced to flee for her life from Germany in the 1930s and to fight from exile against those who claimed to be Wagner's greatest admirers. Friedelind, alone among her family, viewed the Nazi enshrinement of Bayreuth and beatification of Wagner as a perversion of the composer's music and ideals. She resented her English-born mother Winifred's adoration of Hitler, the more so because of his violent contrast to the benign ways of her late father Siegfried, Wagner's only son, a composer of laconically light-hearted operas. When Friedelind fled to Switzerland, Hitler was so dismayed at the defection of a member of the Nazis' Holy Family that he sent a bevy of emissaries alternately to entice and threaten her to return. The last of these was her mother, who crossed the border in 1940 with a final ultimatum: either return to Germany and 'be kept in a safe place, or you will be destroyed and exterminated at the first opportunity.' Friedelind declined and flew to the United States to join the conductor Arturo Toscanini, in a propaganda campaign against the usurpers of Germany and Wagner.

After the War, although she pleaded that she had saved 'her' Jews from extermination, Winifred Wagner was held personally responsible for the nazification of Bayreuth and was forbidden by court order to take any further part in the Festivals in her lifetime. Her sons, Wagner's grandsons, inherited the tarnished Grail and cleansed it of much of its chauvinism.

So sacred was Bayreuth to Nazi ideology that it was temporarily permitted by the Führer to remain an island of racial impurity, for fear that the loss of its Jewish performers would impair the artistic perfection of the Festival. Few of them, however, stayed for long amid an atmosphere of increasing persecution.

Those who left Bayreuth at this time were part of the greatest wave of musical migration in history. With the rise of the Nazis, musical institutions (along with other German enterprises) were ordered to shed their Jews and political dissidents, some doing so with an alacrity that owed more to internal jealousies than to a sudden espousal of the official ideology. Many of those dismissed left Germany as quickly as they could; some escaped before the axe fell; several who were under no threat walked out honourably and defiantly in sympathy with their sacked colleagues.

The list of musicians who went into exile from Nazi Germany reads like a 'who's who' of twentieth-century music. It includes Arnold Schoenberg, deviser of twelve-tone composition, Paul Hindemith, who sought to weld the sounds of industrial society into his music, Kurt Weill, Hanns Eisler and Ernst Krenek, the jazz-influenced younger generation of German composers, and the cerebral pianists, Artur Schnabel and Rudolf Serkin. Of the five top conductors in Germany, Bruno Walter, Otto Klemperer, Erich Kleiber, Felix Weingartner and Wilhelm Furtwängler, all but one emigrated within a year of Hitler's accession; the first two because they were Jewish, Kleiber and Weingartner because they could not tolerate totalitarianism. Only Furtwängler, the maladroit but uncannily effective conductor of the Berlin Philharmonic, remained to endure an uneasy co-existence with the Third Reich, after securing its assurance that his Jewish players would keep their jobs. This, like so many Nazi promises, was soon broken; so too, ultimately, was the conductor, after being made to walk a gangplank of near-collaboration.

With the fall of Austria and Czechoslovakia and the German advances in the early years of war, the tide of musical emigration swelled into a flood. Many refugees were driven from one haven to the next by the approach of evil. Bruno Walter, disciple of Mahler and a legendary Mozartean, left the Leipzig Gewandhaus in 1933 and settled in Austria, where he assumed his mentor's mantle at the Vienna Opera. Driven out by the *Anschluss* of 1938, he settled in France and was awarded its citizenship, only to escape again to the United States when war drew near. Mahler's niece, Alma Rosé, found haven and employment as a violinist in Amsterdam but was trapped there by the Nazi invasion. Captured, she was sent to the Auschwitz concentration camp where she conducted a macabre orchestra formed for the entertainment of genocidal killers until she herself was murdered.

So extensive was the exodus that the German territories were denuded of almost all their outstanding musicians. Those who remained could be counted on the fingers of one hand: apart from Furtwängler, there were the aged Richard Strauss, his favoured conductor and sometime librettist Clemens Krauss (who said he would have gone to Russia or Hell if it meant working with Strauss), and the misanthropic vocal composer Hans Pfitzner.

For the refugees, America, despite its cumbersome and obstructive immigration procedures, offered the best opportunities. New arrivals soon realized, however, that a change of style might be required in their music if it was to satisfy American tastes. To some, such a change was only too welcome, signifying a severance of ties with the horrors of the Europe they had fled. Kurt Weill, whose rich jazzy scores for Bertolt Brecht's social satires were nourished on classical disciplines, abandoned classicism altogether and turned his talents to creating musicals for Broadway. Although he composed a string of box-office bonanzas, his showbiz music has, with the exception of a few songs (*September Song* being the most memorable) been virtually forgotten. His reputation rests on his European works alone.

Sadder was the case of Erich Korngold, a former Viennese child prodigy who won Mahler's admiration with a cantata written when he was ten years old. Hailed as another Mozart (although not by his father, the eminent critic Julius Korngold, who viewed his son's accomplishments with commendable circumspection), he retained a considerable following into adulthood; his opera, *The Dead City*, was one of the great Viennese successes of the inter-War years. But as a refugee in America, the only work he could find was in Hollywood. There he composed film scores with such panache, in movies as disparate as *Robin Hood* and *The Sea Hawk*, that his new-found fame completely overshadowed his reputation. He died embittered at the realization that the second Mozart would be remembered only for his movies.

Korngold's friend and near-neighbour in Los Angeles, Arnold Schoenberg, was also tempted by the movies: was tempted, but did not fall. Schoenberg's close encounter with Hollywood was but one of countless bewildering experiences that befell him in exile. While critics had savaged his work in Europe, they had at least pretended to appreciate his motives. In America, he faced — with great forbearance — a more naïve society, whose leading news magazine, *Time*, made this attempt to summarize his life and work:

For thirty years, bald, parchment-faced, Austrian-born composer Arnold Schoenberg has written music so complicated that only he and a couple other fellows understand what it is all about. This music, which sounds to the uninitiated not only queer, but accidental, has been enjoyed by very few. But it has thrown the world of music into a Kilkenny cat fight. One cat camp maintains that Schoenberg's music, like Einstein's theory, sounds queer because it is way over the average man's head; opponents swear that Schoenberg is pulling everybody's leg, including his own, and that his miscalled music is a gibberish of wrong notes.

Schoenberg had left Berlin in March 1933 after the composer Max von Schillings demanded that the Prussian Academy of Arts rid itself of Jewish influences to conform with the new political order. He went to France (where one of his first acts was to reconvert to the Jewish faith he had abandoned as a youth), then to the United States, where he obtained a succession of poorly-paid academic posts. The last of these was at the University of California at Los Angeles, depositing the ascetic, intellectual composer at the gates of the factories of universal bliss and banalities. While he struggled to make a living from teaching, his friends made approaches to Hollywood to secure him additional freelance employment. Nothing came of these moves until the all-powerful MGM producer Irving Thalberg, godfather to *Gone With the Wind*, happened to hear Schoenberg's atmospheric *Transfigured Night* on the radio. He was even more impressed when he found that the composer had an entry all to himself in the *Encyclopedia Britannica*. Thalberg promptly sent an emissary to commission Schoenberg to compose a score for the film of Pearl Buck's romance of China, *The Good Earth*. The initial contact failed to achieve a meeting of minds, Thalberg's man seeking to fire the impassive composer's enthusiasm with a description of the movie's climactic event. 'Just think,' burbled the envoy,

A terrific storm is going on; the wheat field is swaying in the wind, and suddenly the earth begins to tremble. In the midst of the earthquake, Oo-Lan gives birth to a baby! What an opportunity for music!' Schoenberg paused for a moment, then said mildly, 'With so much going on, why do you need music?

Schoenberg was summoned to meet Thalberg himself. 'What are your terms for writing the music for the movie?' the great producer asked. 'Very straightforward,' said Schoenberg. 'I want fifty thousand dollars.' The mogul did not flinch. 'And I need an absolute guarantee that not a single note of my score will be altered.' Schoenberg also offered to train the movie's stars to deliver their lines in musical conformity with his score, but Thalberg was no longer listening. The idea that a musician could order the most powerful entertainment industry since the gladiators to adapt one of its programmes to the music of a penniless visionary who had never previously composed for the screen was more than his simple business mind could accommodate. It is a measure of their total mutual miscomprehension that Schoenberg told his wife that the reason he had been rejected by Hollywood was that he had demanded too much money . . .

The bitter herbs of Schoenberg's exile were not just fruits of the cultural wilderness in which he found himself but also of the moral wasteland he had left behind. When his devoted pupil Alban Berg died suddenly in Vienna in 1935, Schoenberg volunteered selflessly to complete his almost-finished opera, *Lulu*. However, two days after receiving Berg's score, he returned it to the publishers untouched with the lame excuse that he could not spare the time. In letters to friends, he revealed that his sudden change of mind had been caused by the discovery that Berg had 'thoughtlessly' turned the character of a banker in the opera into an anti-semitic caricature, apparently in the hope of improving *Lulu*'s prospects for performance under the Nazis. The opera, which Berg had dedicated to Schoenberg, was to lie unfinished for another forty years.

In common with most refugees, Schoenberg made few friends among the natives of the country in which he spent his last fifteen years. One exception was his tennis partner, George Gershwin, author of *Porgy and Bess* and as different from Schoenberg as Beethoven from the Beatles. He also played a few sets with sundry of the Marx Brothers, watched once by Charlie Chaplin, whom Schoenberg praised for his movies and criticized for their music. Conscious of the honour, Chaplin admitted to being as flattered by Schoenberg's criticism as by his compliments. These contacts apart, his social life centred on the stifling intimacy of exilic circles, where feuds and fights flourished like bacteria in a test-tube. It was through the whisperings of these coteries that Schoenberg became embroiled in his last great battle.

The uncrowned king of the German-speaking colony of Los Angeles was Thomas Mann, the greatest living German writer, Nobel laureate of 1929, whose exile owed nothing to his race, his politics or even his published works, but to conflict with the Nazis over music. Mann incurred the wrath of the new rulers of Germany in a speech which bluntly challenged their claims to personify the music and ideals of Richard Wagner. If Mann's commitment to music was profound enough to make him leave his homeland, it was also knowledgeable enough to engage him in conversation with the greatest musical thinker of his time. He and Schoenberg also shared a fascination for the Biblical characters Moses and Joseph, around whom each had constructed major works. From their chats in the sunshine and dinner-table candlelight of California there grew Mann's last great novel, *Doctor Faustus*, an allegory of the mixture of genius and madness that inhabits the soul of Germany. Its hero is a fictional composer, Adrian Leverkühn (1885-1943), who is depicted as the inventor of a method of twelve-tone composition.

Schoenberg, whose eyesight was failing, might never have read his friend's book and, had he done so, found no cause for objection, but for the agitation of a self-appointed guardian of artistic properties in the exile community. Alma Mahler-Werfel, widow of Gustav Mahler, sometime girlfriend of Schoenberg's composer brother-in-law Alexander von Zemlinsky, a minor composer herself, and recently the widow of the exiled novelist Franz Werfel, took an emotional interest in musical and literary affairs. She considered it her duty to tell Schoenberg that he should 'do something' about Mann's novel. The composer wrote to the writer that it was wrong of him to attribute the creation of twelve-tone composition to anyone other than himself. After several exchanges, Mann agreed that all future and foreign language editions of *Doctor Faustus* would carry an acknowledgement that twelve-tone composition was invented by none other than Arnold Schoenberg.

But the busybodies of the refugee community would not let the matter rest and incited composer against author until the quarrel erupted into open controversy. Schoenberg sent a furious omni-libellous letter, in which the finger of Alma Mahler-Werfel can be detected busily stirring, to the *Saturday Review of Literature.*

In his novel *Doctor Faustus*, Thomas Mann has taken advantage of my literary property. He has produced a fictitious composer as the hero of his book; and in order to lend him qualities a hero needs to arouse people's interest, he made him the creator of what one erroneously calls my 'system of twelve tones,' which I call 'method of composing with twelve tones.'

He did this without my permission and even without my knowledge. In other words, he borrowed it in the absence of the proprietor. The supposition of one reviewer, that he obtained information about this technique from Bruno Walter and Stravinsky, is probably wrong; because Walter does not know anything of composition with twelve tones, and Stravinsky does not take any interest in it.

I have still not read the book itself, though in the meantime Mann had sent me a German copy, with a handwritten dedication, 'To A. Schoenberg, dem Eigentlicher'. As one need not tell me that I am an 'Eigentlicher', a real one, it was clear that he wanted to tell me that his Leverkühn is an impersonation of myself.

Leverkühn is depicted, from beginning to end, as a lunatic. I am seventy-four and I am not yet insane, and I have never acquired the disease from which this insanity stems. I consider this an insult.

When Mrs Mahler-Werfel discovered this misuse of my property, she told Mann that this was my theory, whereupon he said: 'Oh, does one notice that? Then perhaps Mr Schoenberg will be angry!' This proves that he was conscious of his guilt, and knew it was a violation of an author's right.

Far from being pacified by Mann's printed acknowledgement in later editions, Schoenberg was inflamed still further by its modest wording:

> He calls me 'a (a!) contemporary composer and theoretician'. Of course, in two or three decades one will know which of the two was the other's contemporary.

The magazine solicited a response from Thomas Mann which it published in the same issue (1 January 1949, now a collector's item) as Schoenberg's attack on him. Unhappily for the provocateurs, Mann declined to enter the fray but replied to Schoenberg's wilder accusations with cool dignity. It was thirty-seven years since he had first fought over a composer, then as now championed by the formidable Alma, and he had learned that discretion was better by far than valour. In 1912 the row had centred on the main character in *Death in Venice*, a fanatically self-absorbed homosexual writer, bearing an uncanny resemblance in all but his sexual preferences to Gustav Mahler. His widow was outraged that disreputable habits should be associated with even a fictional representation of her lately-deceased husband, not least because they implied that he had been resistant to her own charms. Peace of sorts was made between widow and writer, but they remained wary of each other and Mann implicitly blamed her in his response for his break with Schoenberg:

> Arnold Schoenberg's letter both astonished and grieved me. If his acquaintance with the book were not based exclusively on the gossip of meddling scandal mongers, he would know that my efforts to give the central figure of the novel 'qualities a hero needs to arouse people's interest' were neither limited to the transfer of Schoenberg's 'method of composing with twelve tones', nor was this characteristic the most important one.
> Instead of accepting my book with a satisfied smile as a piece of contemporary literature that testifies to his tremendous influence upon the musical culture of the era, Schoenberg regards it as an act of rape and insult. It is a sad spectacle to see a man of great worth, whose all-too-understandable hypersensitivity grows out of a life suspended between glorification and neglect, almost wilfully yield to delusions of persecution and of being robbed, and involve himself in rancorous bickering. It is my sincere hope and wish that he may rise above bitterness and find peace in the assurance of his greatness and glory!

But he could not find it, or was not allowed to by his jealous friends. Approached by another magazine, Schoenberg accused Mann of 'an act of revenge' in restricting the acknowledgement inserted in *Doctor Faustus* to a bare minimum. The novelist retorted with disarming detachment:

> You are attacking a bugbear of your imagination and I am not it, so there is no desire for revenge. If you want to be my enemy completely — you will not succeed in making me your enemy.

It was two years before the two weary and elderly gentlemen made up, Schoenberg writing to Mann,

> if the hand that I believe I see held out is the hand of peace . . . I shall be the last not to grasp it at once.

But so deeply had the conflict split the German exiles of California that both men agreed not to make a formal announcement of reconciliation until their supporters had been given sufficient time to get used to living in peace.

The German-speaking exiles were not the only musicians to have found refuge along the Pacific Coast of America — nor were they the only ones to engage in internecine strife. They were joined by waves of Russians, refugees first from the Bolshevik Revolution, then from the Nazi occupation of their European sanctuaries. The musicians of the two colonies had little contact with one another; the Russian composer Igor Stravinsky was acquainted for a while with Schoenberg, but said their wives could not get on with each other. Stravinsky's relations with the other most prominent Russian emigré in California, Sergei Rachmaninov, were also strained. The two composers had little respect for each other's music and it is doubtful if in their long careers they had ever met before reaching Beverly Hills. But in 1941 Rachmaninov, having heard that some of Stravinsky's family were, like his own beloved daughter, trapped in Nazi-occupied France, invited the other worried composer to dinner. After discussing the problems of France, conversation flagged. Neither could bring himself to discuss the other's music. Finally, Rachmaninov scornfully mentioned a popular work of Stravinsky's which had earned him no royalties. Stravinsky retorted that Rachmaninov had also lost all revenue from the works he had published in Russia before he left. The two men glared at each other. Then they proceeded, to the astonishment of others present, to assess amicably how much each had earned from his music. It was the only topic they found in common and it gave them

Sergei Rachmaninov

immense amusement to speculate how much they might have earned from music if political conditions had remained stable.

If they had compared the total sufferings of exile, they would have agreed that Stravinsky's fate had been the harsher. While Rachmaninov was able to support his family from regular American and European appearances as a concert pianist and conductor, Stravinsky's talent as a performing musician was limited and he was forced to rely on variable bursts of compositorial inspiration for sustenance. These sources dried up for a lengthy period after the Revolution and, according to his friend Arthur Rubinstein, were not the only powers he lost in exile. Stravinsky turned up in Paris at the turn of the Gay Twenties penniless and, self-confessedly, impotent. Rubinstein attenuated the first problem by commissioning a piano score for him to play from the material of his ballet *Petrushka*. He tackled the other difficulty with equal delicacy: an expenses-paid evening at one of the more exclusive maisons in Paris, which Stravinsky spent in the secluded company of one Madeleine.

'Cette femme est géniale,' was the composer's appreciative verdict.

Forced to live from his royalties, Stravinsky frequently went to law when he felt his copyright had been infringed. In 1937 he challenged Warner Brothers for using a few bars from his *Firebird* ballet in one of their movies to accompany a seduction scene. Stravinsky sued for 'moral damages' sustained, he claimed, by the suggestion that his music was conducive to licentiousness. Had he brought the case in the United States, he would probably have won part of the 300,000 French francs he demanded in damages. But the outcome of a romantic issue in a court in France is never predictable. Hearing the composer complain that his work was being used to help ruin a young girl's virtue, the Parisian judge demurred: 'But Monsieur Stravinsky, surely that, for a composer, is the greatest compliment in the world!' He was awarded token damages of one franc.

Stravinsky, like most Russian exiles, resisted intense Soviet efforts in the 1920s to persuade him to return home. His music was consequently banned in the USSR until 1962, when Khruschev invited him to visit Leningrad and Moscow and the Soviet Press transformed him at a stroke from a worthless renegade into the greatest living composer. Though Stravinsky's visit was officially represented as a warm homecoming, the composer Dmitri Shostakovich, in his clandestine memoirs, says that Stravinsky forgot and forgave none of the insults that had been heaped on him for half a century. When one of his nastier critics came forward to greet him, Stravinsky stuck out his walking stick instead of a hand. Shostakovich chuckled at his octogenarian truculence and applauded his decision to remain abroad. 'He didn't make the mistake,' he said, 'of Prokofiev, who ended up like a chicken in the soup.'

Prokofiev had been the only major musical figure to succumb to Soviet sweet-talk and return to Russia. There, after a few years of official adulation, he was forced to truckle under to Stalin and make his obeisances in order to survive. His years abroad had produced some of his most enduring works, including three piano concertos and *The Love of Three Oranges*, but these were dismissed as irrelevant when compared to his Russian-based compositions. When he died, the musical functionary Tikhon Khrennikov, once his tormentor, eulogized:

> It was Prokofiev's good fortune to return to his native land at the right time . . .The great artist realized his need for new impressions of life and these he got from his Soviet homeland. It was in the Soviet period of his life that Prokofiev gave the world such brilliant works as *War and Peace, Semyon Kotko, Romeo and Juliet, Alexander Nevsky, Ivan the Terrible,* the Fifth, Sixth and Seventh Symphonies and *all* (sic) the fine compositions that he ever wrote.

Such posthumous acclaim for the one who came back contrasts poignantly with the savage condemnation the Soviet media meted out to the poor wretches who got away. When Feodor Chaliapin, the greatest of Russian singers, died in 1938 at the age of sixty-five, thousands of Russian emigrés flocked to Paris for what amounted to a State occasion for exiles. The funeral service at the Russian cathedral was sung by a famous exiled Russian opera chorus and the cortège proceeded to the courtyard of the Paris Opera. There its most distinguished singers intoned a chorale in memory of the enormous bass who had breathed life into *Boris Godunov,* before a procession of great musicians accompanied Chaliapin to his grave. Back in Moscow, however, *Izvestia,* arbiter of proletarian morality, obituarized in obloquy:

> Chaliapin betrayed his people and sold his fatherland for petty cash . . . Having lost contact with his native soil, he failed to create a single new character on the stage during his stay abroad . . . He left nothing behind him after his death.

Despite the ensuing ostracism, Soviet musicians have continued to emigrate in numbers that alarm the bureaucrats. Yet it is precisely because of the extent of State control that they feel the need to escape. Since 1960 the exodus has included the virtuoso pianists Vladimir Ashkenazy and Bella Davidovich, valued by the Kremlin for their lustre as international prizewinners, and the 'cellist and conductor Mstislav Rostropovich with his wife, the singer Galina Vishnevskaya, both of worldwide reputation. Rostropovich and his wife fell into disfavour in the mid-1970s because of their friendship with the polemical novelist Aleksandr Solzhenitsyn. After having been allowed to undertake a period of residence abroad, they were summarily stripped of their Soviet citizenship and exiled. Vishnevskaya's name was expunged from the roll of honour at the Bolshoi Theatre, where she had been a star for twenty years. In 1981, Rostropovich's sister, Veronica, a player in the first violin section of the Moscow Philharmonic, was forbidden to travel with the orchestra to London, despite a direct appeal on her behalf to President Brezhnev by the conductors Claudio Abbado, Bernard Haitink and Sir George Solti and other leading Western musicians.

Other musicians who have left in recent years include a whole generation of Jewish violinists led by Boris Belkin and Lydia Mordkovich, and the principal conductors of three of Russia's major orchestras: Kyril Kondrashin of the Moscow Philharmonic, Rudolf Barshay, founder of the Moscow Chamber Orchestra and Yuri Aronovich and Maxim Shostakovich, successive directors of the USSR Radio and TV Symphony Orchestra.

Of all these defections, the last was the most disturbing. The post-Stalin authorities had made great efforts to cover up the persecution of Dmitri Shostakovich and to present his life's work as a triumph of Soviet culture. They went so far as to issue a semi-official Shostakovich biography to counter the composer's dissident memoirs, published in the West in 1980, and paraded his son Maxim before the Press to disown the clandestine book. But the conductor was following in his father's footsteps and was finding himself increasingly in trouble with the overbearing State. Matters came to a head in 1980 when he threatened to cancel a prestige visit by his orchestra to France if three Jewish players were not allowed to travel. He got his way, but pressures continued to mount. In April 1981, together with his pianist son Dmitri, he defected after a concert in West Germany and was granted asylum in the United States. His first statement there, having demonstratively renounced his Soviet citizenship, was revealing:

> No matter how difficult it was to leave, it would have been even more difficult for me to stay, to witness the innocent spirit of my son being broken and brutalized as it collided with Soviet reality. Our exodus is a profoundly conscious step, a sign of protest, my spiritual legacy from my never-to-be-forgotten father.

He left behind not only an august position in the musical hierarchy, but what is suspected to be the largest private artistic fortune in the USSR, the royalties from his father's works. The State's loss, however, was greater than his own. With the escape of Maxim Shostakovich, the Soviet Union forfeited a valuable interpreter of his father's symphonies and any residual claim to the composer's loyalty to their oppressive system. There was a shocked reaction of protracted silence from Moscow. Not until eleven days after the defection was the would-be composer Tikhon Khrennikov, head of the Composer's Union, able to announce that Maxim Shostakovich had absconded for 'personal' reasons. 'It will not affect our attitude to his father,' he promised, somewhat lamely. In Washington, meanwhile, Mstislav Rostropovich bubbled over that 'Maxim has done exactly the right thing: it is his answer for the suffering of his father.' Others spoke more soberly of clinching evidence of the bankruptcy of the Soviet musical system, on which the State so prided itself. The cream of Russian music now resided abroad and it was not difficult to draw parallels with an earlier régime that had been abandoned by its music-makers.

Of countless rebuffs that were delivered to the Nazi State by the world's musicians, none was more painful than the boycott proclaimed by

Arturo Toscanini, the most sought-after conductor in the world. Toscanini had become indispensible, in particular to the Bayreuth Festival. He first conducted there in 1930 when he was sixty-three, but his Latin volatility had done much to refresh stolid traditions of Wagnerism. He was a particular favourite with Wagner's own daughters, who viewed his devotion to literal interpretation of their father's scores as an insurance against any innovations that might be attempted by Bayreuth's new manager, their sister-in-law, Winifred.

When the Nazis came to power, Toscanini let it be known that he was unhappy about returning to Bayreuth if the régime persisted in persecuting musicians. When nothing happened to suggest that the policy might change, he joined leading American performers in an appeal to Hitler for an end to political and racial discrimination against musicians. The Nazi response was to ban from German wavelengths the compositions and recordings of all the signatories to the petition. Anxious for her forthcoming festival, Winifred Wagner sped to Berlin to consult with Hitler. Friedelind, her daughter, says the Führer was outraged at Toscanini's intransigence after he had so generously allowed Bayreuth to keep its Jews, but agreed to send a cable to the maestro, saying how happy he would be to greet him in Bayreuth. Toscanini pondered this dubious honour before replying, keeping his options cautiously open:

Your *Excellency*:— For your very friendly writing I want to thank you heartily, only I greatly regret that I could not answer it sooner.

You know how closely I feel attached to Bayreuth and what deep pleasure it gives me to consecrate my 'something' to a genius like Wagner whom I love so boundlessly.

Therefore it would be a bitter disappointment to me if any circumstances should interfere with my purpose to take part in the coming Festival Plays, and I hope that my strength, which the last weeks have taxed severely, will hold out.

He hesitated for a month longer, awaiting a glimmer of light that would permit him to conduct with a clear conscience. But the skies of Germany continued to darken and Toscanini finally cabled Winifred that Bayreuth would have to proceed without him. In a last resort, she sent Daniela, Wagner's daughter, to Milan to try to change his mind; Toscanini, 'with unchangeable friendship for the House of Wagner,' refused. A Nazi newspaper lamented:

The great musician with incorruptible ears, suspicious, pedantically insisting on the last semi-quaver, has heard only the discordant tone of the great orchestra that is Germany.

Toscanini by Caruso

Having snubbed fascism in his own country, Toscanini now transferred his home to the United States, where he became a focus of resistance to totalitarianism. He spurned an opportunistic invitation to conduct in the Soviet Union for the same reason he had withdrawn from Germany and Italy.

Winifred Wagner, frantic to find a 'name' conductor at short notice for the Festival, offered the post to Fritz Busch, head of the Dresden Opera. In open solidarity with Toscanini, Busch declined and shortly afterwards went into exile in Argentina. Substitutes were eventually found in the octogenarian Richard Strauss and the maverick Berlin conductor Wilhelm Furtwängler. Toscanini never forgave either of them for replacing him and obstructed their progress wherever he could (though he continued to conduct Strauss's works). He was, in campaigns against suspected collaborators with an evil régime, as unremitting as in his pursuit of orchestral perfection. He valued moral integrity as highly as tonal purity and pursued both with utter disdain for convention and consistency. Enemy of dictators, he was a tyrant to his orchestras; sworn opponent of persecution, he hounded his enemies mercilessly.

Toscanini was the archetypal conductor, personifying both the power and the mystique of the youngest of all musical species. His ability to transform orchestral standards was as distinctive as it was inexplicable; it gave him licence to act in ways ordinary mortals would never dare.

CHAPTER EIGHT

BATON CHARGE

*T*he conductor is a relatively recent musical instrument, emerging more than a century after the clarinet and barely a hundred years before the Moog synthesizer (which, by promoting the cause of electronic music, may eventually render the conductor obsolete). He rose like Aphrodite from the swelling waves of an orchestral sea when the orchestra became too swollen in size to continue to control itself unguided and it became biologically necessary that one of its members evolve into a biped and stand above his former comrades.

No sooner had this transformation taken place, however, than orchestras began to resent external domination and the freshly-risen conductor to demand ever-greater ascendancy. In these conflicting aspirations lie some of the most awesome of musical conflicts and many of the most fanciful legends.

It might be fairly assumed that the conductor originally took up the baton as the tool of his trade as a means of self-protection and self-assertion. While this is not altogether untrue, there was a sound musical reason: a stick of variable length was found to be the best instrument for indicating a steady beat. Early conductors had tried waving rolls of paper and scrolls of leather but these proved either as ineffective or as disruptive as stamping a foot on the ground. The latter method had prevailed before conductors emerged, when ensembles were led from within by one of their members who would also play the violin or keyboard instrument. This leader, who often composed most of the concert programme, would endeavour, while playing his part, to keep his colleagues in time by periodically waving a bow or hand at them, stamping, shouting and disturbing the harmony he sought to achieve. As both composer and virtuoso, he also had to keep an eye on the audience to make sure they were enjoying the entertainment and was consequently often unaware of what was going on behind him.

The virtuoso French violinist-composer-leader Alexander Boucher was given a salutary lesson in the need to devolve one of his functions to a specialist conductor when he appeared with a good amateur orchestra at a private concert in Belgium in 1820. Boucher, who won his first musical fame leading his classmates at the Lycée des Arts in the storming of the Bastille, bore an uncanny resemblance to Bonaparte and was often mistaken for him. Styling himself 'Alexander, the Napoleon of violinists', his dealings with orchestras were characteristically dictatorial, even when his players were amateurs of noble birth.

At rehearsal he begged the gentlemen dilettanti to fall in right vigorously with their final tutti immediately after the shake of his cadence, and added that he would give them the signal by stamping with his foot. In the evening, when this concluding piece began, it was already very late, and the dilettanti were growing impatient to get home to supper. But when the cadence in which *Boucher* as usual exhibited all his artistic *tours de force* seemed never likely to end, some of the gentlemen put their instruments into their cases and slipped out. This was so infectious, that in a few minutes the whole orchestra had disappeared. *Boucher*, who in the enthusiasm of his play had observed nothing of this, lifted his foot at the commencement of his concluding shake, in order to draw the attention of the orchestra to the agreed signal. His astonishment may be imagined when all that fell upon his ear was the loud stamp of his own foot. Horrified he stared aghast around him, and beheld all the music desks abandoned. The public, who had prepared themselves for this moment, burst into uproarious laughter.

Boucher, who did not share their amusement, silently resolved to play in future only with professionals. However, full-time orchestral musicians can be even more particular about their mealtimes and would much rather forgo a symphony than their supper. Hector Berlioz, one of the pioneers of modern conducting, recalls with fresh resentment in his long-suffering memoirs, his treatment by an orchestra at a concert staged for his wife's benefit. The programme, a long one but not over-long by the standards of those amusement-hungry times, opened with Madame Berlioz in the fourth act of *Hamlet*, followed by a short play by Alexandre Dumas, the elder. The orchestra struck up with two orchestral overtures by Berlioz, Carl Maria von Weber's short piano concerto (*Konzertstück*) played to great acclaim and much feminine audience hysteria by Franz Liszt — an evening's entertainment in his own right — a full chorus by Weber, and, by way of climax, Berlioz's fifty-minute *Fantastic Symphony*. It was a bit too much, Berlioz discovered, for the boys in the band.

I knew nothing of the rule of the Théâtre Italien, that its musicians need not play after midnight, and when, after Weber's *Chorus*, I turned to review my orchestra before raising my baton, I found that it consisted of five violins, two violas, four 'cellos, and a trombone, all the others having slipped quietly away.

In my consternation I could not think what to do. The audience did not seem inclined to leave and loudly called for the symphony, one voice in the gallery shouting, 'Give us the *March to the Scaffold*!'

'How can I,' cried I, 'with five violins? Is it my fault that the orchestra has disappeared?'

Of course my enemies announced that it was my music that had driven the musicians away.

Hector Berlioz

Baton or no baton, Berlioz was helpless in the face of desertion, but continued to believe strongly in the effect of the stick. He would use it, one of his musicians wrote, 'to threaten the big drummer, then he would turn and point it seductively at the flautist. We all feared his demoniac sarcasm and were happy to escape from his clutches.' The baton had an almost magical significance for Berlioz. He once swindled Mendelssohn into exchanging his expensive and imposing pointer, a rod of whalebone covered with white leather, for his own baton, a crude oak branch from which the bark had not been fully stripped. He also took over from Gasparo Spontini, conductor at the Berlin Opera, a field-marshal's ebony swagger-stick capped at each end with a knob of ivory, with which the Italian would exhort his band of German mercenaries in Napoleonic French: 'Allez! Marchez! Au bataille!', reinforcing his commands by the descent of the baton on an offending musician.

The perils of such a weapon are self-evident. Even in the hands of as amiable a conductor as Luigi Arditi, popularizer of Italian opera in nineteenth-century Britain and the United States, it could maim almost by a will of its own. Arditi, as a reward for his success in introducing Bellini's *Norma* to Broadway, was presented with a baton . . .

of Malacca cane, with a topaz of great beauty set at the bottom; while at the other extremity, a little golden Apollo playing on a harp headed an inscription alluding to the production of *Norma*.

I was very proud of this baton, and must have struck up the opening bars of the overture with unusual energy, the Apollo became loosened, and flew off straight in the direction of one of the members of the orchestra, striking him with terrific force on his bald head.

He looked piteously at me, but did not allow the accident to interfere with his share of the overture; and all through the first act my attentions were divided between my score of *Norma* and the hideous lump on the head of my unfortunate flute-player, which seemed to grow larger and larger every minute.

I remember also that when I took my seat in the orchestra the next evening vivid signs of uneasiness were manifest among my musicians, many of whom were looking askance at me, while they brushed and rubbed their handkerchiefs solicitously over their heads, wondering, perchance, which of them would be favoured that night with a burst of Apollo's violent attentions.

On one famous and terrible occasion, the use of a heavy baton proved fatal. The versatile Jean-Baptiste Lully, a century ahead of his time in his orchestral techniques, was the first to succeed in making all his violinists begin together by a uniform stroke of the bow. Unlike his contemporaries, he stood in front of the orchestra and devoted his full attention to securing a cohesive performance. But, progressive though he was, he knew no better way to conduct than to beat time on the floor with a stick. Having wormed his way back into official favour after the last of many homosexual scandals, he composed a *Te Deum* to celebrate the unexpected recovery of the Sun King from a malaise that seemed destined to extinguish his light. During its first performance, Lully became so engrossed in keeping his players together that, while beating time, he crashed the heavy staff down onto his foot. He occasioned a contusion that, in the words of a moralizing post-mortem report, 'from a bad habit of body, brought on a mortification'. The finest royal doctors were unable to bring relief. Lully refused to have his gangrenous leg amputated, the only measure that might have saved his life, and died in agony, a martyr to his conductorship.

Lully's mishap appears to have been unique. The prestige of conductors continued to grow and so did their dexterity with their instrument as they developed the techniques to direct orchestral works of increasing size. Composers in the mid-nineteenth century, following in the direction set by Beethoven, were now writing for ever-larger orchestras. Berlioz, Schumann and Liszt produced symphonies for which a professional conductor was an indispensable as a desk of wind players. By the time they were faced with the massive works of Mahler and Richard Strauss, conductors had developed into virtuoso performers with popular mannerisms which raised their status to equal and even excel that of the great instrumental soloists. The conductor, at the turn of the twentieth century, entered on an era of international super-stardom.

Puffed up by their new-found eminence many became martinets, submitting their orchestras to onslaughts of verbal and physical abuse with little more justification than the gratification of an over-inflated ego. Even the most capable conductors were seized by megalomanic delusions (Bruno Walter's gentle and persuasive manner stands out as a singular exception), permitting themselves excesses that to normal mortals would result in confinement in a penal or psychiatric institution. They became fantasy figures: admired and imitated in front of bathroom mirrors by lowly clerks and hen-pecked husbands, feared and loathed by orchestral musicians.

A characteristic anecdote is told of Serge Koussevitsky, who for twenty-five years governed the Boston Symphony Orchestra with a rod of iron. Visiting the death-bed of one of his musicians, the player, liberated by his impending demise from the inhibitions of caution, proceeded to tell the conductor in clinical detail what he thought of him, pouring out the resentment of years of terrorized subjugation. Koussevitsky listened to the tirade in genuine amazement: he could not believe that one of his 'children' would object to the chastisements which he administered, as he saw it, paternally and in a common interest. He left the bedside shaking his head in bewilderment. The poor musician, however, was to suffer greater agony. He survived his illness and had to return to Koussevitsky's orchestra where he did not have an easy time.

In a generation of autocrats, none was more feared than Arturo Toscanini. His tantrums were musical legends, salted to the point of obscenity by slang and peppered with frequent threats of physical injury to himself and his players. What made them tolerable was only their incontrovertible genuineness and the orchestra's sense that its pain was shared by the conductor, whose most exacting demands were made on himself. In his rages, he would rip pages out of his score, stamp on his watch, rend his clothes and tear his own flesh. He often returned home bleeding from self-inflicted wounds, but only once is he recorded to have injured a player.

In Turin in 1919, while rehearsing Beethoven's Ninth, he became dissatisfied with the performance of one of the second violins. 'What kind of scratching is that?' he demanded, throwing at the man the sopping handkerchief with which he had wiped his brow. 'I am playing, not scratching,' said the violinist. Toscanini charged over to his seat, arms flailing. 'You are rude', the musician managed to add, before Toscanini's baton descended on him. He caught the blow on his bow, which snapped and struck him on the forehead. His colleagues pulled him away and hustled him out of the hall before he could exact retribution. After an interval, the rehearsal continued.

The next day, Toscanini, seeing the offending violinist back in his seat, went over to him and shook his hand. Signora Toscanini made further amends by buying him a new bow. But the violinist was not placated. On the best legal advice, he sued Toscanini for assault; and lost. Under Italian law, the conductor was deemed to have acted under what the Romans called 'the tyranny of the tragic will', and was held not to be responsible for his conduct. It was only when political tyranny seized his beloved country that the maestro was called to account for his actions.

At a typical Beethoven rehearsal in New York, he stormed off the podium yelling threats and curses. 'Call yourselves musicians?' he demanded, pointing at his players one by one. 'Shame on you, and shame on *you*!' The door slammed behind him. A moment later it reopened and his head popped round with a parting cry: 'And shame on Toscanini!'

At times, he might temper a tantrum with a flash of unintentional humour. 'After I die,' he spluttered once, almost speechless with fury, 'I am coming back to earth as the doorkeeper of a bordello.' There was a pause while he let this demeaning fate sink in. 'And,' he added, 'I won't let a one of you in.'

Some weeks after his assault on the violinist, Toscanini met an eloquent journalist, Benito Mussolini by name, and was enrolled as a supporter of his newly-formed Fascist Party. Its programme at the time consisted mainly of moderate Socialist policies aimed at achieving post-war national reconstruction. It was only after the electorate of Milan snubbed him at the ballot box that Mussolini embraced authoritarianism and proceeded to seize power by threat of violence. By the time the Fascists marched on Rome in 1922, Toscanini had long since broken with them and was embarrassed to be reminded of his initial adherence.

Toscanini quickly came into conflict with the totalitarian state. Conducting *Falstaff* at La Scala a few weeks after Mussolini's coup, he ignored demands from Fascists in the audience to play the Party's hymn, the *Giovinezza*. When their shouts persisted during the performance, he snapped his baton in two and walked out. The disrupters were silenced by a promise from the management that their song would be played at the end. Toscanini returned, but when the curtain fell he refused to let the singers reappear for the anthem, exclaiming: 'They are artists of La Scala, not of vaudeville!' Nor would he allow his orchestra to play the *Giovinezza,* claiming they were unfamiliar with the music. To avert a riot, someone plinked out the hymn on a stage piano and the Fascists departed, muttering.

They were not yet confident enough of their power to attack the popular conductor and did not respond when he defied an order to hang Mussolini's portrait in La Scala, nor when he staged a one-man demonstration at the funeral of the Director of the Milan Conservatory, who was hounded by the Fascists into committing suicide. When they finally decided to stage a reprisal, however, they did so with all the brutality for which the conductor so unremittingly opposed their régime.

In May 1931, Toscanini, sixty-four years old, went to Bologna to conduct two concerts. On the eve of the first, he was informed that the presence of two Cabinet Ministers in the audience would oblige him to begin the programmes with the *Giovinezza*; Toscanini refused point-blank. Arriving at the concert hall with his wife and daughter before the performance, his car was surrounded by brawny youths. 'Are you going to play the *Giovinezza?*' one of them demanded. When the conductor shook his head, they seized him and beat him around the face and head. He was hauled out of the mêlée by his chauffeur, while policemen stood idly by, and driven back to his hotel where a Fascist mob gathered under his window and chanted slogans. A message arrived from Party headquarters that he was to leave town before daybreak or they would not be responsible for his safety. Mussolini, initially delighted at the roughing up of his former friend, personally congratulated the Bologna godfathers who had sponsored the assault and ordered Toscanini's passport to be confiscated. But he began to have regrets when a chorus of protests arose abroad, echoed by sporadic pro-Toscanini demonstrations inside Italy. Koussevitsky cancelled his performances at La Scala; other musicians who came to Italy made a point of visiting Toscanini, who was under virtual house arrest. A month later Toscanini's passport was returned and he was allowed to leave and re-enter the country freely.

He went straight to Bayreuth for the Festival, still suffering the after-effects of the mugging. An old shoulder injury began to trouble him and conducting became an ordeal. His depression was deepened by the drift he observed in Germany towards the savagery he abhorred in Italy. To add to his discomfort, there was an unsettling conflict at the Festival between Winifred Wagner's newly-installed management, and the old guard headed by her sisters-in-law; there was also an underlying and unspoken tension between Toscanini and the German conductor with whom he shared the Festival, Wilhelm Furtwängler.

No two musical rivals can ever have been so diametrically dissimilar. Toscanini was short, smartly dressed, exuding energy to the point of explosion, extrovert, effusive in his outbursts. Furtwängler was a tall, fair, gangling man with a giraffe's neck, sartorially dishevelled, meditative, painfully shy, reserved to the point of rudeness. Toscanini dealt with his own contracts and engagements brusquely and efficiently; Furtwängler was pathetically helpless when separated from his orchestral manager, Bertha Geissmar. Their methods of conducting were also antithetical. Toscanini gave a short, precise beat with his baton that was instantly comprehensible to any musician. Furtwängler's handling of the baton was uncertain. It has been described variously as a nervous waggle, a vague quivering motion and a trembling of the hand. It was decipherable only by musicians who had trained under Furtwängler and even they did not understand quite how they responded to it. The conductor Antal Dorati asked his father, who had played under Furtwängler in Budapest, how the orchestra ever managed to start in unison under the conductor's wavering gestures. 'We never start together,' his father replied; it just sounded as though they did. Proof of his genius was supplied by the unequalled Berlin Philharmonic Orchestra, which he led for thirty years, drawing from it a precision that became its hallmark and his own.

The two conductors shared a wary respect for each other's abilities, but had little else in common. When Hitler came to power, Toscanini boycotted Germany, Furtwängler remained. Never a Nazi, he believed that by staying in Germany he could best protect his orchestra and help preserve a modicum of the national sanity. Initially he had some success. The Nazis let him retain Jewish players in the Berlin Philharmonic and encouraged him in a quixotic attempt to lure foreign soloists to play in

Furtwängler depicted in divine birth

Berlin. Yehudi Menuhin, Pablo Casals, Artur Schnabel, Fritz Kreisler and Josef Hofman refused outright. The violinist Bronislaw Huberman replied in an open letter that his rejection of Nazi Germany

> is not a question of violin concertos nor even merely of Jews; the issue is the retention of those things that our fathers achieved by blood and sacrifice, of the elementary pre-conditions of our European culture, the freedom of personality and its unconditional self-responsibility.

Huberman went instead to Palestine where he founded an orchestra composed of exiled Germans, whose ranks were later swelled by refugees from Nazi-conquered nations. Toscanini travelled to the Holy Land to conduct its inaugural concerts.

Only the Swiss-born pianist, Alfred Cortot, consented to play in Berlin, where he became a convert to Nazism. Furtwängler, ever more isolated, came under unrelenting pressure to give formal acknowledgement to the New Germany by playing its strident anthems and hailing its leaders with an outstretched arm. Slowly the screws of the police state tightened on the conductor. His appeal to Hitler for the reinstatement of his fellow conductors Bruno Walter and Otto Klemperer was contemptuously rejected by the Propaganda Minister, Josef Goebbels. He continued to resist the changes and finally came into open conflict with the Nazis over his right to decide what music he conducted. Early in 1934 he gave the first performance of a set of three suites from a forthcoming opera *Matthias the Painter (Mathis der Maler)* by the modernist composer Paul Hindemith. It was a tremendous success with the audience but the Nazis vilified the music in their newspapers and refused permission for the opera to be performed. Furtwängler responded with an article in the *Deutsche Allgemeine Zeitung*, one of the last relatively free newspapers, maintaining that Germany could ill afford to dispense with Hindemith, having lost so much other genius, and concluding naïvely: 'What would happen if vague political denunciations were to be applied constantly to artists?'

The newspaper was snapped up on the streets and printed extra editions; not long afterwards it was brought under rigid Party control after its editor was killed in a suspicious accident. Furtwängler conducted twice on the day his article was published. Both audiences rose to cheer him for fully twenty minutes before he could nervously give his baton its first waggle. Goering and Goebbels were present at the second demonstration and understood its implications. When Furtwängler followed his printed protest by resigning on the following day from the Berlin Philharmonic and the Berlin Opera (along with Erich Kleiber, who managed to leave the country), he experienced for the first time the penalty of Nazi disfavour. His passport was seized and he was confined, like Toscanini in Italy, to effective house arrest. Worse, he was cut off from his personal manager Bertha Geissmar, whom the Gestapo now felt free to persecute for her Jewish ancestry. Dr Geissmar, who in the past had extricated Furtwängler from the consequences of many indiscretions (she had once viciously slapped down his hand as he was about to shake on a rash agreement to conduct the Vienna Philharmonic, taking him aside and reminding him forcibly that his principal loyalty was to Berlin), was no longer able to help. She was lucky to be allowed out of

Germany and settled in London, where Sir Thomas Beecham employed her to direct his affairs.

Furtwängler was eventually permitted to emerge from seclusion on the personal order of Hitler, who acknowledged him as Germany's finest conductor. But other Nazi leaders had marked him down as a troublemaker and lost no opportunity to expose him to humiliation. In 1938, they launched a drive to replace Furtwängler with an up-and-coming young conductor from Salzburg who had made a name for himself in Aachen, where he had pragmatically joined the Nazi Party. They secured his appointment to the Berlin State Opera and Goebbels's newspapers trumpeted the accomplishments of this new star whom they dubbed *Das Wunder Karajan* — The Wonder Karajan.

Furtwängler's supporters among the Nazi hierarchy sprang to his defence. A campaign of Byzantine intrigues broke out among followers of the two conductors, a battle which lasted long after the War. When his opponents protested to Hitler at Furtwängler's conscientious refusal to conduct in the occupied countries, his supporters hinted that they might take issue with the fact that Herbert von Karajan's wife was half-Jewish. When Karajan seemed poised to replace Furtwängler at the Berlin Philharmonic, supporters of the incumbent arranged for him to receive call-up papers. Karajan's dispatch to the Russian Front was averted only by a chance remark to his dentist on the day before his departure. The dentist telephoned his daughter, who happened to be Goebbels's secretary, and Karajan's mobilization was promptly annulled.

Furtwängler remained in Germany until the end of 1944. At the orchestra's last concert that year he invited the Minister of Armaments, Albert Speer, a middle-class music-loving technocrat, to his dressing-room to ask him, 'with disarming unworldliness . . . whether we had any prospect of winning the war.' Speer replied that the situation was hopeless and advised Furtwängler to take the opportunity of a concert tour in Switzerland to remain abroad — particularly since his old enemies Goebbels and Himmler were contemplating a final revenge for his many acts of disobedience. 'But what will become of my orchestra?' Furtwängler demanded, 'I am responsible for it.' Speer promised to take it under his personal protection and claims to have thwarted a last-ditch attempt by Goebbels to mobilize the musicians into the defence of Berlin. 'I alone raised this orchestra to its special level,' the Propaganda Minister had bragged. 'It can go under together with me.'

The Philharmonic survived him, though, and continued playing among the ruins of Berlin under the baton of a brilliant young Rumanian, Sergiu Celibidache, who was studying music in the city when it fell and was possibly the only person there capable of wielding a baton whom the Allies were certain was not a Nazi. Furtwängler and Karajan were both banned from conducting for two years until they had been cleared by de-nazification courts. When Celibidache abdicated his position in 1951 to go East in search of a mystic philosophy, Furtwängler resumed the principal conductorship. Although he was succeeded on his death by Karajan, the Nazi-inspired conflict between them continued to the last: as long as Furtwängler conducted the Berlin Philharmonic, Karajan was banned from its rostrum.

Their tenure under the Nazis also engendered considerable opposition abroad, an antagonism that was led by their fellow-conductors and, in Furtwängler's case, by his old rival Toscanini. The Italian maestro had originally sympathized with Furtwängler's political dilemma in Germany and did not condemn him for remaining. When Toscanini quit the New York Philharmonic in 1936, it was Furtwängler whom he recommended to the orchestra as his successor. The proposed appointment, however, aroused a storm of protest from both anti-Nazis, who objected to his acceptability in Germany, and pro-Nazis, who wanted him to stay in Germany. Furtwängler withdrew his candidacy with a cable that encapsulated his innocent view of the world:

Political controversy disagreeable to me. Am not politician but exponent of German music which belongs to all humanity regardless of politics. Propose postpone my season in the interest of Philharmonic Society until the time that public realizes that politics and music are apart. Furtwängler.

What set Toscanini firmly against Furtwängler was his decision later that year to conduct again at the Bayreuth Festival, which for the Italian symbolized his own boycott of the Nazis. That Furtwängler should conduct for Hitler at Bayreuth was unforgivable. The two conductors met for the last time in 1937 in neutral Austria at the Salzburg Festival and relations between them were icy. By the next Salzburg Festival, Austria had fallen to the Nazis and Furtwängler once again filled a Toscanini vacancy, by taking over his production of *The Mastersingers*. Toscanini went back to Palestine, blithely ignoring fears for his safety in the Arab-Jewish troubles.

After the War Furtwängler, though he resumed most of his European engagements, was never allowed back into the United States. Each time an American concert tour was mooted it provoked fierce resistance, surreptitiously conducted, many believed, by Toscanini. Orchestras threatened to strike, newspapers said they would not review his concerts, stevedores warned they would not handle the Berliners' baggage. Furtwängler died in 1954, predeceasing Toscanini (who was twenty years his senior), a forlorn figure, as brave a man as his opponent but not as resolute in putting his principles into practice.

Arnold Schoenberg, spiritual leader of the exiles, who had no particular sympathy for Furtwängler, was almost the only voice to speak out against Toscanini's exploitation of emotive issues to pursue a personal vendetta. 'This powerful man,' he wrote in 1946,

> whose vocabulary is not great enough to explain his ideas to musicians, the man who throws a golden watch on the floor in anger at his verbal impotence — this man is capable of keeping a Furtwängler, who is many times his superior, from conducting in America and the rest of the world.

It was Karajan who took Furtwängler's orchestra to America in the year after his death, but the demonstrations he faced were so unsettling that no further tour was conducted for some years.

Political concerns and rivalry with each other, engaging though they may be, are not the principal conflicts of a conductor's life. That distinction is reserved for his regular confrontation from the rostrum with players whose reaction to commands varies from passive resistance to open mutiny. The hardest are the early days, when almost every young conductor has difficulty in convincing a world-weary band that he has something new to offer. Even Artur Nikisch, the Hungarian wizard who preceded Furtwängler at the Berlin Philharmonic, encountered orchestral rebellion in his youth. At twenty-two he was hired to conduct the Leipzig Gewandhaus Orchestra by its impresario Angelo Neumann who, with full confidence in his abilities, immediately went on holiday. His vacation was disturbed by a telegram from Leipzig reading:

> 'Orchestra refuses to play under Nikisch. Too young!'
> Just as I was about to leave for Leipzig an idea struck me and I telegraphed — 'Don't postpone *Tannhäuser* on any account. Keep to programme, Nikisch conducting rehearsal to-morrow. Call meeting of orchestra *before* rehearsal, and show them clearly they are exceeding their rights in this matter. After having explained their rights and their limitations tell them, if they are still of the same mind, they may hand in their resignations at the *Tannhäuser* rehearsal tomorrow; and at the end of the overture may say whether they will hold to their decision or not. In case the orchestra should then resign I shall come directly back to Leipzig.'

One rehearsal with Nikisch was enough to convince the Leipzigers that they had a genius on their hands and would look foolish if they drove him out. When Nikisch put his baton down, the orchestra rose to cheer him and — uniquely — begged him to extend the rehearsal.

Nikisch had achieved triumph over massed adversity without uttering a harsh word. 'Perhaps you would be kind enough to play that again?' was his most severe admonition. As he matured, he remembered to greet each new orchestra with a broad smile and tell them how proud he was to conduct such a truly wonderful band of players. He flattered his musicians and they loved him for it; after his initial setback at Leipzig, there is scarcely another conflict in his career. He disappears from our narrative as unexpectedly as he entered it.

Another gentle man, an American, won his spurs as a conductor through his excellence in the martial arts. John Philip Sousa's first salaried engagement was as leader of the Band of the US Marines, which he served with distinction and bravery from 1880 to 1892. He liked the army so much that when he got out he formed his own military band of civilians, composing for it around a hundred popular marches, among them *The Stars and Stripes*. But until he became master of his own band he found orchestral musicians hard to live with, especially in those mid-Western territories where a man was reputedly a man and a musician could ill afford to be much less.

I went to the theatre and found the orchestra in the music room under the stage. The leader said, 'You might as well know the boys and I'll just introduce you. What is your name?' 'My name,' I answered, 'is Sousa.'

'Well, Sousa,' this with an awkward bow, 'allow me to introduce Professor Smith, our second fid; and, Sousa, this is Professor Brown, our clarinet player; and, Sousa, this is Professor Perkins, our bull fid, and this,' pointing to a cadaverous-looking fellow, 'is Professor Jones, who agitates the ivories on our pipe organ. Sousa, these are Professors Jim and Bill Simpson, solo and first cornet; this is Professor Reed, who whacks the bull drum, and yours truly, solo trombone. Now that all of us know each other, what is your overture?'

I explained that the overture we used I had written myself and it had met with some favour.

'I ain't sayin' that's so or not, but it won't go here. Will it boys?'

A unanimous 'No' from the orchestra dispelled any doubt as to their feelings. I expostulated with warmth and injured pride:

'But you have never heard my overture, you know nothing about it, and I can assure you it is all right.'

'It may be all right in Chicago or Bosting, but I tell you it won't go here. I got the overture that our people want and that's the one we are going to play tonight.'

Not wishing to end a promising career abruptly in the OK Corral, Sousa backed down, but soon discovered that the professorial ensemble was barely competent to play even the easiest music. 'This is the rottenest orchestra I ever heard,' the young conductor declared, urgently beckoning to the sheriff before the musicians could reach for their holster instruments.

The inability of an orchestra to play music that is beyond its capabilities is a frequent cause of strife. Rehearsing *Pierrot Lunaire* in Vienna in 1913, Arnold Schoenberg was confronted first by the violinists who could not abide the sounds they were making ('You are just playing badly,' he insisted), then by a horn player who simply could not get his mouth round Schoenberg's dissonances. Maddened by his own limitations, the musician stood up and challenged his colleagues in the strings: 'If you won't kill him, I will!' Horn aloft he rushed at the composer, whose balding head was buried in his gigantic score. He was overpowered by Schoenberg's pupils and sent home to practise his part alone. He locked himself in a room for four days and did nothing but play Schoenberg's score. When he emerged, he had mastered the part and considered it the most beautiful music he had ever set lips on. He rushed round to Schoenberg's house to apologize for his behaviour; the composer stared at him blankly, as unmoved by his enthusiasm as by his previous antagonism.

Sometimes the roles are reversed when the orchestra can play a new score but its composer cannot conduct it. Claude Debussy, arriving in London to conduct his three *Nocturnes* in 1909, found an orchestra at the Queens Hall that had been well-trained by Sir Henry Wood. His rehearsal went off without incident, but on the night of the concert Debussy lost his way among the rapid changes of beat in the second *Nocturne,* which shifts swiftly between three and five beats in a bar. Beating three where five were indicated, and five instead of three, Debussy came unstuck. Tears of shame trickling down his cheeks, he tapped on his desk for the orchestra to stop and dropped his arms abjectly to his sides. To his anguish, the orchestra ignored him and carried on playing the complicated piece in perfect time, with sublime disdain for the hapless conductor. The audience gave them a standing ovation and insisted on having the piece repeated. In the encore, the orchestra generously allowed Debussy to conduct.

The obduracy of orchestral players has driven even the toughest of conductors to despair, desertion, dementia and close to self-destruction. Sir John Barbirolli, the affable Anglo-Italian who succeeded Toscanini at the New York Philharmonic, was driven out after seven mutinous years. His successor, the tyrannical Artur Rodzinski, whose first act as conductor was to fire fourteen players, lasted barely half as long. He was forced to quit in 1947 and promptly took over the Chicago Symphony Orchestra. There he survived only three months before being sacked for last minute program changes, causing confusion in rehearsals, exceeding the budget by $30,000 and attempting to secure a three-year contract,

of which the last offence was, presumably, the most heinous in its presumption.

The gruff and unpopular Otto Klemperer was subverted more insidiously by his players. After falling through the railings of a podium in 1933, his health was permanently impaired and he underwent a succession of debilitating and disfiguring brain operations. When he was ready to resume conducting, malicious musicians put about rumours that Klemperer had escaped from a lunatic asylum and was considered dangerous. However much he denied the reports, there were many who were only too glad to believe them. To counteract the slanders, Klemperer sank his life's savings into a concert at Carnegie Hall, where he convinced the public that he was as sane and competent as any conductor.

He endured further misfortunes in later years, including an accident in which he sustained severe burns through smoking in bed and then trying to douse a smouldering sheet with the only liquid at hand: whisky. He managed to overcome calamity with an extraordinary resilience and lived to the age of eighty-eight, conducting almost to the last.

His constitution would have been envied by his stricken mentor, Gustav Mahler. If any conductor can be said to have been driven to an early grave by his orchestras, it is Mahler. His death at fifty shocked even his fiercest opponents and the last journey of the dying man from Paris to Vienna resembled the funeral cortège of a monarch, with civic and musical personalities turning out to pay homage at each railway station where his train stopped. While he was vigorously alive, though, he had earned the unremitting hatred of orchestral musicians of whom he demanded more in effort and intelligence than any conductor had previously dared. He required that every player should be a virtuoso on his instrument and was particularly feared by back-desk players whom he made stand up in rehearsal and play their parts solo.

He first conducted at the age of eighteen at Hall in Upper Austria. It was an inauspicious start, in which his duties included wheeling the impresario's baby in its pram during intervals. But he quickly established a reputation for orchestral achievement which began to spread around the provinces of the crumbling Empire and into Germany. Between 1882 and 1888 he was hired and fired successively at Laibach, Olmütz, Cassel, Prague, Leipzig and Budapest. The orchestra at Cassel, rehearsed beyond endurance, plotted to cut short his career by giving the young upstart a physical beating. Warned of their plans, Mahler disdained precautions. On the day scheduled for the attack he tore into rehearsal and put the

Mahler conducting

players so furiously through their paces that they had not the energy left at the end to carry out their plan. Glaring at them one by one, Mahler slammed down the lid of his grand piano and stalked out without a word.

Despite the upheavals that attended his activities, Mahler's prestige continued to rise in a spiral of mobility that conquered many of Europe's musical summits before his thirtieth birthday. In Budapest he impressed the young Richard Strauss, who recommended him to his own sponsor, the veteran conductor Hans von Bülow, who in turn helped him obtain the post of chief conductor at the Hamburg Opera. Six years later, at only thirty-seven, he was appointed to the premier opera position in Europe, Director of the Vienna Opera. Over the next decade he instigated what is still recalled as the Golden Age of Vienna Opera, the most exhilarating, provocative and revolutionary period in the history of musical performance in a city that considered itself to be the fount of musical performance. But the price of his zealotry was high. The horizons of music were littered with the victims of his aspirations; he himself became their last casualty.

He stormed into Vienna as though he meant to demolish and reconstruct its venerable musical foundations: which he did. '*Tradition ist schlamperei!*', tradition is sloppy, he proclaimed to a city whose religion was tradition. Confronting the Vienna Philharmonic Orchestra, the world's finest not least in its own estimation, he treated veteran musicians like novices and made them repeat familiar music over and over again until he was satisfied. Rehearsing Beethoven's Fifth Symphony, which had received its première in Vienna a century earlier, he made the experienced orchestra play the ominous opening bars time and again until several musicians got up to leave in a rage and others defiantly laid down their instruments. 'Gentlemen,' barked Mahler. 'Save your fury for the performance and then we might at last have the opening played as it should be.'

The orchestra, a self-governing body, rid itself of the troublesome conductor for its concerts as soon as it could, but was forced to continue to serve him at the Opera House, where both orchestra and conductor were Imperial employees. To try and bring about Mahler's dismissal, musicians intrigued against him in Court and spread scandalous rumours in the Press. His decade in Vienna was a constant struggle with all the forces of the musical establishment, some of whom stooped so low as to align themselves with the gutter anti-semitic newspapers (Mahler had been born a Jew, but converted to Roman Catholicism to qualify for the Vienna appointment). When one violinist remarked to another that Mahler was no more severe than Hans Richter, he was told unequivocally: 'That is true. But Richter is one of us. We can take it from him.'

What hurt Mahler more than the conspiracies and insults, more than the conservative and racialist demonstrations during his concerts, what was probably the final straw that made him quit Vienna in 1907, was the persistent rejection by both orchestra and public of the symphonies he devoted all his spare time to composing. To orchestral players at the turn of the century, Mahler's symphonies were the most difficult, part for part, they had ever encountered. If Mahler expected orchestral musicians to be of soloist standard in conventional repertoire, in his own music he made demands that would tax even virtuosi. His scores exposed musicians' inadequacies, making them detest him all the more. The public, hearing music that was startlingly unusual and badly played, responded negatively. After one disastrous première, Mahler told the orchestra that he felt 'like a general abandoned by his troops'.

Only the younger generation continued to support him, flocking to his operas and concerts with an adulation that bordered on idolatry. Mahler responded to their ardour by searching constantly for fresh challenges. He was among the first to lend an ear to the extraordinary idea propounded by Schoenberg that tonality was obsolete. He disagreed violently with what Schoenberg said, but, like Voltaire, would fight to the death for his right to say so. One of his last acts as a dying man was to send money to Schoenberg; among his last words were: 'Schoenberg, if I go, he will have nobody left.'

When he left Vienna, driven out by his musical enemies, he died the death of a dream. Vienna had been the pinnacle of his life's ambition as a conductor, the directorship of its Opera a prize he had aspired to since his childhood in rural Moravia. Cut adrift, he sailed to New York but quickly despaired of transforming American standards of musicianship. All he cared for now were his family and his symphonies, scribbling away frantically at his scores until the coronary illness contracted in Vienna overwhelmed his weakened frame. He died within four years of giving up Vienna, leaving behind a gigantic reputation as a conductor and a legacy of four extraordinary song cycles and ten engrossing symphonies, the last one unfinished.

Mahler's music, like Schoenberg's, did not only outrage orchestras. The most eminent composers of the day confessed themselves baffled by his unique musical language, in which the sublime alternated and mingled imperceptibly with the banal. Johannes Brahms, who thought him an excellent conductor, expressed reservations about his symphonies. On a country walk, when the older man grumbled that music had reached its peak and was now in decline, Mahler interrupted him as they crossed a bridge and pointed downwards at the flowing brook below. 'What's that?' asked Brahms. 'The *last* ripple,' said Mahler ironically. 'Well, it all depends,' Brahms conceded allegorically, 'whether it is going down to the sea or whether it will lose itself in a swamp.' Brahms' adversary, Anton Bruckner, whose gigantic symphonies Mahler helped rescue from obscurity, also had little enthusiasm for the younger man's compositions. Even Arnold Schoenberg, Mahler's protégé and beneficiary, at one time doubted his greatness as a composer, though he later told his own pupils that he learned more about counterpoint from watching Mahler knot his tie than from three years' study at a conservatory.

Mahler's most crushing disappointment, however, was the rejection of his music by Hans von Bülow, the conductor who had done more than anyone to advance the 'new' German music of Wagner, Liszt, Bruckner and Brahms. Bülow had also salvaged from a Russian oblivion what was to become one of the perennially most beloved concert works, Tchaikovsky's first piano concerto. The composer had intended the concerto for Anton Rubinstein, but the latter, the most celebrated Russian musician of the day, having heard Tchaikovsky play the concerto through on the piano, pronounced it unplayable, inept, trivial, partly plagiarized, and worse. Only one or two pages were worth saving, Rubinstein said, the rest should be burned. Tchaikovsky scratched out Rubinstein's name on the dedication, replacing it in desperation with Bülow's, and sent the score to the conductor in Germany. Bülow's reaction was the very reverse of Rubinstein's. He found the concerto lofty, strong and original, 'qualities which compel me to congratulate not only the composer, but all those who will enjoy the work in the future'.

Bülow's perceptiveness was combined with a conductorial arrogance, an utter disregard for conventional musical wisdom and accepted political authority. He treated his audiences as serfs and his aristocratic patrons as little higher. When booed while conducting a work by Liszt, Bülow stopped the orchestra, turned round and announced: 'It is against the rules to boo here. Would those who are doing so please leave the hall.' Applauded for an inspired performance of Beethoven's Ninth, he bowed to the audience, thanked them and ordered them to sit down again while he repeated the entire symphony. He ensured that they endured the full hour of the encore by ordering the doors of the auditorium to be locked. When he had a political point to make, he used his podium as a platform. Angered at young Kaiser Wilhelm's sacking of the venerated Bismarck, Bülow prefaced a Berlin performance of Beethoven's Eroica Symphony with a brief sermon on its composer, ending rebelliously, 'and I dedicate this performance to Chancellor Bismarck, the Beethoven of German politics.'

It was in this maverick arbiter of modern music that Mahler placed his faith for recognition as a composer. Shortly after joining the Hamburg Opera, he visited his fellow-conductor with a score under his arm. Bülow agreed to listen to Mahler play through part of his Second Symphony on the piano, but when the composer looked up from the keyboard he saw the old conductor standing by the window clasping his hands to his ears. Alarmed, he rose from the piano, but Bülow, without removing his hands from his head, motioned for him to continue. When he had finished there was a silence. Then Bülow said, more in bewilderment than reproach, 'If that was music, I no longer understand anything about the subject.'

Mahler's dejection was overwhelming; he spoke of being condemned to compose forever for the drawers of his desk. It was some years before he could summon the defiance to proclaim, prophetically: 'My time will come.'

He was, incidentally, not the only great conductor to harbour the notion that he was an important composer. Weingartner, Klemperer and Furtwängler all set great store by their own compositions, but few other conductors believed in them. By way of contrast, Bülow and Toscanini both composed in their youth, but gave up the vice once they acknowledged their inadequacy.

The only consolation that Mahler could find in Bülow's rebuff was the knowledge that the conductor was by now too worn to care much for innovatory music. He was ageing fast, tired, ill and, above all, war-weary. He had spent almost the whole of the previous half-century, from his teenage years, fighting at the epicentre of the greatest conflagration music has known. Wherever the battle raged, Bülow was there with his baton raised, fighting first for one side, then for the other. It cost him dearly. He lost the love of his life, his young family, temporarily his sanity and ultimately his faith in human nature.

CHAPTER NINE

CIVIL WAR

$\mathcal{O}$f all wars, none is more savage than one fought among citizens of the same nation. The grievances of a civil war run deep and are not easily healed by peace treaty. The last of the generation of combatants must die before all hard feelings are laid to rest. Civil dissension, wrote Shakespeare, is a viperous worm that gnaws the bowels of the commonwealth. Cicero acknowledged even greater foreboding: 'Any sort of peace with our fellow-citizens seems to me preferable to civil war.' It is in the nature of proximity, however, to breed dissent and few fellow-countrymen are more certain to arouse national controversy than two composers who take up arms against each other.

In the 1890s, two opera composers plunged Italy into civil strife in a struggle over a libretto. Giacomo Puccini and Ruggero Leoncavallo, born within a year of each other and rising stars of the post-Verdi generation, were both scouting around for a new opera to follow their first triumphs, Puccini's with *Manon Lescaut* and Leoncavallo's with the short *Pagliacci* (destined to form the tireless Cav-and-Pag double bill with Mascagni's *Cavalleria Rusticana*). By coincidence they stumbled separately on a fifty-year-old novel depicting the everyday melodramas of the artistic community of Paris. Puccini, warned by his publisher Ricordi that Leoncavallo was writing an opera from the same book as he, preserved strict silence. Leoncavallo, however, blabbered on blithely about his work to anyone who would listen, including Puccini to whom he showed his scenario. When Leoncavallo, over beer at a Milan café, finally wheedled Puccini out of his secrecy, they almost came to blows. Abandoning their drinks, both composers raced over to their publishers, and then back to their composing desks. Next morning, *Il Secolo*, a newspaper owned by Leoncavallo's publisher, carried banner headline news of his forthcoming opera. The evening paper *Corriere della Serra*, sympathetic to Ricordi, carried exclusive news of Puccini's next project. Throughout the ensuing controversy, Puccini remained unperturbed: 'Let him compose and I shall compose and the public will judge.'

Justice being blind, the public received Puccini's *La Bohème* very coolly at its Turin première under Arturo Toscanini. By contrast, Leoncavallo's opera, also entitled *La Bohème* and finished fifteen months later, had enormous success at its première in Venice, thanks in no small way to the extraordinary début of a young tenor, Enrico Caruso. It was given at Vienna (against the advice of Gustav Mahler who protested that Puccini's work was superior), but thereafter rather suddenly lost ground to its rival, which rose to become one of the most durable international box office successes. Leoncavallo became convinced that he had been the victim of sabotage, as his opera gradually sank into near-oblivion. Its American première was not given until 1960, its English only in 1970.

By coincidence, Puccini's next opera again involved him in a confrontation with a fellow-Italian composer over a libretto. Puccini had been offered by Ricordi a chance to set to music a French play by Victorien Sardou in which Sarah Bernhardt had given one of her most memorable performances, but he did not care much for the subject. Ricordi handed the play to another of his contracted composers, Alberto Franchetti, known as the Meyerbeer of Italy, whose private fortune enabled him to write music without having to earn a living from it and to finance the most lavish productions of his operas. Franchetti set to his task ambitiously and showed his initial sketches to the venerated Verdi, who was so impressed by the libretto that he declared he would have coveted it for one of his own operas if only he were a few years younger.

When Puccini heard of Verdi's verdict, he immediately changed his mind about the opera. He instructed Ricordi that he would now write *Tosca*, and he alone. The publisher, realizing that Puccini was a better prospect than Franchetti, was faced with the delicate task of relieving the other composer of his libretto without starting a war within his own publishing house.

Franchetti, still cock-a-hoop from Verdi's encomium, was approached without warning by a long-faced deputation of publishing staff. Reconsidering the Sardou play, they said, it was not really suitable for Italian opera. It contained an attempted rape and a violent murder which would revolt the pure-minded public, and the plot was anyway too melodramatic, not realistic enough, too risqué, too bland, too foreign, insufficiently cosmopolitan. As reservation followed contradictory reservation, Franchetti's confidence in the opera ebbed away. When Ricordi offered him an option to withdraw from his contract, he seized it with grateful relief. The very next day, Ricordi commissioned Puccini to compose *Tosca*.

It was a libretto again that lay at the heart of the operatic quarrel which provoked civil war in the placid by-waters of English music. For fifteen years or more, the English-speaking world found as much fascination and amusement in the fights of Gilbert and Sullivan as in their light operas. Arthur Sullivan and William Schwenck Gilbert had been from the outset an unlikely pair of collaborators. Sullivan, an inventive melodist, was deemed the brightest hope for English music since Handel, his youthful suite to Shakespeare's *Tempest* enrapturing critics as exacting as Rossini and Charles Dickens. Gilbert, a barrister of biting and occasionally sadistic wit, took pride in being totally unmusical. 'I know only two tunes,' he boasted. 'One is "God Save the Queen". The other isn't.' Sullivan, though of working-class origins, possessed such natural grace that aristocracy and even royalty fawned at his feet. Gilbert was a middle-class man with social ambitions, most of them frustrated. Even when their partnership was at its most fruitful, Gilbert and Sullivan saw nothing of each other socially and surprisingly little of each other at work, much of their collaboration being conducted by correspondence.

Aside from these contrasts of personality, they differed fundamentally in attitude to their joint work. While both men wrote light operas for the money, Gilbert saw the comedies as an end in themselves, but Sullivan was primarily interested in using them as a source of income while composing serious music. After he was knighted in 1883, the musical expectations of Sir Arthur rose even higher than the fond hopes that had been cherished of a mere Mr Sullivan. Queen Victoria herself commanded him: 'You ought to write *grand* opera, Sir Arthur, you would do it so well.' By this time, however, his youthful spark was gone and anything he did without Gilbert was little above mediocre. When the Queen ordered a Command Performance, it was not an oratorio or symphony that she wanted but *The Gondoliers*. By a quirk of cultural snobbery, the programme on this occasion advertised Sullivan's authorship in big letters but omitted Gilbert's name altogether. The librettist was made to wait almost a quarter of a century longer than the composer for his knighthood.

These snubs rankled greatly with Gilbert, who saw himself as the motivating member of the partnership. 'The verse always preceded the music, or even any hint of it,' he told an interviewer. His was also the dominant personality:

> My boy you may take it from me [he wrote in *Ruddigore*]
> That of all the afflictions accurst
> With which a man's saddled
> And hampered and addled
> A diffident nature's the worst.

Yet when Sullivan overcame his natural diffidence to announce, after completing *Princess Ida*, that he would not write another comic opera, Gilbert was lost for words. It was left to their business partner Richard D'Oyly Carte, whose Savoy Theatre was founded on Gilbert and Sullivan successes, to remind Sullivan that he was bound by a five-year legal agreement with himself and Gilbert to compose on demand. Gilbert followed this threat by submitting a new libretto for Sullivan's approval, for, as he disingenuously put it, 'in all the pieces we have written together I have invariably subordinated my views to your own.' Sullivan's resistance crumbled under this double assault and he countered feebly that all he wanted was a more realistic plot. The new libretto was, however, the most unrealistic plot of all, a satire on English manners set in ancient Japan, called *The Mikado*. It became their greatest success.

More rows followed over *Ruddigore* and *The Yeomen of the Guard* and, though it was announced that they had 'buried the hatchet completely' with *The Gondoliers*, it was the prelude to a fight that broke up the partnership. The tone of their exchanges had been growing ever sharper.

Dear Sullivan:
Your letter has filled me with amazement and regret. If you are really under the astounding impression that you have been effacing yourself during the last twelve months . . . then there is most certainly no *modus vivendi* to be found that shall be satisfactory to both of us.

My dear Gilbert:
I was so annoyed at your abrupt letter to me that I thought it wiser not to answer it without a few days' delay . . . All I ask is that in the future my judgement and opinion should have some weight with you in the laying out of the musical situation . . .

If you will accept all this in the spirit in which I write we can go on smoothly as if nothing had happened and, I hope, successfully. If not, I shall regret it deeply, but, in any case, you will hear no more recrimination on my part.

Dear Sullivan:
. . . when you deliberately assert that for twelve years you, incomparably the greatest English musician of the age — a man whose genius is a proverb wherever the English tongue is spoken — a man who can deal *en prince* with operatic managers, singers, music publishers and musical societies, when you, who hold this unparalleled position deliberately state that you have submitted silently and uncomplainingly for twelve years to be extinguished, ignored, set aside, rebuffed and generally effaced by your librettist, you grievously reflect, not upon him, but upon yourself and the noble art of which you are so eminent a professor.

Once *The Gondoliers* was staged, Gilbert discovered a new *causus belli*. Examining the accounts, he found that £500 had been deducted from his royalties by Carte for re-carpeting the Savoy Theatre. He protested to Sullivan, but the composer perversely took the impresario's side. Gilbert called in his solicitors. British and American newspapers, which had long entertained their readers with the latest imbroglios in the partnership, assigned special correspondents to the dispute. Barely a day went by without a fresh slander to be reported. With *The Gondoliers* playing to packed houses at the Savoy, Gilbert applied for the theatre to

Gilbert vs *Sullivan* (Spy)

be declared bankrupt and a receiver appointed. The full panoply of British justice was invoked to examine the carpet tiff and Carte's accounts were found wanting, though not excessively so.

Gilbert, having been awarded £1,000 and his legal expenses, offered to resume the partnership, but Sullivan had used the rupture to begin work at last on a grand opera. *Ivanhoe*, when performed, was moderately successful, but not in the same financial league as the Savoy operas. Gilbert, who declined Sullivan's invitation to the première, was gratified by its relative failure; and said so. But his own attempt to write a comic opera with another composer also flopped. Each dismayed by his individual incompetence, Gilbert and Sullivan found themselves thrown back into an uneasy embrace. But they had fought each other to a standstill and the title of their reconciliatory opera, *Utopia Limited*, was no more than an effort of wishful thinking.

If such controversy was notable for its rarity amid the propriety of English music, it was, a short swim across the Channel, the very life-blood of French musical activity. Barely would a year go by in France without a fresh scandal to intrigue music lovers, summoning them to clamber once again onto the barricades of musical strife with the same familiarity and eager anticipation with which they took their seats in the concert hall.

A regular cause of contention were the annual, nationally-contested prizes for musicians — prizes which were fought over uninhibitedly by competitors, judges and the general public with equal commitment.

Hector Berlioz was baptized in the flames of disputatiousness, when he applied in 1827 for the valuable *Prix de Rome*, which guaranteed its recipient five years' income while he studied in Italy and Germany. Berlioz quickly discovered that Cherubini, his old enemy and director of the Conservatoire, was moving heaven and earth to stop him winning. Parties were formed, pledges trothed, duels fought. One of the judges later disclosed that Cherubini's men had clinched the issue with the chauvinistic assertion that 'Berlioz is no good at all. His head has been turned by this fellow Beethoven, a German, and we will never manage to set him right again.' Fortunately for Berlioz, and thanks to a growing clamour from his friends, he won the prize at the fourth attempt.

The *scandales Ravel* at the turn of the twentieth century followed a similar pattern. Maurice Ravel entered for the *Prix de Rome* but was defeated owing to the machinations of Théodore Dubois, Director of the Conservatoire, and others who believed his music did not conform to theoretical disciplines. Ravel applied successively for four years, achieving at best an honourable mention as runner-up. In the meantime, he wrote a string quartet and a song cycle, *Shéhérezade*, which won him enough admirers to raise a vociferous inquiry as to why this most promising of French composers was being denied encouragement by a conclave of arid academics. Their agitation did not win Ravel a prize, but, when the judges once went so far as to eliminate him from the final round, the storm broke and Paris divided itself into camps of pro and anti-Ravel. The prize became a political issue and Dubois, the most powerful musical functionary in the nation, was forced to resign from the Conservatoire. He was succeeded by Gabriel Fauré, a respected composer and Ravel's teacher, but the professorial intrigues against the unorthodox young composer continued. Two years later Ravel was indicted for plagiarizing Debussy in a song cycle, *Histoires Naturelles*. Ravel acknowledged Debussy's influence, but denied copying him. The Press strove mightily to fan the flames, but the scandal was short-lived since Debussy declined to press charges (mindful of Ravel's support as a Pelléastre during his own troubles). The intrigue, however, ended their friendship. Ravel remarked, 'It is probably better for us now, for illogical reasons, to be on frigid terms.'

If competition for student prizes was fierce, the fight among mature musicians for positions of honour and influence was ferocious. It was waged not only among musicians, but involved the petitioning of support from members of the Cabinet, army generals, leaders of the Church, courtesans, prominent restauranteurs and anyone else whose influence might be brought to bear. Passions could run so high that, after one such affray, a musician considered on high authority to be one of the five greatest piano composers since Beethoven (the others being Chopin, Liszt, Schumann and Brahms) withdrew in a huff from musical life and did not return for a quarter of a century. In 1848, Charles Henri Valentin Alkan, a prodigious pianist whose skills were envied by his friends Chopin and Liszt, applied for the vacant post of Head of the Piano Department at the Conservatoire. His appointment was viewed as a foregone conclusion — he was beyond dispute the foremost French composer for the piano — and Alkan did not trouble to canvass support. It was to his amazement that, shortly before the election, he learned that the composer Daniel Auber, all-powerful Director of the Conservatoire, had thrown his weight behind another candidate. To add indignity to calculated insult, Auber was backing one of Alkan's own pupils, Antoine François Marmontel, who was by no means his best student. Alkan frantically sought support among musicians and writers, but Auber's favourite got the job.

In shame and fury, Alkan became a recluse, disappearing from the concert platform, publishing few new compositions and keeping in touch only with a handful of close friends. He had been almost wholly forgotten when he reappeared suddenly and without explanation in a series of unpublicized recitals at the Érard Hall in Paris early in the 1870s. These concerts, unnoticed by the public, were attended in the main by the finest musicians of the day, eager to discover a pianist who had outshone Chopin and Liszt. Alkan's revival came to an end when he died suddenly, alone in his apartment, crushed in a bizarre accident by a falling shelf of scriptural tomes. He might have been lost altogether to posterity had it not been for a fulsome tribute that appeared in a famous book on pianists by none other than his ungifted pupil and triumphant rival, Marmontel. As a result, some of his music has survived to be played by the few modern master-pianists who can surmount its knuckle-twisting complexities.

Alkan's life and solitary death bear more than passing resemblance to those of another combative pianistic recluse, the eccentric Erik Satie. Like Alkan's, Satie's career had two distinct periods separated by a disappearance. He emerged as a composer in 1888, shortly after leaving the Conservatoire where he failed to graduate, composing in a style that influenced his friend Claude Debussy. Neither of them had much success initially, but when Debussy's hour arrived Satie, perhaps in a fit of jealousy, vanished from musical life. His small reputation was kept alive only thanks to Debussy's popular orchestration of his *Gymnopédies*.

He re-emerged from a suburban seclusion in 1905, creating a stir by registering as a thirty-nine-year-old student at music school and publishing a series of individualistic piano works with eye-catching titles: the *Bureaucratic Sonatina, 3 Automatic descriptions* and the *I-want-you waltz*. His music was cool and skeletal, a sharp contrast to the prevailing heavy orchestrations of the post-Wagner establishment. It appealed instantly to the younger generation, who were also attracted by his outrageous pronouncements: that, for example, music should be like furniture, an aural wallpaper that blends unnoticed into an everyday background (anticipating, by half a century, the rise of Muzak); or that one piece, aptly entitled *Vexations*, should be repeated in performance 840 times (so far as is known, its full première has yet to be given). Satie became a middle-aged cult figure, elder statesman to *Les Six*.

Now it was Debussy who bridled at his friend's new-found celebrity and took to ridiculing his compositions and theories. Satie ('I have never written a note I didn't mean') defended them hotly, too hotly, in a letter of counter-blast which Debussy wept over when he received it on his deathbed. Satie repented for this act of querulousness: 'How I must have made Debussy suffer as he lay dying,' he mourned. But his regret did not curb his pugnacity, nor restrain his urge to create the widest possible strife from the pettiest of his feuds. Before long he fell out with cinq of *Les Six*, but the younger composers were too involved in their own pursuits to spare much thought for the foibles of an old man. Unable to provoke them, Satie broke with the group altogether after a dinner party at which Georges Auric carelessly or maliciously stabbed his treasured

Satie by Cocteau

black umbrella as it stood forlornly in the puddled receptacle by the front door.

Of *Les Six* only the agreeable Darius Milhaud remained his friend. When the others sought to visit him on his hospital deathbed, Satie refused to admit them. 'Debussy,' he said bitterly, 'died without seeing me again.' After his death, Milhaud and Satie's estranged brother went to his bachelor room in the suburb of Arcueil to dispose of his effects. They were the first strangers to enter the room for twenty-seven years.

Domestic fights among musicians are not peculiar to France, or Italy, or England, but rage wherever music is played. In Russia, the Mighty Handful, as Balakirev, Borodin, Cui, Mussorgsky and Rimsky-Korsakov were collectively known, fought among themselves and with such upstarts as Peter Ilyich Tchaikovsky over which among them deserved to be called a genuine Russian composer. In the next generation, partisans of

Rachmaninov and Alexander Scriabin, continued the contest, fighting on while the first composer had a nervous breakdown and pausing only briefly when the second died an early death. In exile in the United States, Rachmaninov sustained the feud by ostracizing another distinguished Russian emigré, the conductor Serge Koussevitsky, who had been Scriabin's principal sponsor. Such musical civil wars respect no national frontiers and transcend social revolutions and international wars. Even a common political enemy — the Bolshevik Revolution — was not enough to reconcile Rachmaninov to Koussevitsky.

But the greatest of music's civil wars was instigated by Richard Wagner. It ranged over half a continent and raged unabated for more than half a century, continuing long after the death of its protagonists. It persisted through continental wars and revolutions, violating every frontier in Europe: it engaged not only the greatest musicians of the age but their wives, children, servants and tradesmen, even their cats and dogs; it created misery and entertainment, martyrs and heroes, greatness and pettiness, in almost equal measure.

Without wishing to apportion blame, the origin of the pan-German conflict between the followers of Richard Wagner and Johannes Brahms is rooted inescapably in the incandescent character of Wagner. While every original thinker creates opponents, Wagner's special gift was to express himself so bluntly that he gave offence to someone with almost every utterance. He scattered his shot widely and wildly, wounding supporters as often as opponents. Wagner tolerated no half-friends and regularly put his closest followers to tests of fidelity that would estrange any but the most besotted. Even King Ludwig of Bavaria, his financial saviour, was submitted to acts of insolence and treachery that few monarchs would endure with impunity. For many, the agony of retaining Wagner's friendship was sharper than the pain of his enmity.

His aggressiveness was sustained by a belief in his own genius that was absolute. His self-assurance affronted establishment composers such as Felix Mendelssohn (who, though only four years Wagner's senior, had been launched by the most prolific childhood talent since Mozart's), and made such rising contemporaries as Berlioz and Schumann distinctly uneasy. Yet, for each enemy that he made, Wagner's immense charisma attracted fresh recruits to his camp, led by the composer and pianist Franz Liszt, and his pupil, the callow but clear-sighted pianist and conductor Hans von Bülow.

While it is not possible to set a date for the outbreak of war, the first significant confrontation can be traced to an unhappy Dresden evening in 1848 when Wagner and Liszt paid a supposedly friendly call on Robert and Clara Schumann. The contrast between the two sides was striking. Liszt, the suave, disreputable (by reason of his non-marital liaisons) man of the world and Wagner, restless in his provincial position, faced the respectable Schumanns, who had settled in Dresden in search of a peaceful life and wanted nothing more than to live quietly, make music, and have lots of children. When Wagner began attacking the recently deceased Mendelssohn, Schumann, already prone to the depressive attacks that would kill him eight years later, stormed out and locked himself in his bedroom. It was left to the angrily protective Clara to show her guests the door.

Though relations were strained by this outburst, they were not ruptured. The Schumanns continued to see Wagner and Liszt and to share common friends, among them the Hungarian-born violinist Joseph Joachim, who had played as a wonder-child under Mendelssohn's immaculate baton in Leipzig and was now leader of Liszt's orchestra at Weimar. He was also a regular concert partner of the Schumanns, playing duets with Clara, the foremost woman pianist, and helping her in the crises of her husband's increasing mental instability. Joachim worshipped Schumann, but also admired Liszt, who introduced him to the exiled Wagner when they visited Strasbourg in 1853. Unaware that he was shaking hands with the anonymous author of *Judaism in Music* (which he had condemned when it was published), Joachim was impressed by Wagner and astounded by *The Ring of the Nibelungen*, which the composer read aloud to his friends for the first time at this meeting. Joachim volunteered to lead the violins in the orchestra at the première of the great trilogy, an offer which lapsed two years later when he recoiled from the composer after the racialist tract was republished under Wagner's own name. In 1857 Joachim broke with Liszt as well, condemning his drift towards musical bombasticism and the campaign of vilification mounted by his acolytes against Schumann and the traditionalists. His parting letter to Liszt conveys more sorrow than anger and reflects the grief felt by many of the combatants as they took up positions against their former friends.

Dear Liszt, [wrote Joachim],
I will not longer conceal from you what your manly spirit has a right to demand: I am quite impervious to your music; it contradicts everything in the works of our great masters, on which my mind has been nurtured since my early youth. If I should ever be robbed of that which I love and admire in their works — that which *I* feel to be music — your tones would not, even in part, fill the monstrous and over-whelming void.

How can I fraternize with those who, under your banner, make it their lives' work to make your works known — I speak of the noblest of your supporters — *versus* the recognized achievements of the great musicians?

Your awe-inspiring industry, and the numbers of your devotees will soon allay the pain of my loss, but, however you may take my letter, believe one thing of me: that, for all that you have been to me, for the affection which you entertained for me in Weimar, for all those things which I attempted to learn from your divine gifts, I shall never cease to regard myself as — Your most grateful pupil,

JOSEPH JOACHIM

Even before he formally joined them, Joachim had already performed an invaluable service to the anti-Wagnerians four years earlier; he had introduced to them a young man whose genius might equal Wagner's and who could carry their standard into battle against him. Visited one day by an itinerant Hungarian violinist of his acquaintance, Eduard Reményi, Joachim was struck by his accompanist, a shy twenty-year-old whom Reményi had come across playing the piano in a squalid sailors' tavern in Hamburg. The young man had learned his trade the hard way — he had been hired out to entertain at brothels since he was a child — but possessed an inner tranquillity which shone through his playing. Joachim engaged him in conversation. Though only two years in age separated the musicians, they were at diametrically opposite poles of the musical globe, one playing his instrument to royalty, the other to prostitutes and pimps. Yet the disparity did not prevent Joachim from appreciating his visitor's considerable talent, an impression that was strengthened when the young man showed him some of his furtive piano compositions. Joachim dashed off a glowing letter of recommendation and dispatched him impartially first to Liszt, then to Schumann. Liszt received the young man warmly and, after dinner, invited him to play some of his music. When he timidly declined to perform for the assembled audience of princes, princesses and musical personages, Liszt himself strode to the piano and played, sight unseen, a scherzo by the youth. Liszt's praise for this composition did not alleviate the young man's discomfiture and it was some months before he summoned the courage to present himself to Joachim's other renowned friend. Schumann's reaction was even more overwhelming. He hailed the youth as the Messiah he had been praying for and acclaimed his 'Coming' in the *Neue Zeitschrift für Musik*:

He has arrived, a young man at whose cradle the heroes of old stood guard. His name is Johannes Brahms; he came to me from Hamburg . . . Even his outer appearance shows all the attributes which indicate that here is a Chosen One . . .

In a note of thanks to Joachim he added: 'I believe Johannes to be the true Apostle, who will also write Revelations.' This prediction was not to be fulfilled until after Schumann's death, since the bashful Brahms was so inhibited by this acclamation that he almost dried up musically. It was four years before he produced his first orchestral composition and more than twenty before his First Symphony appeared. But if he was stunned by Schumann's recognition, he was reassured by a great bond of affection that grew between himself and Robert and Clara. When Schumann was committed to an asylum after trying to drown himself in a fit of depression, Brahms and Joachim rallied to his bedside in the two years until he died and did what they could to help Clara, who had been left destitute with seven small children on her hands. It is one of the abiding controversies of musicology as to whether Brahms and Clara Schumann became lovers, either before or after Robert died. She was fourteen years his senior, still a beautiful woman, and that part of their correspondence which they did not destroy points to a profound and complex attachment, mutual and lifelong, which may or may not have enjoyed sexual consummation. Whatever their relationship, a strong Brahms-Clara Schumann-Joachim axis formed during the tragedy and with it the resolve to resist the assaults of the Wagner-Liszt camp.

The battle lines having been drawn, the weapons primed, there now ensued — as in all Great Wars — a hiatus of phoney war. Hostilities were so quiescent in the ensuing years that it became possible for Brahms and Wagner to work together in Vienna in 1862. Brahms even enjoyed a brief friendship with Wagner's mistress from Zurich, Mathilde Wesendonck, inspirer of Isolde.

When they were introduced, Wagner exercised his charm and enlisted Brahms to help copy orchestral parts for a concert of excerpts from his unperformed operas. 'A selection from *The Mastersingers* was allotted to him,' wrote Wagner, 'and indeed Brahms' behaviour proved unassuming and good-natured. However, he showed little vivacity and was hardly noticed at our gatherings.' The contrast between the extrovert, egotistical, exuberant Wagner and the self-effacing Brahms, could hardly be more incisively observed.

They met, though, in a fateful year. 1862 was the year in which Wagner alienated Hanslick by lampooning him in *The Mastersingers* and transformed the critic into his most powerful enemy. Hanslick retaliated with a barrage of hostile articles to which Wagner responded in kind and the battle began in earnest. When Hanslick met and praised Brahms, Wagner was quick to counter the critic's claims, calling Brahms boring and uninventive, a scribbler masquerading as a composer, 'a Jewish czardas player'.

The hostility quickly spread beyond Germany and Austria, as partisans of both camps declared themselves in most European countries. Berlioz came out against Wagner ('If he only knew how cordially I can hate,' he wrote to Joachim); Wagner promptly put about a rumour that his enemy Meyerbeer had bribed Madame Berlioz with a valuable piece of jewellery.

The Norwegian composer Edvard Grieg forgot his gallantry and slapped the face of Dame Ethel Smyth when she dared to criticize Liszt. In London, the Principal of the Royal Academy of Music warned his star pupil:

I am sorry you are going to Bayreuth, for every presence there gives countenance to the monstrous self-inflation. An earthquake would be good that would swallow up the spot and everybody on it, so I wish you were away.

An American critic joined the fray: 'Wagner, thank the fates, is no hypocrite. He says out what he means, and he usually means something nasty.' Another countered: 'Brahms might occasionally put a little more melody into his work, just a little, now and then, for a change.' Mark Twain, an agnostic pilgrim to Bayreuth, commented raspingly on *Parsifal*: 'The first act of the three occupied three hours, and I enjoyed that in spite of the singing.'

Such foreign breezes of humour blew a touch of light relief into the Germanic seriousness of the conflict. Claude Debussy, having relented of a period of Wagnerian influence, inserted an infantile parody of the opening of *Tristan* into *Children's Corner*, written for his small daughter. Sir Arthur Sullivan, who dismissed the Nordic heroes of *The Ring* as 'thieves, liars and blackguards', caricatured the entire cult in *Iolanthe*. Such satires earned their authors the unqualified hatred of true Wagnerites whose adoration was so devout that they would later purchase in Venice the gondola in which the Master had sailed on his last holiday in Venice and the railway coach in which his mortal remains were conveyed back to Bayreuth.

Such relics were not only valued by Wagnerians but were also coveted by their opponents for the secrets they might yield. A typically sordid tussle took place in 1877, when the voluminous correspondence between Wagner and a milliner fell into unscrupulous hands in Vienna. The letters were offered for sale to Brahms and he laughed loud and long on reading them, since they showed the 'Musician of the Future' to be engrossed in the minutest details of precisely which fabrics he needed to furnish a room in which his inspiration could flourish.

Dear Miss Bertha [Wagner had written],
You are well acquainted with the models I need for my house robes. Can you get me some dark pink satin? Can the enclosed shade of light pink be bought for 4 or 5 florins? Have you any of the dark yellow material from which we made the drapes for the little table? . . .

Dear Miss Bertha,
Unfortunately I cannot send you any money this week as my affairs
are not going well. Do not worry, though. I most urgently want to
reimburse you as soon as possible.

Dear Miss Bertha,
Now how much will such a dressing-gown cost? . . . (my sketch
enclosed)

Brahms was enthralled by this trash and sent it to Daniel Spitzer, a
journalist, who bought the letters and published them in the *Neue Freie
Presse*, Hanslick's newspaper, to raucous amusement in Vienna coffee
houses. From high-minded critical assaults, the conflict had descended
into pettiness and bigoted acrimony. When Wagner died in 1883, Brahms
sent a wreath to Bayreuth. The widow Cosima pointedly set it to one side
and declined to acknowledge its receipt. 'Why should I acknowledge it?'
she declared. 'The man who sent it is no friend of our Art.'

Wagner's death, a cataclysmic event which sent his supporters weeping
into the streets and caused at least one suicide, served only to intensify
hostilities. For want of a more imposing commander, his followers
seized on Anton Bruckner, a retiring symphonist, to lead them into
battle. The unsophisticated Bruckner, who had expressed his devotion to
Wagner by falling on his knees and kissing the Master's hand ('Do calm
yourself, Bruckner,' Wagner had muttered irritably), was never a match
for Hanslick's sophistry. Moreover, Brahms, who had viewed the contest
between himself and Wagner as a clash of values between an orchestral
and an opera composer, was infuriated to find himself opposed by a
fellow-symphonist. Brahms was convinced that Bruckner was an
impostor created specifically to annoy him and schemed to deny Bruckner
any advancement in Vienna. His campaign was made easier by the fact
that the audiences which had adored Wagner's bombast and eroticism
could not fathom Bruckner's gigantically innocent symphonies. After
conducting the première of his Third, entitled the Wagner Symphony,
Bruckner turned round from the podium to find that the entire Wagner-
loving audience had left before the end. Only his own pupils remained
to applaud.

Even these disciples could not be counted on for unqualified support.
The violinist Fritz Kreisler, who studied under Bruckner as a boy, relates
how he and his classmates involved Bruckner's dog, 'Mops', in the War.
While his master was at lunch, the rascals submitted the unfortunate
animal to pre-Pavlovian conditioning, playing a Wagner theme on the
piano while kicking the dog and following it with a motif from Bruckner's
Te Deum, during which 'Mops' was rewarded with titbits to eat. When

Bruckner returned, his pupils presented the simple man with incontrovertible evidence that while his own music was pleasing to the dog, his beloved Wagner's made it yelp in terror and run howling from the room.

Attempts to conciliate between Brahms and Bruckner were futile, though a brief lull set in after they were brought together at a restaurant and amused one another by calling spontaneously for the same simple dish. Bruckner became consumed with jealousy when Brahms was offered a doctorate by Cambridge University (he declined it, since he disliked the English) and petitioned universities great and small, among them some very young American colleges, for a similar honour. He was finally elevated by the University of Vienna only a few years before he died. Brahms, nine years his junior, made to attend Bruckner's funeral but turned away at the cathedral door, murmuring 'Soon my coffin'; six months later he too was dead, ravaged by cancer of the liver.

The once shy and agreeable young Brahms had grown into a bluff but tetchy bachelor, whose friends, like Wagner's, learned to beware of his sudden and unprovoked assaults. He alienated Joachim, his discoverer, by blunderingly and uninvitedly taking the side of his wife Amalie during the break-up of their marriage. Relations were only repaired by a penitent dedication of Brahms' elegiac Double Concerto for violin and cello to his benefactor. He insulted Hanslick, his campaign manager, by presenting the intellectual critic with a dedication of nothing more weighty than a playful opus of waltzes. He became estranged for a while even from his beloved Clara, first in a quarrel over the editorship of Robert's Spring Symphony, then over a sweet young girl who had caught his eye. Clara, while she might have renounced her own claim to Brahms, could not bear to see him flirting with others.

Nor did he show any greater consideration to new supporters, refugees from Wagner's testing standards of friendship. His treatment of the conductor Hans von Bülow, Wagner's most notable renegade, who devoted his later years to spreading the gospel of Brahms, was almost Wagnerian in its insolence. On two significant occasions he wrested the baton from Bülow at performances of his Fourth Symphony, snubbing the conductor before prestigious audiences after having allowed him to popularize the symphony throughout the provinces. Bülow avenged himself in Hamburg, Brahms's home town. Resuming the podium to direct a Beethoven symphony, Bülow turned to the audience and observed that the city of Hamburg had reason to be proud of having given birth to a great master, one who had suffered neglect but was now receiving due recognition. 'I refer of course to . . .' he paused for effect. 'Meister Johannes Brahms,' murmured the glowing Hamburgers. 'Felix Mendelssohn,' declared Bülow with evident satisfaction. Shocked whispers of protest broke out and Bülow conceded that 'Mendelssohn is dead, Kaiser Wilhelm is dead; but Bismarck lives on, Brahms lives on!' before racing into the vivacious opening bars of Beethoven's Eighth.

He was wounded nonetheless by Brahms's behaviour and shortly afterwards resigned from the Meiningen Orchestra which, during his tenure, he had made available to the composer for symphonic experiments. They did not meet for more than a year until Brahms, in a delightful gesture, left at Bülow's Vienna hotel an unsigned card bearing a few bars of music. Bülow recognized it instantly as a quote from Mozart's *Magic Flute* sung to the words, 'Shall we never meet again, beloved?' He went straight round to Brahms' house to be reconciled.

Bülow's arrival in the Brahms camp was doubly welcomed since it coincided with the defection to Wagner of one of Brahms' staunchest allies. The conductor Hermann Levi had lived out an emotional tug-of-war for close on a decade, loving Brahms as a friend but being attracted aesthetically to Wagner's writings and music. When he crossed the lines, he met Bülow coming the other way and took over the conductor's post in Munich.

The loss of Bülow and the manner of his going were the heaviest blows suffered by the Wagner side. Not even his blindest admirers could condone the composer's treachery towards a trusting friend who had followed Wagner throughout the tribulations of exile, copying his manuscripts, conducting his works and making himself helpful in every way possible. Bülow had been so preoccupied with the Wagner cause that he failed to notice that his wife Cosima, Liszt's daughter (whom he had married, as a friend crudely put it, 'to give the illegitimate child an honourable name and through it to bring peace of mind to the father'), was making herself available to Wagner. Whatever his motives in marrying her, Bülow loved Cosima passionately and was deeply attached to their children, little realizing that only the eldest two were his own.

His suspicions were first aroused by an innuendo-ridden article about Cosima and Wagner in a Bavarian newspaper. Bülow demanded a retraction and called out the editor to a duel. Neither satisfaction was granted. When other newspapers picked up the scandal, Cosima threatened King Ludwig that if he did not declare his faith in the propriety of her relations with Wagner, she, Bülow and Wagner would all leave his country. 'My royal lord,' she wrote, 'I have three children to whom it is my duty to preserve their father's honourable name unstained.' Ludwig, blackmailed, became party to the perjury.

Bülow may well have been the last man in the German-speaking world to discover the adultery and the shock almost killed him. Tempted to commit suicide ('My situation is so incredibly and uniquely horrible that any other way out demands superhuman courage'), he resisted, in order to protect his children and the reputation of his father-in-law, Liszt. His farewell letter to Cosima portrays his struggle to retain a semblance of human dignity:

Wagner and Cosima, Bülow trailing behind

> My suffering is so great that I can allow myself to express it, since I
> refrain from accusing anyone of being responsible for it but myself.

Liberated from the service of Wagner, Bülow embraced the creed of
Brahms with the fervour of a convert. Though he abstained from
attacking Wagner, his popularizing efforts on behalf of Brahms gave the
anti-Wagnerians strength in the area they most needed, the public heart.
Without the trappings of stage drama, Brahms' music was less readily
appealing to audiences than Wagner's; in Bülow's hands it became
widely comprehensible and attractive. The conductor also embraced the
composer as his personal saviour. 'I have him to thank for being restored
to sanity, for being alive even. Most of my existence has been misspent
on my former father-in-law, that charlatan and his brood, but the
remainder belongs to the true saints of Art and above all to him, to him,
to him . . .' Yet he never ceased to mourn the loss of his first allegiance
and burst into tears when a veteran Wagnerian reproved him, after a
performance of the *Tannhäuser* overture, with a reminder, 'of the time
when we both worshipped that ideal, to which *I* have stayed faithful.'
  Nor had he heard the last of Wagner. With a grossness that scarcely
bears contemplation, the Master of Bayreuth sent an emissary to Bülow
at Meiningen demanding to borrow his excellent orchestra to play his

Siegfried Idyll to the conductor's former wife on her birthday. That Bülow did not shoot the envoy is to his eternal credit.

In Bülow, Wagner acknowledged with regret that he had lost his most faithful interpreter. He almost lost Liszt as well, appalled by the antics of his daughter with his protégé. Cosima remained cool towards her father for the rest of his life, transferring all her allegiance to Wagner. When Liszt died inconveniently during the Bayreuth Festival, three years after Wagner, she had him buried in haste in order not to lose a single night's opera.

In Cosima, Wagner gained his most fanatical follower, one who pandered to his every wish and urged him on to ever-greater excesses of self-gratification (except where other women were concerned: she took emphatic exception to Wagner's autumnal dalliance with the novelist, Judith Gautier, daughter of the great French writer). To the end of her long life, outlasting all of Wagner's friends and enemies, she kept the controversies alive, regardless of personal cost. In 1914, half a century after her adultery with Wagner, she was sued by Isolde Beidler, *née* von Bülow, for the right to be recognized as Wagner's daughter (which she undoubtedly was) and to share in his inheritance. After an acrimonious hearing, the Bavarian Civil Court ruled that there was no proof that Cosima, whatever her relations with Wagner, had not also cohabited with her lawful husband between 12 June and 12 October 1864, when Isolde might have been conceived. Phrenological and blood tests which could have shown that Isolde and Wagner's son Siegfried shared the same parentage were not admitted in evidence; a neighbour's testimony that Bülow had once caught the adulterers in the act was dismissed as inconclusive. Cosima, rather than acknowledge an old sin with the grace of age, aggressively maintained the deception of Wagner's inviolability to the last and dismissed from her life the favourite among her daughters.

She lived to be an indomitable ninety-two, wearing black for her husband to the day of her death. In marrying her, Wagner had transformed both his destiny and his music. Cosima carried the pursuit of musical warfare into the home, storming and capturing the musician's last citadel. Nor did she fight there single-handed.

CHAPTER TEN

ON THE HOME FRONT

$\mathcal{C}$osima was not Wagner's first connubial firebrand. He had previously spent twenty years married to Minna Planer, an actress four years his senior. Minna wanted her husband to settle down and write simple operas that everyone could understand and she told him so, often. She braved the poverty of his youthful Parisian adventure without complaint but baulked at having to uproot herself again because her hot-headed husband had got mixed up in a revolution. She had responsibilities of her own, having to support her much-younger sister Natalie, whom everyone but Wagner knew was her illegitimate daughter. She stayed in Dresden when Wagner fled and, though she rejoined him some years later in Switzerland, the marriage was effectively over. It had been a stormy union, with Wagner tormented initially by her infidelities and Minna affronted later on by his. Although Cosima did her best to malign Minna's memory in the memoirs Wagner dictated to her, his first' wife's influence was substantial and not altogether as deleterious as indicated by H. L. Mencken in a sardonic appraisal of Wagner's marital disturbances.

It must be plain that the presence of such a woman — and Wagner lived with her for twenty years — must have put a fearful burden upon his creative genius. No man can be absolutely indifferent to the opinions and prejudices of his wife. She has too many opportunities to shove them down his throat. If she can't make him listen to them by howling and bawling, she can make him listen by snuffling. To say that he can carry on his work without paying any heed to her is equal to saying that he can carry on his work without paying any heed to his toothache, his conscience, or the zoo next door. In spite of Minna, Wagner composed a number of very fine music dramas. But if he had poisoned her at the beginning of his career it is very likely that he could have composed more of them, and perhaps better ones.

It was, however, no longer fashionable or entirely safe for a musician to murder his wife for the sake of his music and Wagner was sensible enough to let nature take its course. In the meantime, he embarked with Cosima on what they sought to portray, somewhat heavy-handedly, as an ideal love-match.

Cosima appeared to have lost the shyness she had evinced towards me and a very friendly manner had taken its place. While I was singing *Wotan's Farewell* to my friends I noticed the same expression on Cosima's face as I had seen on it, to my astonishment, in Zurich on a

186

Cosima

187

similar occasion, only the ecstasy of it was transfigured into something higher. Everything connected with this was shrouded in silence and mystery, but the belief that she belonged to me grew to such certainty in my mind, that when I was under the influence of more than ordinary excitement my conduct betrayed the most reckless gaiety. As I was accompanying Cosima to the hotel across a public square, I suddenly suggested she should sit in an empty wheelbarrow which stood in the street, so that I might wheel her to the hotel. She assented in an instant. My astonishment was so great that I felt all my courage desert me, and was unable to carry out my mad project.

One way or another he got her to the hotel, and entered eventually on a second eventful marriage. But while Cosima was more openly worshipful than Minna she exerted no less an influence on his music, at least in Mencken's view:

Cosima Liszt-von Bülow, had far more intelligence than Minna, and so we may assume that her presence in his music factory was less of a handicap upon the composer. Nevertheless, the chances are that she, too, did him far more harm than good. To begin with, she was extremely plain in face — and nothing is more damaging to the creative faculty than the constant presence of ugliness.

Moreover, Cosima had shoddy tastes, and they played destructively upon poor Wagner. There parts of *Parsifal* that suggest her very strongly — far more strongly, in fact, than they suggest the author of *The Mastersingers*.

I do not here decry Wagner; on the contrary, I praise him, and perhaps excessively. It is staggering to think of the work he did, with Minna and Cosima shrilling in his ears. What interests me is the question as to how much further he might have gone had he escaped the passionate affection of the two of them and of their various volunteer assistants.

Wagner's wives and the turmoil of his personal life undoubtedly affected his music, although the composer resisted overt attempts by both Cosima and Minna to influence his ideas. Other less massively self-assured composers, however, turned to their wives for both guidance and inspiration. Sir Edward Elgar, the first great English composer for two centuries, would never submit a manuscript to his publisher without first having made whatever amendments Lady Alice gently suggested. He also blissfully immortalized his wife as the first of his fourteen *Variations on an Original Theme*, popularly known as the *Enigma Variations*, a series of character sketches in music.

A mere sketch of his wife, though, would not have satisfied the Bavarian composer Richard Strauss. He found her the most endlessly fascinating creature in his life and created entire symphonies and operas about her. To a casual observer, Richard Strauss was the archetypal hen-pecked husband. A mild-mannered, unprepossessing man who looked less like a musician than a suburban bank manager, he married in 1894 a sharp-tongued, strong-willed shrew, who combined the bellicosity of her military upbringing with the pretensions of the operatic soprano that she became. Pauline de Ahna did not sweeten her nature while Strauss was wooing her and it may have been her very vehemence that attracted the composer. The first of the violent and embarrassing scenes that would make Pauline's name feared by musical managements and society hostesses across Europe took place early in their courtship. Singing under Strauss's baton in a rehearsal of his immature opera, *Guntram*, she stopped suddenly in mid-phrase and demanded, 'Why don't you interrupt me?' 'Because you know your part well,' Strauss replied gently. 'I want to be interrupted,' she shrieked, throwing her heavy score at the conductor's head; it fell short, hitting a second violinist. Strauss followed the singer to her dressing-room, from where shrill screams and loud banging were soon heard. Alarmed for the safety of their conductor, the orchestra dispatched a delegation of its burliest players to intervene. When the leader poked his head timorously around the door of the dressing-room, he was greeted with a shy smile from Strauss and the explanation that 'I must inform you that Miss de Ahna has just accepted my proposal of marriage.'

Strauss's friends were appalled by the announcement, none more than Cosima Wagner, who had ear-marked the eligible composer-conductor for one of her own daughters. Pauline was never invited again to sing or stay at Bayreuth. It was no loss to her, for she gave up singing when she married and devoted the rest of her life to instilling some much-needed discipline into Strauss's easy-going ways. For a man who liked nothing more from life than a stroll in the sunshine, a game of cards and a friendly chat, it was like marrying a regimental sergeant-major. Every morning as soon as he finished breakfast she would command, 'Now, Richard, go to your study and compose.' He would obey, meekly and gratefully, and not re-emerge before lunchtime.

She demanded public recognition of her domestic domination and contrived to create marital 'scenes' in the most auspicious of settings. After the Vienna première of *Feuersnot* (*Fire-famine*), when Strauss greeted her with a cheery, 'Well, Pauksl, what do you think of that for a success?' she shrilled in reply: 'How dare you show yourself to me? You make me sick!' Gustav Mahler, who was familiar with Pauline's public paroxysms, hustled the couple away to the privacy of his office. Pauline reappeared eventually, followed by a dishevelled Strauss. 'I am going to the hotel to spend the evening alone,' she declared to Mahler. 'I'll take you there,' offered her discomfited husband. 'You will walk ten paces behind me,' she stipulated. Strauss rejoined the Mahlers later at a restaurant, apologizing that 'My wife's a bit rough, but that's what I need.'

She almost wrecked a performance of Strauss's opera, *The Woman without a Shadow*, by abusing its star, Lotte Lehmann, during the interval with, 'an unfortunate remark of purely personal nature which with the best will in the world I could not excuse on the grounds of her well-known temper.' Only with difficulty was Lehmann induced to continue.

Under the Nazi régime, Pauline's social misdemeanours verged on the criminal and landed her husband in frequent trouble with offended Gauleiters. She hated Hermann Goering in particular and once threw out of her house the wife of Clemens Krauss, who dared to visit her in a mink coat she had been given by the Reichsmarschal. Sailing ever closer to the wind, she loudly assured a second-rank Nazi leader, Baldur von Schirach, that he would still be welcome at her house when the war was over and 'the rest of the Nazi gang got what they deserved'.

The Nazi attitude to Strauss declined from initial veneration, through dismay at his Jewish daughter-in-law and his stubborn collaboration with the exiled librettist, Stefan Zweig, to outright fury at his wife's indiscretions. They virtually banned celebrations of his eightieth birthday and, towards the end of the War, mercilessly refused the old man permission to go to Switzerland for urgent medical treatment.

For all the discomfort she caused him, Pauline was utterly devoted to Strauss. When he died in 1949, she survived him by less than a year. Yet the very ugliest of her public outbursts were reserved for assaults on her husband's most intimate sensibilities. Asked once if she was thinking of having another child, she brayed, 'Another one? You don't know how difficult it was to get him to start the first one!' At a ceremonial dinner in his honour she proclaimed that Strauss's compositions should be reclassified as 'Strauss de Ahna', since she was equally responsible for them.

Pauline began to appear in Strauss's music early in their acquaintance, first as a rich theme pregnant with the eroticism of an unconsummated union in the tone poem *Don Juan*, then as an acutely nagging violin solo in *A Hero's Life*. In the *Domestic Symphony* she emerged as a rounded but still prickly maternal presence. Strauss deliberately scandalized audiences in this symphony with music that depicted the everyday activities of the middle-class family, from mealtimes, to bathing baby to conjugal relations. He gave one of its first performances in a shrine of bourgeois observances — a New York department store. If the symphony was to represent the composer's own marriage, one knowing American critic sniped, 'the wife would be portrayed on trombones . . . the husband on a second violin.'

Strauss's fascination with his wife's personality reached a climax in

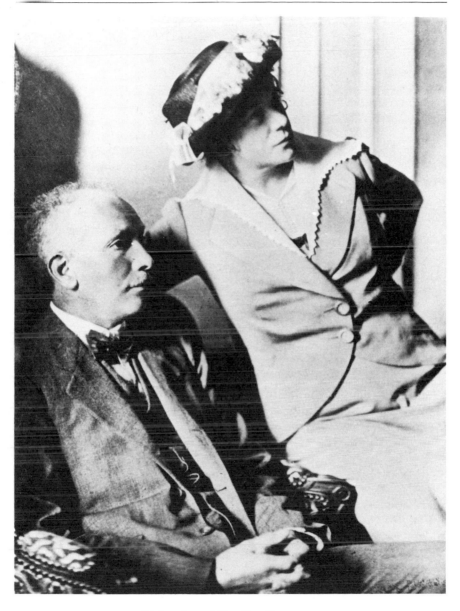

Richard and Pauline Strauss

the opera *Intermezzo*, founded on a marital incident of mistaken identity. Opening his mail, while Strauss was away on a concert tour, Pauline found a love letter addressed to her husband from a woman who signed herself 'Mitzi Mücke'. She went straight to a lawyer and filed for divorce, refusing to answer Strauss's bewildered letters until he came home.

Although Strauss protested in vain that he had neither heard of Miss Mücke nor wanted to, Pauline demanded that he prove his innocence. He mobilized friends into an amateur detective squad and tracked down his correspondante to an unsavoury bar, where she pursued a traditional occupation. Questioning revealed that Miss Mücke had consorted with visiting musicians whom she had pressed for complimentary tickets to a concert as a token of their appreciation. Not having any tickets to hand, they assured her that their friend Herr Stransky would attend to the matter. When no tickets arrived, the resourceful Miss Mücke had looked him up in the telephone directory and, finding no Stransky, or even Straussky, settled on the nearest phonetic approximation, one Richard Strauss, conductor, of 17 Joachimsthaler Street, to whom she wrote a reminder about her tickets, couched in the fondest terms. Only when this exhaustive evidence was produced did Pauline allow herself to be placated.

Mindless of any personal embarrassment, Strauss saw the makings of an opera in his comedy of errors and asked his greatest librettist, Hugo von Hofmannstahl, to write a script. He declined, objecting that the story was in the poorest of taste; when Strauss persisted, Hofmannstahl directed him to an unmusical writer whom he particularly disliked. In the end, Strauss sat down and wrote the opera himself, embellishing the Mitzi incident with some extra characters and details but staying close to historical truth.

To play Pauline's part, tantrums and all, Strauss picked Lotte Lehmann whose voice was most like hers. In rehearsal, he frequently interrupted Lehmann with the comment: 'My wife would not do that.' For added verisimilitude, he had the stage design modelled on his home and the leading characters made up as facsimiles of their real-life counterparts. 'All the same, it's a happy marriage,' sang the protagonists in the closing duet.

The première of *Intermezzo* was a voyeur's delight, the audience easily identifying the living heroes and crowding around Strauss and Pauline in the foyer with open curiosity. Lotte Lehmann, recalling Pauline's many insults, resolved to give Frau Strauss a taste of her own medicine. She strode through the crowd to Pauline and cattily declared: 'This opera is a marvellous present to you from your husband, isn't it?' A hush fell as the fashionable gathering awaited an outraged response. For once, Pauline disappointed. With a severe glance at her husband and a promise of malice to come, she proclaimed: 'I don't give a damn!'

Few contemplated Pauline's perversity with greater distaste than the fastidious Gustav Mahler, whose association with Strauss was founded on mutual musical respect rather than any friendly feeling. They conducted one another's works whenever possible, but when they met socially they had little in common, a gulf that was widened by the contrasting natures of their wives.

Mahler had married late and unexpectedly. He was forty-one, the most famous man in Vienna after the Emperor, ascetic, puritanical, to all appearances a confirmed bachelor who was wedded undeviatingly to his work. He fell to the charms and perseverance of a twenty-two-year-old girl who believed herself destined to inspire great art. Alma Schindler, daughter of a distinguished Viennese painter, had been flirting since puberty with the high-minded, arousing gossip over her pursuit of the Art Nouveau eroticist Gustav Klimt, and scandal over her extra-mural relations with her music teacher, the composer Alexander von Zemlinsky. It was the subject of Zemlinsky that provoked a heated argument with Mahler shortly after they were introduced, the nubile student reproaching the most powerful musical director in the Empire for his neglect of her teacher. Mahler was first amused by the girl, then fiercely attracted by her. Alma quickly jettisoned Zemlinsky (though she persuaded Mahler to produce his opera), seduced Mahler and persuaded him to marry her.

If Pauline imposed discipline on Strauss's lethargy, Alma brought tranquillity and domesticity into Mahler's muddle. But while Frau Doktor Strauss, though a former singer, took no particular interest in her husband's output, Frau Direktor Mahler avidly awaited each new song, movement and symphony. Alma demanded to be Mahler's inspiration but, though her influence was evident from the outset, it was not until the marriage verged on collapse that she changed the course of his music.

The Mahler marriage has been eloquently chronicled by both partners, Alma in a volume of candid if not always truthful memoirs, and Mahler in his late symphonies. Their nine years together passed through three distinct triennial phases. Initially, Mahler was the dominant partner, treating Alma almost like a pupil and basking in her admiration. Even when he insisted that she give up her own ambitions to compose she complied, albeit grudgingly. This first period of marriage was comfortable for the composer; two daughters were born and the soundness of his domestic life was reflected in the new expansiveness and confidence of his Fifth Symphony.

In its middle stage, however, the relationship lapsed into complacency and indifference. Mahler was engrossed in his fights at the opera and the symphonies he was planning, while Alma was becoming increasingly resentful of her subsidiary role. Matters came to a head in tragedy. Mahler had insisted on setting to music a gloomy cycle of poems by the orientalist Friedrich Rückert entitled *Kindertotenlieder* (*Songs of the Death of Children*), overriding a superstitious appeal from Alma, who begged him not to tempt fate. When their elder daughter, Mahler's favourite, was carried off by a sudden bout of scarlet fever at the age of four, both parents reproached themselves and were unable to find solace in each other. 'Suffering estranged and separated us,' Alma wrote. She suffered a physical collapse; Mahler, half-jokingly, submitted himself to a medical examination and was found to have a heart ailment that might prove fatal at any time.

They entered the final phase of their life together in grief and upheaval. They uprooted themselves from Vienna on the pretext that Mahler could no longer tolerate the intrigues at the opera and accepted engagements in the New World. As they travelled back and forth across the Atlantic, Mahler became aware that Alma was slipping away from him. His attitude towards her transformed. He became an ardent lover and considerate husband, pouring out his love desperately and vehemently in three last symphonies. Alma, though, retreated further. She began to flirt provocatively with younger men, allowing the composer Hans Pfitzner and the pianist Ossip Gabrilowitsch to court her openly. Sent to a sanatorium to recuperate after another collapse, she met a young architect who aroused her dormant physical passions. Her lover wrote to her begging her to elope with him; in his agitation — Freud would say, intentionally — he addressed the love letter to Herr Direktor, not Frau Direktor, Mahler.

Mahler, terrified that he might lose Alma, turned for help to Sigmund Freud, whose psychoanalytical theories were still generally viewed as crackpot. Freud's analysis, on the basis of a single afternoon's conversation, was inspired. Mahler, he said, had nothing to fear, since both he and Alma had found their ideal in each other. He wanted a fragile, careworn woman like his mother; Alma required an older, accomplished man like her father: they were admirably suited. (Freud wrote later that Mahler had comprehended his new science more profoundly than anyone of his time.) Notwithstanding this diagnosis, Mahler never felt sure of Alma again. Rescinding his ban on her musical activities, he encouraged her to resume composing and had her songs published, performed and publicized until even the flattered Alma admitted that his praise for her small talent was exaggerated. Increasingly wracked with pain, the dying man was tortured above all by the fear that his wife was forsaking him. As he agonized over the labour of composing his Tenth Symphony, he scribbled across its pages love poems to Alma and entreaties to the Almighty to save his afflicted soul.

> You alone, you alone, you alone
> know what it means.

and:

> In your hands I commend my soul.

and:

> To live for you;   (Für dich leben;
> To die for you.   Für dich sterben.)

He had completed only two movements of the symphony when he contracted a fatal infection. Alma brought him back from New York to die in Vienna, aged fifty. For a year afterwards she was prostrate with grief and contemplated suicide. Her surviving daughter and her friends restored her will to live and with it the realization that she was only thirty years old, still beautiful and still capable of fulfilling her self-ordained mission to inspire creative artists. Gradually, she allowed herself to be wooed by former suitors such as Pfitzner and Gabrilowitsch (who was already married to Mark Twain's daughter, Clara), as well as by new admirers in the composer-conductor Franz Schreker, Dr Joseph Fraenkel, the eminent American physician who attended Mahler in his last illness, and the pioneering Austrian biologist Paul Kammerer, who threatened to shoot himself at Mahler's grave if she did not yield to his demands. She had a violent affair with the visionary artist Oskar Kokoschka, who immortalized their union in several paintings. So intense was her spell over this young man that his mother became alarmed and lay in wait for Alma with a loaded revolver. In 1915, she married Walter Gropius, the revolutionary architect, founder of the Bauhaus, who had pursued her in Mahler's penultimate year. However, she soon deserted Gropius for the novelist Franz Werfel, author of *The Song of Bernadette*, who became her third and last husband.

Musical divorces could be contested as fiercely as marriages, with battles for the custody of instruments and scores. Johann Strauss senior, first of the Viennese Waltz Emperors, was relieved when his wife Anna applied to terminate their marriage. He had given her ample cause by publicly siring a brood of seven with his milliner mistress. He was not prepared, however, to pay adequate maintenance for his first family, so Anna safeguarded her interests by sending in bailiffs to confiscate all the instruments of the most famous waltz band in Europe until its conductor-manager paid his social dues.

As a further musical redress for her humiliations, Anna prompted her eldest son, named Johann after his father, to set up his own band in competition. Johann senior, who had overlooked the gifts of his eponymous heir, announced a boycott of any inn or dance-hall which engaged his son and orchestrated a cacophony of Press abuse against the upstart. His former wife, however, knew as many trade secrets as he and succeeded in securing a venue for her filial champion. Johann junior's début in 1844 was packed to the rafters by music-lovers, curiosity-seekers, friends and relatives, disrupters hired by his father and a large contingent of police who were kept busy throughout the evening. The young conductor, nineteen years old, dressed in a blue uniform with silver buttons that could have been his father's, was distinctly nervous.

Josef, Johann and Eduard Strauss

But, after some indifferent overtures, he captured the audience with waltzes he had composed himself. Only the deaf would have failed to recognize a talent that was superior to his father's.

Overnight, Johann junior became the talk of foot-tapping Vienna, his father all but forgotten. The older man resorted to gimmicks, by expanding his orchestra to a complement of 220, but the battle was lost and he had to make the best of being second best. The familial rivalry, never truly quiescent, flared up again four years later when father and son found themselves on opposing sides of the 1848 revolution. In a bid to regain his lost eminence, Johann senior composed the enormously popular *Radetzky March* in honour of the Imperial Field Marshal who had subdued rebellion in the Italian provinces. His son countered with a *Revolution March* and enlisted his band to entertain the insurrectionists. When the revolt was crushed, he narrowly escaped prosecution and was viewed with permanent disfavour in Franz Josef's court. But Johann senior was unable to enjoy a reward for his loyalty; he had died, aged forty-five, of meningitis, caught from one of the children of his second family. Barely had his eyes closed, than his descendants fought a deathbed battle for possession of his valuable scores and instruments. The legitimate children won, Johann junior assuming command of his father's orchestra and achieving a virtual monopoly of Viennese light music that lasted half a century.

But Johann junior's own life, plagued by marital turbulence, was never as gay as his music. His first wife died of a heart attack during a row with him over financial provision for her pre-marital illegitimate offspring, who grew more numerous each time Strauss asked after them. His second cuckolded him with a theatre director. Only with his third spouse did he find peace.

Those composers, however, who shied from the perils of wedlock, could find the unmarried status equally disruptive to their work. Johannes Brahms, disappointed in love by Clara Schumann's responsibilities towards her young family, never married. He found his simple pleasures among the fifteen thousand prostitutes of Vienna, who, loose in lips as in morals, would discomfit him with a cheery 'Good evening, Doctor Brahms' as he walked along the Ringstrasse in the company of the most exalted citizenry. Red-faced, he offered an aghast society matron the extenuation that, 'At least I have never ruined a decent young girl.' He was fortunate to avoid the syphilis which impelled Franz Schubert, Hugo Wolf and lesser composers to insanity and early death and robbed Josef Mysliveček, the 'Divine Bohemian', of his nose, sacrificed to a surgeon in a quack attempt to assuage the infection.

The supremely innocent Anton Bruckner, a reluctant bachelor, was nearly blackmailed into an unsuitable marriage by a chambermaid who convinced him that he had somehow compromised her virtue. Only with difficulty were his friends able to buy her off. Bruckner was also prone to random seizures of romance. He was forever imagining himself in love with young girls, strangers whom he met in church or while walking in the woods, and was often disappointed when they failed to turn up for a second rendezvous. He presented himself to the father of one chance encounter and solemnly asked for the hand of a daughter whose name he barely knew. Bewildered, as his frequent proposals of marriage were spurned, he went to his grave unsullied by carnality, his music a testament to his state of grace.

Beethoven, too, fell in love regularly, unrequitedly and often with controversial consequences. The title of his best-known instrumental duet had to be changed because of a quarrel with its violinist over a girl. Originally called the **Bridgetower Sonata**, the work was dedicated to an English mulatto violinist, son of an African Prince and a Polish girl, who captivated Vienna in 1804 with his talents. When George Augustus Polgreen Bridgetower (known to the Germans as Bridgethauer and to

Beethoven even more phonetically as Brishdower), a pupil of the extraordinary Jarnovick, played the new sonata with Beethoven, the composer jumped from his piano stool and embraced him in delight. They became close companions and were inseparable until the handsome half-caste captured the current object of Beethoven's desire. The composer scratched out Bridgetower's name on the dedication page of the sonata, opus 47, and replaced it with that of a French violinist Rodolphe Kreutzer (inaptly, since Kreutzer was never skilful enough to play the sonata that bears his name). Bridgetower, who forfeited posterity for the flash of a pretty girl's eye, returned to England and died in obscurity and poverty in Peckham.

Luckier in love than Beethoven was Robert Schumann, although his attempt to marry engaged him in a protracted legal struggle with his piano teacher, an ambitious man who refused to become the father-in-law of a mere musician. Schumann was eighteen when he went to study with Friedrich Wieck and fell in love with his ten-year-old daughter, Clara, who was already an accomplished concert pianist. Wieck, having encouraged Schumann to give up his law studies and devote himself to music, frowned on the romance, saying that he intended a better match for his daughter. When Clara reached seventeen, Schumann was made forcibly aware that his visits to the Wiecks were becoming too frequent and too lengthy. On her eighteenth birthday he asked Wieck unsuccessfully for her hand. Schumann, in despair, took to drink and became a stage-door Johnny, following Clara on concert tours from town to town in the hope of seeing her after a performance. A year later Robert and Clara filed suit jointly against her father, demanding permission to marry. Wieck failed to attend court, made excuses, applied for postponements, issued counter-suits, anything to save his talented daughter from Schumann. When he was compelled to face the summons, he alleged that Schumann had insufficient means, was a poor composer, was likely to be unfaithful to his bride, was temperamentally unstable and drank too much. The court dismissed all his objections except the last and ordered the reluctant father-in-law to submit evidence of intemperance. Wieck prevaricated seven months longer until, seeing Clara become totally estranged from him, he relented. After a twelve-year courtship, Robert and Clara were married and lived together blissfully for a further twelve years, their union releasing from Schumann's fertile talent a flood of music that had stagnated during the frustrations of the battle for his bride. Ultimately, though, Wieck was proved right: Schumann *was* impecunious, did drink too much and was certifiably unbalanced. He departed the marriage in a straightjacket, leaving Clara penniless.

The legal fighting did not end with his death. A century later, in New York, in 1954, four of Schumann's grandchildren sued a Hollywood studio for causing them 'loss of social standing, humiliation and other mental anguish' by portraying their grandfather in the movie *Song of Life* as insane and their grandmother as the mistress of young Brahms. The case was peremptorily dismissed, the court taking their great-grandfather's view that Schumann was indeed deranged.

Hector Berlioz, too, was driven to the point of madness by a lady pianist who provoked him into attempting to commit two murders and suicide. Marie Moke entered Berlioz's life while he was hopelessly in love with an Irish Shakespearean actress named Henriette Smithson, who, alarmed by the vehemence of the composer's amorous protestations, refused to see him or even accept his letters. In his misery, Berlioz composed an autobiographical symphony, modelled on De Quincy's *Confessions of an Opium Eater*, a *Fantastic Symphony*, depicting:

> a young musician of unhealthily sensitive nature (who) has poisoned himself with opium in a paroxysm of lovesick despair . . . Too weak to cause death, it throws him into a long sleep accompanied by the most extraordinary visions.

These include a witches' orgy and a fantasy that he has murdered his beloved and is being marched to the scaffold. While writing the symphony, Berlioz became first disenchanted then disgusted by the aloof Henriette. Instead he turned to Marie Moke, an eighteen-year-old fellow-teacher at a boarding school, to whom Berlioz had been carrying secret love letters from the German pianist Ferdinand Hiller.

When he sought permission to marry Marie, her parents demanded that he prove his worth as a musician. Happily, his *Fantastic Symphony* fitted the bill. The première 'had a frantic success,' he wrote,

> they actually encored the *March to the Scaffold*. I am mad! Mad! My marriage is fixed for Easter 1832, on condition that I go to Italy for a year. My blessed symphony has done the deed and won this concession from her mother.

With the *Prix de Rome* in his pocket and his future happiness assured, Berlioz set off for Italy. There, while working on a fundamental revision of the *Fantastic Symphony*, he received a letter from Madame Moke announcing her daughter's engagement to Camille Pleyel, wealthy son of the piano manufacturer. She took the trouble to deny that she had ever promised Marie to Berlioz and urged the composer not to kill himself in disappointment. Berlioz's reaction was more ambitious than even she had feared.

In two minutes my plans were laid. I must hurry to Paris to kill two guilty women and one innocent man; since, having carried out the act of justice, I too must die.

He rushed out to a milliner's and ordered a lady's maid's costume as disguise, then raced back to his hotel to leave directions on the unfinished revision of the *Fantastic Symphony* for the conductor Habeneck to complete its scoring. He then packed a suitcase with two pistols and two small bottles containing strychnine and laudanum and departed for Paris. On the first stage of his journey he rehearsed his plan to enter the Moke home disguised as a maid bearing a letter from her mistress.

While it was being read, I would pull out my double-barrelled pistols, kill number one and number two, seize number three by the hair and finish her off likewise; after which, if this vocal and instrumental concert had gathered an audience, I would turn the fourth barrel upon myself. Should it miss fire (such things happen occasionally), I had a final resource in my little bottles.

Arriving at Genoa, he found that his costume had been stolen. Resolutely, he bought another before proceeding to Nice, where he experienced a conversion. According to the self-mocking account in his memoirs, when the stage-coach stopped to change horses he suddenly realized that he was hungry, not having touched food since he left Florence and, this physical desire reawakened his love of life. A more likely explanation, confessed in a letter, is that in frustration at the delays in his mission, he swallowed the contents of one of his small bottles, instantly regretted his suicide attempt and dosed himself with sea water until he had rid himself of the poison. Weakened, he had no stomach left for murder and spent a month recuperating among the orange groves.

On his return to Paris, Berlioz found Henriette Smithson in town, miserable after the failure of a theatrical tour. His infatuation revived and was received with greater sympathy. When she broke her leg and was kept off the stage, he felt this was an omen that he should protect her. The *Court Journal* in London reported acidly that:

Miss Smithson was married last week in Paris to Delrioz (sic), the musical composer. We trust this marriage will insure the happiness of an amiable young woman, as well as secure us against her reappearance on the English boards.

It achieved the latter objective, but not the former. Henriette, who had never matched Berlioz's fury of adoration, soon resented his rising fame and the decline of her own. She berated him for betraying her with other women and he, in growing disenchantment, gave grounds for her accusations. When she tried to prevent him from going on foreign tours, he surreptitiously smuggled his music score by score out of their home until he had extricated himself entirely. He moved in with his mistress Marie Recio, an indifferent singer, but found he had merely jumped from the frying pan into the fire. 'I should deserve to be in Hell, if I were not there already,' he wrote. Recio gave him no chance to escape, accompanying him on tours and singing at his concerts, to the embarrassment of all concerned. She fought with Henriette over the money each was receiving from the beleaguered composer and, when Henriette died in 1854, gave Berlioz no rest until he married her. Berlioz mourned to the last the withering of his love for Henriette, but voiced little regret over Marie's death eight years later. As for Marie Moke-Pleyel, he never mentioned her name after abandoning his attempt on her life. She became the second most famous woman pianist in Europe (after Clara Schumann) and a respected professor of music at Brussels for a quarter of a century. Such is the fate of a siren.

Half a century later Debussy, too, left his wife for a singer. Emma Bardac was the estranged wife of a banker and it was swiftly alleged that her principal attraction for Debussy was the huge stipend she received from her former husband. The scandal burgeoned when Lily, the wife she supplanted, had the poor taste to attempt suicide. She failed, the bullet causing a serious chest wound, and some of Debussy's friends earned his animosity by paying her hospital fees. Rumours flourished that Debussy had taken cash from her bedside table. Several versions of this story began to spread. Alma Mahler, who resented Debussy's opposition to her husband's music, wrote that Debussy, finding Lily unconscious, stripped her body of all valuables before sending for a doctor. Another tale suggested that Debussy tried, but failed, to murder his wife. Had he done so, it would not have been musically unprecedented. The fame of the Italian lutanist and composer, Carlo Gesualdo, rests equally on his originality as a madrigal composer and his savagery as a wife-killer. As the Scots composer, Cecil Gray, put it: 'It was not until Gesualdo gave up murder that he seriously took to composing.'

Don Carlo Gesualdo, Prince of Venosa, was heir to no gentle tradition of music-making, but to a line of robber barons. The most celebrated of his ancestors had distinguished himself by losing his head to a marauding Greek army, his severed skull being fired by catapult into the besieged city he had been defending. As he grew up in the 1560s, young Carlo's imagination was nourished on such tales, but he did not take them too seriously since he was only a second son and consequently not expected to perform acts of valour. He showed an early gift for music and would gather his friends to a quiet castle outside Naples, where they would while away the summer nights in song, Gesualdo accompanying on his lute. Like warfare, women played little part in his life and he was able to approach his thirtieth year without troubling to encumber himself with a wife and family.

Then, disaster struck. His elder brother Luigi died suddenly and childlessly and Carlo became heir to the princedom. Not only did this entail administrative and occasional combative duties, but it became necessary for Carlo to marry and sire a few scions, or the noble House of Gesualdo would disappear. The bride chosen for him was his first cousin, Donna Maria d'Avalos, a 'surprising beauty' of twenty-one years old, who 'had already given ample proof of her fecundity'. She was a passionate woman, whose first husband had died from what was diagnosed as an excess of conjugal carnality. She enjoyed a brief second marriage before giving up her spouse (thanks to a papal indulgence) to marry the last of the Gesualdos.

Carlo approached his new tasks dutifully. The estates flourished, the first years of his marriage seemed happy and a son was born to ensure continuity of the line. But tragedy was at hand, set in motion by the innate restlessness of his new wife, and chronicled in immaculate detail in two family histories (liberally translated by Cecil Gray):

> The enemy of the human race, unable to endure the spectacle of such great love and happiness, such conformity of tastes and desires in two married people, awakened in the bosom of Donna Maria impure desires and a libidinous and unbridled appetite for the sweetnesses of illicit love and for the beauty of a certain knight. This was Fabrizio Carafa, third Duke of Andria and seventh Count of Ruovo, reputed to be the handsomest and most accomplished nobleman of the city.

What began with an innocent dance at a ball progressed into exchanges of glances, words, secret messages and, fatefully, assignations:

> The first occasion of their coming together was in a garden in the Borgo di Chiaia, in the pavilion whereof the Duke did lie concealed, awaiting his beloved who, on pretext of diversion and entertainment, was taken there. And she, while walking there, affected to be overcome by some bodily pain, and separating herself from her escort, entered into the pavilion wherein lay the Duke, who, without the loss of one moment, put into execution the work of love. Nor was this the only occasion on which they came together for these enjoyments, but many and many times did they do so

. . . many and many of which encounters are described in fascinating but irrelevant detail by the local historians.

Before long, news of the affaire reached Don Giulio, Carlo's uncle, who, nursing a penchant for the lovely Maria, invited her to the pavilion in his own garden. When she declined, the evil Giulio went to her husband. Meanwhile, Duke Fabrizio, having heard that the Gesualdos were becoming suspicious,

gave pause to his pleasures; but Donna Maria, unable to endure this remission, solicited the Duke that they should resume again . . . And so did they continue in their delights.

Until one day when Carlo returned unexpectedly from a hunting expedition and found the lovers asleep in bed, sated with pleasure.

Shaking off the dejection into which this miserable spectacle had plunged him, he slew with innumerable dagger thrusts the sleepers before they had time to waken.

And after he had ordered that their dead bodies should be dragged from the room and left exposed, he made a statement of his reasons for this butchery, and departed with his familiars to his city of Venosa.

And this tragedy took place on the night of the 16th October, 1590. The bodies of the wretched lovers remained exposed all the following morning in the midst of the hall, and all the city flocked to see the pitiful sight.

The lady's wounds were all in the belly, and more particularly in those parts which she ought to have kept honest; and the Duke was wounded even more grievously.

Too beautiful, too alike, too unfortunate were this unhappy couple.

At the hour of vespers the bodies were removed for burial amidst the lamentation of the entire city.

Such was the end of impure desires.

For the sanguinary Gesualdo, however, it marked the beginning of his musical career. The assault released volumes of sweet madrigals from his quill. He remarried without further brutal incident and devoted the rest of his life to music.

CHAPTER ELEVEN

CASUALTY LIST

*I*f music be the food of love, as Shakespeare has asserted, love has been shown to contribute just as much feud to music. While musical blood has been shed for reasons as diverse as professional jealousy, a refusal to play an encore and smoking a cigar at the wrong time, it is romance which has created the greatest toll of casualties. With Donna Gesualdo's fate fresh in mind, we turn to the unsolved mystery of the assassination of the Italian composer Alessandro Stradella.

Stradella, virtually forgotten nowadays, was a musician of no mean ability, rated by Burney as the finest vocal composer of his century, the seventeenth. He was also 'an exquisite singer', the finest in Venice and the vicinity where he was hired by a Senator to train the voice of his betrothed, a noble Roman lady, by the name of Hortensia. Before long, Stradella's attentions strayed from his pupil's larynx to more endearing parts and the peculiar intensity of the singing lessons was soon the subject of comment among passing gondoliers. The Senator's suspicions were aroused and Stradella and Hortensia prudently eloped.

> The Venetian suitor, enraged at their escape, determined to satiate his revenge by having them assassinated, in whatever part of the world they could be found. For this purpose he hired two desperate bravadoes for a large sum of money and the promise of a still larger reward when the work should be accomplished. The assassins proceeded directly to Naples, the place of Stradella's nativity, supposing he would return thither for asylum.
>
> After many fruitless researches in that city, they arrived in Rome, on an evening when there was to be a grand *funzione*, accompanied by music, in the church of St John of Lateran. Entering with the crowd, they beheld Stradella. It was an oratorio of his own composition, in which he was to sing a principal part. Delighted at having at length found their victim, having almost despaired of meeting with him, they resolved to lose no time; the performance was not to close till dusk and they determined to take this favourable opportunity for executing their purpose. They then ran over the whole church to ascertain if Hortensia was among the spectators. They were occupied in this search, when, after other pieces executed by common performers, Stradella began to sing. They stopped in spite of themselves; they listened to his sublime tones. Assassins as they were, their rocky hearts were softened. What a reflection, that in the whole world there was but one such perfect singer, and they were about to extinguish for ever that enchanting voice that had not its equal on earth! Remorse filled their hearts; they shed tears, and before Stradella's part was finished, had made up

their minds to save the lovers, whose death, on receiving the wages of blood, they had sworn upon the Holy Evangelists.

The ceremony over, they waited a long time for Stradella, outside the church. At last they saw him come from a private door, with Hortensia on his arm. They approached; complimented him on his oratorio, thanked him for the pleasure he had just given them, and confessed that it was to the impression which his voice had made upon them, and the tender feeling which it had excited, that he owed his life. They explained to him the fearful motive of their journey, and advised the lovers to quit Rome without delay.

They headed for Turin, where Stradella was appointed concert-master to the Duchess of Savoy and Hortensia was sent to a nunnery to recover from her excitement. The impressionable assassins returned meanwhile to Venice, claiming they had failed to find the fugitives. The furious Senator hired another pair of detective-cutthroats in their stead and, according to the French biographer Stendhal (from whose account these extracts are taken), enlisted Hortensia's family in the mission of vengeance by convincing her father that he was honour bound to kill the lovers.

One evening, as Stradella was taking the air on the ramparts of Turin, he was attacked by three men, who stabbed him in the breast and left him for dead. They were the aged father of Hortensia, and two assassins, who, as soon as they had committed the deed, fled for an asylum to the palace of the French ambassador.

The assault had been witnessed by numbers of persons, who were walking in the same place. The noise of the transaction spread through the whole city, and reached the ears of the Duchess, who instantly ordered the gates to be shut, and the assassins to be demanded of the French ambassador. But, as they had made his palace their sanctuary, he insisted on the privileges granted to men of his function, refused to give them up, and finally favoured their escape.

The resilient Stradella, however, recovered from his chest wounds, although he was never able to sing again. Learning that his prey had eluded him yet again, the Venetian took matters into his own hands. Donning disguise, he took up residence in Turin to observe the miscreants at close quarters.

A year passed. The Duchess of Savoy, more and more touched with the situation of the two lovers, who had suffered so much and who seemed born for each other, resolved to sanctify their mutual passion, and had the ceremony of their marriage performed in her own palace. Shortly after this, Hortensia, wearied with her residence at the convent, wished to take an excursion to Genoa. Stradella conducted her thither.

The morning after their arrival, they were both found poignarded in their beds.

The culprit was never apprehended, and the facts of the crime have come increasingly into question in the three centuries since it was committed. Stradella was certainly murdered in 1682 but by whom and whether Hortensia died with him remains open to speculation. Burney, writing almost a century after the event, and Stendhal, later still, assumed that both lovers were put to death at the hands of the Venetian. This conclusion provided the theme for no fewer than four nineteenth-century operas. Some modern musicologists contend, however, that the composer was slain by Hortensia's brothers, at her behest, when she found he was being unfaithful. A third account, put forward by *Grove's Dictionary*, maintains that Stradella was killed by a soldier in the Piazza Bianchi, after a dispute with one of Genoa's leading families over a further affair of the heart.

A hundred years later, the philandering violinist Giuseppe Cambini narrowly avoided a similar fate when he seduced and made off with a young lady from Naples. They boarded a departing ship in the Bay, moments before her avenging family caught them, only for the ship to be seized by pirates. Of Cambini's beloved, no more is heard. The musician spared himself a watery death by producing his violin and entertaining the buccaneers with the latest airs. They sold him into slavery, but he fiddled his way to freedom and set off for Paris, where he arrived in good time for the French Revolution. He prospered in the new political climate, churning out hundreds of hymnal banalities for the masses and became music director of a munitions factory. But apparently he loved nocturnal pleasures too much to keep a steady job and was soon back on the streets, reduced to hawking his compositions under the more imposing name of Luigi Boccherini (his erstwhile teacher who, being dead, could not complain). Cambini disappeared from Paris during the Napoleonic era and died in circumstances as untraceable as his fiancée's.

One entry above Cambini in the musical reference books there lives and violently dies another casualty of musical strife, Robert Cambert, harpsichordist and founder of the first French opera company. Evicted from Paris in 1672 when Jean-Baptiste Lully secured a royal musical monopoly, Cambert went to London and established a Royall Academy of Musick of his own. Five years later he was murdered; how, why and by whom remains a mystery. The prime suspect was his valet, though others included his many rivals on both sides of the Channel. Some even say he died a natural death, the victim of nothing more criminal than an act of character assassination.

Quite why so many musical murders should remain unsolved is in itself a mystery, particularly when professional jealousy presents itself as a clear-cut motive. In one of the most puzzling cases, Jean-Marie Leclair, a leading French violinist and composer, was stabbed to death one October evening in 1764 when he returned home from work. Leclair had powerful friends at Court and the police investigation was unusually thorough. It found three principal suspects: Leclair's estranged wife, who was also his publisher, the gardener who discovered his body the next morning and his nephew, an up-and-coming violinist, Guillaume-François Vial, in whom his wife was taking a pronounced interest. According to *Grove*, the evidence against the rival musician, preserved in the French National Archives, is so conclusive that it is inexplicable that he escaped prosecution. Possibly he was saved on the strength of his own Court connections; alternatively, the authorities may have decided that, having lost one violinist to an assassin, they could ill afford to sacrifice another to the public executioner.

Hardest of all to substantiate are the legends of poisoning that flourish when a promising musician dies prematurely. Doubtless some of these tales are true, particularly in medieval Italy where poison was a proven means of obtaining a social advantage. Few, though, have been proven. Visiting Italy in 1776 Doctor Burney was astonished to learn that Giovanni Battista Pergolesi, composer of a renowned *Stabat Mater*, who had died forty years earlier aged twenty-six, was believed to have been poisoned by a rival. Burney brought proof that Pergolesi had died of consumption, scourge of the poor, and had achieved no success in his lifetime to inspire homicidal envy, but his protestations did not allay the legend.

The most famous allegation of poison concerns the death, at thirty-five years and ten months of age, of Wolfgang Amadeus, beloved of God, Mozart. The allegation that he had been poisoned by Antonio Salieri arose within weeks and swiftly became accepted, without a shred of real evidence, as a popular truth. The Russian poet Alexander Pushkin made it into a 'short tragedy', whose theme was that Salieri had murdered Mozart not out of base envy but as an act of musical self-defence, to protect traditional values from his revolutionary innovations. Rimsky-Korsakov adapted Pushkin's fanciful poem into an imaginative opera entitled *Mozart and Salieri*. In 1980, Peter Shaffer's play on this threadbare but compelling theme became one of the award-winning productions in the West End and on Broadway. To examine the case against Salieri, we must trace Mozart's activities in his last months on earth.

Mozart received the first premonition of his death in July 1791. As he was putting the final touches to *The Magic Flute*, a haggard stranger dressed in grey appeared at his door and offered him a commission from his employer to write a requiem. The fee was generous and carried a condition: the composer was to observe strict secrecy about the work. Mozart accepted, but was disturbed by the mysterious nature of the request. Only long after his death was it discovered that the commission had come from Count Walsegg-Stuppach, a Viennese courtier, who wanted to pass the requiem off as his own tribute to his deceased wife.

Mozart began composing it immediately but was interrupted by an invitation to write an opera for Prague, for the coronation celebrations of Leopold II as King of Bohemia. Ever short of money, Mozart accepted. He is said to have written *The Clemency of Titus* (*La Clemenza di Tito*) in only eighteen days. Late in August, as he was about to board the carriage for Prague accompanied by his wife Constanze and his pupil Franz Xaver Süssmayr, the enigmatic emissary suddenly approached him to ask how the requiem was proceeding. Mozart fobbed the man off with a promise to complete it when he returned to Vienna, but, weakened by overwork, poor diet and persistent maladies, he was haunted by the reappearance of this shadowy apparition.

He spent a month in Prague and was ill intermittently throughout. The opera was coolly received at first but gained popularity as the coronation festivities warmed up. Mozart took leave of his friends in Prague with tears in his eyes. To their consternation, he said he did not expect to see them again alive.

He returned to Vienna for the première of *The Magic Flute* on 30 September. Again the audience responded cautiously, a notable exception being Antonio Salieri who, as Mozart observed in a letter, greeted each new aria with 'Bravo' and 'Bello'. The opera gradually grew more popular; at one performance, Mozart enlivened proceedings from the wings by playing a glockenspiel deliberately out of time with Papageno's song. He seemed cheerful, youthful and not unwell until

one fine day in autumn his wife drove with him to the Prater. As soon as they had reached a solitary spot and were seated together, Mozart began to speak of death and said that he was writing this requiem for himself. She tried to talk him out of these gloomy fancies but in vain and his eyes filled with tears as he answered her, 'No, no I am but too well convinced that I cannot last long. I have certainly been poisoned. I cannot rid myself of this idea.'

All the while he continued working at the *Requiem*, pausing only to compose his sublime clarinet concerto and a cantata for his masonic lodge. He became so obsessed with morbid thoughts, that a doctor ordered the *Requiem* score to be taken away from him. When his spirits rose again, the *Requiem* was returned to him, but so did his illness.

About the 21st of November his hands and feet began to swell, he was seized with sudden sickness and an almost total incapacity of motion. In this state he was removed to the bed, from which he never rose again . . .

Throughout his illness, music was still a subject of the greatest interest to him. The *Requiem* lay almost constantly on his bed and Süssmayr was frequently at his side receiving instructions as to effects . . . At two o'clock on the day . . . of his death . . . he desired the score of the *Requiem* to be brought and it was sung by his visitors round his bed; himself taking the alto part . . . They had proceeded as far as the first bars of the *Lacrymosa*, when Mozart was seized with a violent fit of weeping.

These recollections, published by the English writer Edward Holmes in 1845, were assembled from first- and second-hand observations of Mozart by relatives and friends in his dying days. The account of his last moments on 5 December, 1791, is given by his sister-in-law Sophie:

As I approached his bed he called to me, 'It is well that you are here: you must stay tonight and see me die.' I tried as far as I was able to banish this impression, but he replied, 'The taste of death is already on my tongue — I taste death . . .' Süssmayr was standing by the bedside and on the counterpane lay the *Requiem*, concerning which Mozart was still speaking and giving directions . . . As he looked over the pages of the *Requiem* for the last time, he said, with tears in his eyes, 'Did I not tell you that I was writing this for myself?'

On the arrival of the physician, Dr Closset, cold applications were ordered to his burning head, a process endured by the patient with extreme shuddering and which brought on the delirium from which he never recovered. He remained in this state for two hours, and at midnight expired.

At the moment of Mozart's death, the only suspicion of foul play lay in his uncanny presentiment of mortality and his hysterical accusation that he was being poisoned. While the symptoms of his last illness do not rule out poisoning, the continuous small doses required to escape detection could only have been administered by friends and relatives who attended the dying man. If Salieri poisoned Mozart, he could only have done so with an accomplice.

Doctors who examined the body, and professors who subsequently re-examined their findings, found no trace of poison. The cause of death was diagnosed variably as: a severe military fever, rheumatic fever, a deposit in the head and a dropsy of the heart. Mozart received a pauper's funeral and was buried in an unmarked mass grave in St Marx church-yard outside Vienna. When posterity sought to make amends and rebury him with honours, his corpse could not be found. Salieri, Süssmayr and three other musicians are said to have been the only mourners at the graveside; other accounts say the funeral was unattended.

Süssmayr completed the *Requiem*, which was first performed at a concert for Constanze's benefit in January 1793; Salieri helpfully attended the rehearsals. (Count Walsegg-Stuppach performed the work as his own composition ten months later; not for a further six years were the disputes over its ownership resolved.)

It was some weeks before the whispers began. First it was mooted without medical proof that Mozart's death was due to kidney failure, a common outcome of poisoning. A Berlin newspaper reported that his corpse had swelled up after death. Emperor Leopold died suddenly; he, too, was alleged to have been poisoned. Reports that Mozart had talked of being poisoned began to spread but, though fingers pointed at Salieri as the composer who stood most to gain from Mozart's elimination, he was not the only natural suspect. Mozart in his short life had made many musical enemies. Genius had been only too conscious of its superiority over mere mortals and was never slow to demonstrate the disparity. Mozart would 'die laughing', in his own offensive phrase, when he heard his inferiors play the piano, his favourite instrument. Of the respected Abbé Vogler, he remarked unpleasantly, 'It was unendurable . . . his sort of sight-reading is like shitting to me;' of another rival, 'I wiped the floor with him;' of Muzio Clementi, who almost defeated him in a piano duel, 'A charlatan, like all Italians . . . he has not the slightest expression or taste, let alone feeling.'

It was on Salieri, however, as the highest ranking rival, that public attention became fixed. He had been vanquished musically time and again by Mozart but succeeded by guile and gregariousness in attaining State honours which were consistently denied to Mozart. Though an agreeable companion and a conscientious teacher of music, as Beethoven, Schubert and Liszt would attest, Salieri could be ruthless when his interests were threatened. He had intrigued ceaselessly against Mozart in court and was probably responsible for Da Ponte's banishment from Vienna when the librettist abandoned Salieri's operas for Mozart's. Publicly his behaviour towards Mozart was rarely improper and often generous, but he cannot have regretted the departure of so overwhelming an opponent. Shortly after Mozart's death, he is reported to have said: 'He is gone — good riddance, or we should all have been starving before long. What killed him? His immorality — just listen to *Don Giovanni*!'

Salieri was soon made aware that he was suspected of having murdered Mozart, but did not take the charge seriously. When Rossini visited Vienna in 1822, he was able to taunt Salieri cattily about his reputation as a latter-day Borgia. 'It is lucky for Beethoven,' Rossini remarked, 'that, in self-preservation, he avoids having you at meals. Otherwise you might pack him off to the other world as you did Mozart.' 'Do I look like a poisoner to you?' Salieri retorted mildly. Rossini acknowledged that he seemed more troubled by attacks on his music than by criminal imputations.

A year later, however, Salieri became fatally ill and Vienna's newspapers outdid each other with reports that, in delirium, he had confessed to killing Mozart. He tried to commit suicide by cutting his throat but his life was saved and he was consigned to an asylum. Newspapers reported fresh admissions of guilt, but Salieri's admirers, Beethoven among them, stoutly insisted that the 'confessions' were the fantasy of a deranged mind. The deaf Beethoven's notebooks, through which he conducted conversations, are littered with jottings by visitors informing him of Salieri's latest indiscretions. Beethoven pooh-poohed their tittle-tattle and scribbled loftily: 'I still call myself Salieri's pupil' — this testimonial coming from a man who had just completed his titanic Ninth Symphony. When he learned that Salieri had been retired by the Emperor on a full pension, Beethoven was delighted: 'This proves he is innocent. He is just sick.'

Another former pupil, the pianist-composer Ignaz Moscheles, visited Salieri on his deathbed in the common ward of a Vienna hospital.

> Our meeting, [writes Moscheles] was a sorrowful one; for already his appearance shocked me, and he spoke to me in broken sentences of his nearly impending death. At last he said, 'I can assure you as a man of honour that there is no truth in the absurd report; of course you know — Mozart — I am said to have poisoned him; but no — malice, sheer malice; tell the world, dear Moscheles, old Salieri, who is on his death-bed, has told this to you.'

Yet the evil he was alleged to have done lived after him. Even Moscheles, defender of his good faith, conceded that 'morally, he doubtless poisoned by his intrigues many an hour of Mozart's existence'. Without a trace of evidence, the two composers have entered popular history as murderer and victim. Perhaps it is the very absence of proof that makes their final confrontation so intriguing. Had Salieri been detected, tried, convicted of murder and judicially condemned to death, the episode would have given rise to fewer literary extravaganzas.

While jealous murders are mostly insoluble, there is firm proof of many attempts by musicians to put their rivals out of action by means of injury. Leopold Sylvius Weiss, an influential German lutanist, had his thumb almost bitten off at the knuckle by a violinist he overshadowed at a recital in 1722. Miraculously, he recovered sufficiently to resume playing within a year. The flamboyant American pianist Louis Moreau

Gottschalk, a precursor of Liberace, was the victim of a similar assault in Spain in 1852. Gottschalk, who was recognized by the array of medals that clanked against his chest as he played the piano, cultivated a feminine hysteria in his audience that equalled the raptures aroused by Liszt and Paderewski. In Valladolid, he so enchanted the Infanta, sister of the King of Spain, that she baked him a cake with her own fair hands. This royal conquest, however, was viewed with less enthusiasm by the owner of the hornier hands whose duty it was to play for Her Majesty year in, year out.

> Leaving the Court in one of the Court carriages, he heard his name called, and stopping the coach he found he had been called by the pianist of the Court, who came running up. Gottschalk opened the coach door, when the pianist, seeing Gottschalk's fingers grasping one side of the opening, quickly shut the door upon them. The pain was so great that Gottschalk immediately fainted, and was taken to his hotel. On examination it was found that his little finger was very much injured, and the surgeons feared they would have to amputate it. To this Gottschalk would not consent, as it would prevent him from ever playing again. He was ninety-one days in recovering. What was very remarkable, instead of injuring, it absolutely benefited his finger, which became more powerful than ever, and enabled him to execute certain passages with more *éclat* than before.

A travelling musician, like the modern professional footballer, is at personal risk not only from the local players he shames but from the emotions he kindles in adversary audiences. The prudent Paganini would never mount a stage without first ascertaining the situation of its exits; even so, he often barely escaped the vengeance of crowds he had taunted with his fiddle. Rossini, less fleet of foot, suffered a memorable pummelling in Rome after the première of his *Barber of Seville*, his brand new jacket torn from his retreating back and his body bruised by missiles. Unwilling to face a further test of his popularity, he cried off sick just before the second performance and was awoken in bed late that evening by a tumultuous roar in the streets outside his hotel. He jumped out of bed and hid in a stable in the rear courtyard. The tenor Manuel Garcia, the Count in the opera, found him there and urged him to accept the exuberant apologies of an audience which had changed its mind about his masterpiece. 'Tell them,' replied Rossini, still bitter about his jacket, 'that I fuck them, their bravos, and everything else. I am not coming out of here.' Garcia, loyally delivering the composer's message, was hit in the eye by an admonitory orange from Rossini's restless admirers. The proprietor of the hotel came running. 'They'll burn the building down if you don't come out,' he quavered. 'Look, they are breaking my windows.' But Rossini refused to emerge and the crowd eventually dispersed. He complained later that he had suffered as much from Roman adulation as from castigation: he was made to pay for damage to the hotel and caught a cold from sleeping the rest of the winter night in a room with a broken window.

Jealousy and misplaced enthusiasm apart, political reasons also figure highly as a cause for assaults on musicians. Toscanini was beaten up by Fascist thugs for refusing to conduct their anthem. His German rival Furtwängler narrowly escaped serious injury when former concentration camp inmates waylaid him as he entered a concert hall in Vienna in 1947, seeking to exact physical retribution for his apparent collusion with the Nazis. The Jewish violinist Jascha Heifetz was savagely assaulted in Jerusalem in 1953, for playing music by a composer who was listed by the Government as a Nazi collaborator.

Heifetz, who performed the most florid extravagances with icily unemotional perfection, encountered opposition in Israel as soon as he announced that he would be playing the violin sonata by Richard Strauss. When asked discreetly to drop the sonata from his programmes, he refused. To a formal request from the Minister of Education he retorted: 'I recognize only two kinds of music — good music and bad. Good music is for all those who have ears to listen.' Threats against his life were made by the Betar movement, a right-wing youth organization led by the former terrorist leader who would later become Prime Minister, Menahem Begin. Heifetz's first concert was in the port city of Haifa, which had a large population of refugees from Germany. A police squad protected him inside the hall. But there was no trouble and the audience was so enthusiastic that it appeared that Heifetz had won a victory for musical tolerance.

He played Strauss again in Jerusalem. After the recital, Reuters reported,

> he drove back to the King David Hotel. As he got out of the car, a young man leapt at him and attempted to smash his arms. They are insured for a six-figure sum.
>
> With an instinctive movement he averted the full weight of the blow, but received a wound on the right arm which bled profusely. The attacker ran away and the iron bar, wrapped in paper, was found later in a wood in the neighbourhood . . .
>
> An unidentified man telephoned the Israeli state broadcasting station and said: 'The attempt to break Heifetz's arms was made by the Hebrew Youth Organisation. We warn the artist to leave the country immediately.'

Heifetz was rushed to hospital, where his wounds were treated. On the following night, his right hand plainly swollen, he played courageously at Rehovot. But he cancelled his last concert in Tel Aviv and announced on departure that he would never return. The Israel Philharmonic Orchestra roundly condemned the 'cowardly' assault; official reaction was more ambiguous.

It was fifteen years before Heifetz let himself be persuaded, by his chamber music comrade, Gregor Piatigorsky, to revoke his boycott. His return to Zion was hailed as something of a political triumph: the ingathering of the farthest exile. His reconciliation concert in Jerusalem was attended by President Zalman Shazar, Prime Minister Golda Meir, most of her Cabinet and the cream of Israeli society. Heifetz, true to character, made no concession to emotion and played a programme that ran higher in the brow than most of the occasional concert-goers would have wished. Unmoved by an applause that demanded an emotional gesture, Heifetz conceded a single encore and departed without comment, never to return.

To refuse to play an encore altogether was unthinkable. A century earlier such an act was reputed to have provoked a homicidal assault on a renowned conductor and threatened briefly to provoke full-scale war between two European empires. In April 1870, word reached Vienna that Josef Strauss, second of the waltz brothers, was lying grievously injured in Warsaw, where he had been beaten up by Russian officers after refusing them an encore. Gentle Josef, according to his brother Johann junior the most gifted of the Strausses, was the one most beloved of the Austrian public. He had never wanted to be a musician and was advanced on a successful career as an industrial engineer when Johann collapsed in 1853 from overwork and begged his brother to take over the family business until he recovered. 'But I can't play the violin,' Josef protested. 'You are a Strauss,' said Johann, 'you'll learn.' His first tentative waves of the baton were sympathetically received by the Viennese and Josef, encouraged by their response, quickly grew in confidence. He took violin lessons and was soon a competent performer. More pertinently, he studied harmony and composition so diligently that within months he was submitting his own original waltzes for the delectation of the most discriminating audiences. In contrast to his famous father and brother, who composed mainly in the ebullient major key, Josef used the contemplative minor for his waltzes and thus distinguished himself as the most sensitive of the Strausses. At Johann's insistence, he gave up engineering altogether and applied himself to waltzing, camouflaging in such titles as *The Course of My Life is Love and Joy* his vocational regrets and the inherent melancholy of his nature.

In 1870, Josef took his orchestra for a tour of Russia. Assembling his band in Warsaw, he found that seven musicians had deserted along the way. Replacements were despatched from Vienna, but the delay irked

Melancholy Josef Strauss

Josef, who longed to return home to his family. He was further irritated by a nagging quarrel with his first violinist, who, petulantly, kept fluffing important entries. After three fractious concerts, Strauss found himself losing control of the orchestra in the fourth. As he strained to hold his forces together, he suffered what must have been a stroke, fell off the podium and down four steps, banging his head and sustaining concussion. He was carried away bleeding from the nose, mouth and back of the head. During the concert, a group of Russian officers and

217

their disreputable female consorts had tried to enter without tickets and were blocked by a porter, named Stroutza. One of the lieutenants drew his sword and hit the porter on the head; he collapsed, bleeding. Strauss and Stroutza were rushed to hospital. Sensationalist or sloppy journalists jumbled the two names and the wires to Vienna buzzed that night with the news that Josef Strauss, Austria's favourite, had been brutally assaulted by legions of the Tsar. Retribution was demanded in banner headlines. Hapsburg armies were put on alert. The tension was defused by the Russian Governor-General of Warsaw, Grand Duke Constantine, an amateur violinist who had played under Johann Strauss's baton, who made the Austrian Consul issue a swift statement clarifying the confusion.

Johann sped to Warsaw together with Josef's wife, but left her to cope with the sick conductor, while he took over his brother's scheduled concerts to prevent rival waltz bands from stealing a march on the Strauss monopoly. Josef's ailment was diagnosed as a brain tumour. He was carried back to Vienna in agony and died within days of arrival, aged forty-three.

Rumours continued to flourish after his demise. It was put about that the 'body' brought back to Vienna was nothing more than a wax effigy of Strauss, the widow having been bribed with roubles. A sworn deposition by the Austrian priest who had given Josef the last sacrament laid that fable to rest, but the legend that one of the Strauss family was murdered by Russian soldiers still appears as fact in many an otherwise infallible work of reference. Josef remains the least known of the Strauss brothers; his only daughter died in 1920, apparently of starvation.

Fatal confusions of musical identity are not uncommon, particularly in circumstances of civil upheaval. On 30 June 1934, during the Night of the Long Knives in which Hitler destroyed the brown-shirted legions of Ernst Röhm's SA, four members of Himmler's ascendant SS called at the Munich apartment of Dr Willi Schmidt, a well-known music critic. They disturbed him in his study playing the cello and took him away without explanation. When a coffin was brought back to his widow some days later, she was told not to look inside. It transpired that her husband had been confused by the SS with another Willi Schmidt — a German name as common as John Smith — a prominent brown-shirt who was scheduled to be purged.

Eleven years and a World War later, a few miles away across the border in Allied-occupied Austria, the last of the great musical innovators was killed by an American soldier who mistook him for a black marketeer. Anton von Webern, pupil of Arnold Schoenberg, had fled Vienna as the Red Army approached and took refuge with relatives in the village of Mittersill, near Salzburg. Webern had survived the Nazi régime with difficulty. Though a 'pure German', his music and radical twelve-tone philosophy were outlawed as 'cultural Bolshevism' and he was reduced to giving private lessons and reading the proofs of approved composers for a benevolent publisher. Webern greeted the end of the war with relief, hoping it would enable his music to be heard again.

Post-War conditions in Mittersill were severe. There were shortages of all essentials and the composer shrunk to fifty kilograms in weight from the ravages of dysentery. Matters seemed to be improving in September 1945, when one of his sons-in-law, a former Nazi storm-trooper, began negotiating contraband deals with American soldiers. In celebration of his sudden fortune, he invited the Weberns to their first square meal

Anton von Webern

since the War and, as a special treat, procured for the smoke-starved composer a priceless American cigar for his post-prandial pleasure.

After dinner a party of soldiers called to speak to the son-in-law, apparently about business. Webern and the ladies withdrew to the only other room, where his grandchildren were asleep. Itching to smoke the cigar, the composer stepped outside into the darkness to light up. As he puffed away peacefully in the cool night air, one of the soldiers who had come to arrest his son-in-law brushed past him. Alarmed, the soldier drew his pistol and fired three times. Webern died within minutes.

Repercussions of the tragedy reverberated for a decade. Webern's daughter was immediately hauled off to prison with her husband, both charged with illegal dealings. His distraught widow, left behind to look after her small grandchildren, was to die prematurely four years later, reproaching herself to the end for having ordered her husband outside for his smoke. Webern's daughter was released after interrogation, his son-in-law was jailed for a year. A United States Army inquest returned an open verdict on Webern's death, but the nervous soldier who had shot him became obsessed by the accident. Returning home to North Carolina, he took to drink and, ten years to the month after the composer's death, died of the effects of alcoholism. The death of a great musician does not, in itself, signal the end of discord.

CHAPTER TWELVE

PARTING SHOTS

*D*eath, for all its seeming finality, is one of the untidier of Nature's phenomena. There are always loose ends to be tied up, affairs to be settled, projects to be completed or abandoned, outstanding disputes to be resolved.

It is rare for a composer to die with an empty desk; when he does, that in itself is cause for tongues to wag. When Joseph of the Strausses was taken so suddenly from his brothers, he left behind no unpublished waltzes. Officially this was attributed to the neatness of his scientifically-trained mind, which composed frugally for the occasion, producing a solution for each fresh problem. But rumours soon circulated that Johann, the executor of Josef's will, had retained his brother's notebooks and was issuing Josef's last creations as his own. Though this would have been wholly out of character for Johann, who showed exceptional consideration for Josef's bereaved family, the slander was given substance by the youngest and least of the Strauss brothers, Eduard, known as Handsome Edi, in a casual remark in his memoirs.

Nor was this Eduard's principal sin against his brothers after their deaths. Jealous at having been largely excluded by Johann and Josef from their compositional collaborations, he claimed in his memoirs that the three brothers had pledged that the survivor among them would destroy any musical arrangements left by the others, to prevent them falling into the hands of competitors. No sooner did his book appear in 1906 than Eduard made good his 'promise' by carting crate after crate of irreplaceable manuscripts to an industrial furnace for incineration. Mounds of documents — not just scores, but family documents that were embarrassing to the insignificant survivor — vanished into flames, feeding the furnace for two days and nights. As an act of musical fratricide, it is without parallel, denying Johann and Josef Strauss their last right of reply to Edi's falsehoods.

Johann Strauss's Vienna card-partner, Johannes Brahms, was another who died with an empty desk; so too, by odd coincidence, did his arch-rival Richard Wagner, though inevitably for differing reasons. Brahms became aware of the malignancy of his disease just soon enough to put his affairs in order. Wagner died with upturned palms apparently because *Parsifal* had consumed the last of his creative energies.

Parsifal was itself the centre of a major international controversy twenty years later. Its composer had ordained that the 'sacred festival drama' was to be staged only at his self-consecrated shrine at Bayreuth, in order that its receipts could be enjoyed exclusively and eternally by Cosima and their family. However, his decree was void of any legal force and as soon as its copyright expired the opera, like any other, entered the public domain for performance wherever, whenever and without payment of royalties. American copyright laws being more liberal then than most, it was in New York that Wagner faced his first posthumous battle. As soon as Wagner's US copyright expired in 1903, Heinrich Conried, the newly-appointed German-born manager of the Metropolitan Opera, announced the world première (outside Bayreuth) of *Parsifal*. The announcement provoked a storm of outrage from the entire copyright-shackled European world of opera, sanctimoniously horrified at the American 'sacrilege'. Only the conductor Felix Weingartner remained dispassionate enough to observe that if Wagner had genuinely wanted *Parsifal* to remain in Bayreuth he need not have published it and the original manuscript could have remained a family secret. Conried shrewdly offered to cancel his production if the leading German opera houses undertook to forgo the work when their own national copyright restrictions lapsed. When they failed to respond, he went ahead.

Cosima and Siegfried Wagner applied for an injunction in a New York court to stop the performance; it was refused. Conried offered them a gratuitous $20,000; they spurned it. The Richard Wagner Society of America protested vehemently against the flouting of the Master's wishes; it was ignored. Delegations of clergymen descended on the Mayor of New York demanding that he ban the opera as a blasphemy — not least because the première was ingeniously scheduled for 24 December; they were turned away. *Parsifal* survived its transplantation. In the event, every major opera house violated Bayreuth's master-given lien over the opera.

The sanctity of a composer's wishes cannot, it seems, be defended in perpetuity. An injunction by Edvard Grieg, the first composer to express a distinct Scandinavian identity in his music, was observed by reverent Norwegians for 114 years, but succumbed ultimately to an act of subversion and a powerful threat from the Soviet Union. Grieg had written a symphony in his student days at Leipzig, a competent work, though unmistakably influenced by the Mendelssohn-Schumann school. It was applauded in his native Bergen in 1865, but was withdrawn two years later by the composer, dissatisfied at its lack of national character. Within another two years Grieg had written his famous piano concerto and won acclaim (from Liszt, among others, who mastered its knuckle-twisting complexities at sight) as the voice of Norway. In 1874, aged thirty-one, he received a pension from the Norwegian Government which enabled him to devote the rest of his life to creating such national monuments as the *Peer Gynt* (written as incidental music to Ibsen's play) and *Holberg* (commemorating another national dramatist) suites. Across the title page of his youthful symphony he now scrawled: 'Is never to be performed'.

Grieg died in 1907. His wish was respected until 1981, when a researcher at Oslo University abstracted the score from its library, photocopied it and took the copy to Moscow. A Soviet orchestra recorded the symphony and the Russians generously offered Norway's state radio the first opportunity to broadcast the tape. If they declined, it was made clear, the Soviet Union would be only too honoured to stage the world's first broadcast performance of an unknown work by the patron musical saint of a neighbouring, none-too-friendly, nation. Faced with this ultimatum, Norway caved in. The broadcast première was given by the Bergen Symphony Orchestra, from Grieg's home town, and relayed prestigiously across Europe on the Eurovision network. To allay the national humiliation altogether, the Norwegian Prime Minister, Dr Gro Harlem Brundtland, added her personal seal of approval in a sleeve note to the commercial release of the recording.

Another storm in the far north blew up over the musical legacy of the most prolific melodist of all, Franz Schubert. At his death in 1828, at the age of thirty-one, he left behind more than six hundred songs, nine symphonies, fifteen string quartets, eleven piano sonatas and a diversity of inventions for various combinations of instruments and voices. His death was scarcely noticed by the musical community, which was preoccupied by rumours that Ludwig Spohr, the ephemeral violinist-composer, had died ('a serious loss at any time, but at the present irreparable', mourned one London paper). Schubert's massive pile of manuscripts was left to his brother, who tried with little success to have them published. Bundles of immortal music languished unopened in publishers' vaults, in the cupboards of cheap lodging houses and on the rubbish piles of Vienna. Schubert's Ninth Symphony, the Great C major, was only discovered ten years after his death by Robert Schumann, who persuaded Mendelssohn to conduct its première in 1839 at Leipzig.

More than a quarter of a century elapsed before another Schubert symphony, greater still, received its first performance. The *Unfinished*, for which Schubert had written two movements, was in the possession of a fellow composer Anselm Hüttenbrenner. He waited until 1865, by which time Schubert's music was becoming popular, before showing it to a publisher, but then only on condition that one of his own mediocre works was comparably published and performed. Hüttenbrenner's neglect may be partly excused by the fact that Schubert had made no attempt to finish the work and obviously regarded it as an abortive venture. For a man who could write eight songs in a day, he would not waste time over a symphony which resisted easy completion. He might also have been repelled by memories of the indignities of a venereal disease and its unsavoury treatment that he endured at the time of its composition.

However sordid its origin, the symphony was an instant success on performance and appealed in ever greater degree to successive generations of music lovers. It became an early bestseller on gramophone records and, as the centenary of Schubert's death approached, the moguls of the record industry sought to capitalize on its potential.

The first scheme they devised was to stage a competition for composers to 'complete' the *Unfinished Symphony* with an up-beat final movement. Musical reaction to this plan was so violent that it was swiftly abandoned and replaced by a Schubert Memorial Prize, offering ten thousand dollars — an amount greater than Schubert's lifetime earnings — for a new symphony which best conveyed the 'spirit' of Schubert's lyricism. An International Grand Jury of the Russian composer Alexander Glazounov, the English scholar Donald Tovey, the Danish symphonist Carl Nielsen, the Austrian conductor Franz Schalk, the American conductor Walter Damrosch, the Spanish musical writer Adolfo Salazar, and others of equal distinction, was convened. Amid the popping of flashbulbs and champagne corks, the judges awarded the Schubert Unfinished Prize to a Symphony in C major by a Swedish composer, Kurt Atterberg. The new symphony was immediately performed and recorded to near-unanimous acclaim. A notable exception was the English writer, Ernest Newman, to whom the work sounded a little too familiar to be wholly original:

Atterberg may have looked down the list of judges and slyly made up his mind that he would put in a bit of something that would appeal to each of them in turn — a bit of *Schéhérezade* for the Russian Glazounov, a bit of *Cockaigne* for Mr Tovey, a bit of the *New World Symphony* for Mr Damrosch, a bit of Granados for Salazar . . . But I wonder if there may not be another explanation . . . Atterberg is not merely a composer. He is a musical critic . . . Suppose he looked round with the cynical smile that, as all the world knows, all critics wear, and decided to pull the world's leg?

The hoax was elaborate and gravely embarrassing to all involved, except Atterberg, who bragged in an article entitled *How I Fooled the Music World* that his symphony was intended to satirize the wave of Schubertophilia in general and opportunistic commercialism in particular.

The desire to bring to fruition the unfulfilled ambitions of a dead composer harbours both a challenge to his friends and a pecuniary incentive to his family. It is also a perpetual source of conflict. When Mozart died, his widow Constanze sought to relieve her desperate poverty by publishing his last works. She handed the incomplete *Requiem*, however, not to Mozart's pupil Süssmayr who had followed the work from its inception but to another composer, Josef Edler von Eybler. If Süssmayr resented her decision, as he must have, he showed little sign of it. He was rewarded some months later with the task of completion when Eybler proved unequal to it, but has received little credit for his pains. Mozart scholars still get hot under the collar over just who wrote what in the *Requiem*, their antagonism to Süssmayr fuelled by a jealous suspicion that he was probably Constanze's lover before Mozart died. Consummation, in musical terms, can be a thankless act.

The widow of Carl Maria von Weber, the opera composer most admired by Wagner, found herself in similar straits to Constanze when her husband died suddenly aged thirty-nine, while conducting in London in 1826. Weber had left unfinished some preliminary sketches for a comic opera, *The Three Pintos* (*Die Drei Pintos*), but had written only seven of the opera's seventeen songs and scored a mere eighteen bars. His widow despatched the sketches hopefully to his friend Giacomo Meyerbeer, who retained the score for twenty-six years before returning it with apologies. The Weber family had abandoned hope when, in 1887, Weber's grandson, Carl, an army officer, showed the material to the ambitious junior conductor at the Leipzig Gewandhaus. Gustav Mahler devised a method of completing the opera with music from themes in other Weber works. He set to with a will, eagerly assisted by young Weber and his wife, Marion, and created a successful new opera, conducted by Mahler at a momentous Leipzig première more than sixty years after the death of its composer. Its immediate consequences, however, gave no cause for celebration. While reconstructing the opera, Mahler fell in love with Marion, 'a beautiful person . . . the sort that tempts one to do foolish things.' She inspired him to write his own First Symphony and they plotted to elope together. Mahler waited for her on a train poised for flight, but she failed to arrive at the station in time. Carl von Weber, unwilling to create a scandal for fear of prejudicing his army career and reluctant to offend Mahler in whose hands part of his grandfather's destiny lay, was consumed with impotent jealousy. After some months, it unbalanced his mind. Travelling by train one day to Dresden, he suddenly drew his revolver and alarmed fellow-passengers by shooting out the headrests between their seats. When his ammunition ran out, he was overpowered, arrested and consigned to a lunatic asylum for the rest of his life.

Mahler, plagued in his own last years by marital jealousy, expressed his fears in his Tenth, unfinished, Symphony, which itself generated prolonged posthumous strife. Thirteen years after his death, his widow, Alma, commissioned a young composer Ernst Krenek, who had recently married Anna, her surviving daughter by Mahler, to complete the symphony. Krenek found the task impossible and instead worked up a full orchestral score from the two unrelated movements which Mahler had left almost finished. His contribution was amended by Alexander von Zemlinsky, Alma's pre-Mahler teacher and lover, and Franz Schalk, Mahler's former deputy conductor, who directed the first performance. Their composition by committee was flawed, inevitably. It was also crippled by disjointedness, since the two movements were intended by Mahler as the symphony's first and third; the middle clue was missing. Yet for almost forty years this was the only glimpse musicians and public were allowed into Mahler's last masterpiece.

In a characteristic gesture of extreme candour, Alma published a facsimile of most of the manuscript pages of the symphony, revealing the dying composer's agonized jottings about her infidelity. But she continued to resist demands for a re-examination of Mahler's original score of the Tenth. In the 1940s she consented to let Schoenberg see the manuscript, but the great revolutionary was by then severely hampered by failing health and eyesight.

In 1960, for the centenary of Mahler's birth, a musicologist working for the BBC prepared an unauthorized revision of the two known movements. When he heard it performed by orchestra, Deryck Cooke resolved to go further and try to fill in the missing links for the second, fourth and fifth movements, much as Mahler had done for Weber's opera. His initiative was fiercely opposed by the survivors of the Mahler circle. The conductor Bruno Walter, Mahler's acolyte, convinced Alma to forbid performances of Cooke's work. But the ranks of the faithful were being thinned by age and the new Mahlerians soon spied their grail through the gaps. When Walter died in 1962, the eighty-three-year-old Alma was cajoled into listening to a recording of Cooke's version of the two movements. She was overcome — she had not realized, Cooke said, 'how much Mahler there was in it' — and showed the scholar pages of the manuscript she had been withholding.

Alma, who died in New York in 1964, did not live to hear Cooke's 'performing version' of the complete symphony. Its publication met with mixed, and heated, reaction. There were many who welcomed it as an imaginative evocation of Mahler's last thoughts, but a phalanx of prominent musicians led by Leonard Bernstein and Pierre Boulez, protested vigorously against it. The controversy continues and even now several musicians are embarked on their own personalized and competitive versions of Mahler's Tenth. To a composer who felt so misunderstood in his lifetime, the impassioned arguments over each of his last semi-quavers would afford Mahler wry amusement.

Yet Alma's greatest contribution to posthumous discord did not involve any of her three husbands. Long after her death, it is gradually becoming apparent that her energetic, busybody personality was at the heart of the suppression of what many believe to be the greatest twentieth-century opera.

In the creative intimacy of inter-War Vienna, Alma created a salon for her favourite composers, artists and writers, most of them members of the avant-garde. Among the musicians were the leading figures of the Second Vienna School, though of its founding trinity of Schoenberg, Berg and Webern, only Alban Berg became a regular visitor. Schoenberg lived mostly in Berlin and the introverted Webern had little in common with the socialite Alma, who publicly deprecated the effects of his radical asceticism on Schoenberg, his teacher. With Berg, though, she enjoyed a profound and lasting friendship. He was one of few who called her by Mahler's pet name, 'Almschi'. To cement their relationship, Alma went to great lengths to cultivate Berg's wife, Helene, although the two women were unlikely companions. Alma, buxom, passionate and hedonistic, contrasted sharply with the willowy, pale and self-denyingly slim Helene, whose regal bearing owed to more than coincidence: she was believed to be the illegitimate daughter of the Emperor Franz Josef. Berg had courted Helene with an insistence that recalled Schumann's pursuit of Clara. She was slow to respond initially and let herself be escorted by others, but Berg's passion and endurance were immense and ultimately overwhelming. Like the Schumanns, they encountered fierce resistance from her civil servant father, who objected to the young man's impoverished state, his choice of career, poor health and the fact that his only sister was an overt lesbian. For three years he vetoed their marriage. When he resigned himself to the inevitable, it was with the proviso that both bride and groom convert from Catholicism to Protestantism, so that they could get divorced easily if the match, as he expected, failed.

Such fond hopes were frustrated. The marriage was, to all appearances, serenely happy and ended only with Berg's premature death in 1935. To the carefully selected edition of his letters that she released for publication, Helene appended the briefest of prefaces:

> For twenty-eight years I lived in the Paradise of his love. His death was a catastrophe I only had the strength to survive because our souls were long ago joined together in a union beyond space and time, a union through all eternity.

Helene had taken little interest in Berg's music, but he did not seem to need her encouragement, so confident was he of its merit. In 1910 he told his idol, Mahler, that he would not waste time as a conductor or performer: he was a composer. The ailing titan replied, with a measure of personal regret, 'Yes, that is how it should be.'

Berg's first steps as a composer were catastrophic. His early works were hooted and hissed in some of the worst audience disruptions in musical history. On the most notorious occasion, Berg's friend Adolf Loos, the fanatically purist architect, had to be restrained from beating up his hissing neighbours, while Oscar Straus, benign composer of the feather-weight *Chocolate Soldier*, grappled with furious concert-goers who wanted to attack the musicians, delaying them just long enough to enable the performers to escape. Berg was less disturbed by such scenes than Schoenberg and proceeded quietly, almost pedantically, towards his own inescapable destiny. In May 1914, a year after the concert disaster, he saw a theatre performance of an early nineteenth-century tragedy about a jealous soldier and his love and decided to transform

Alban Berg

Wozzeck into the first twelve-tone opera. Six years and a world war later he finished the work, which he dedicated to his close friend Alma Mahler. A further five years elapsed before an opera house was induced to produce it. The first performance in Berlin in 1925 was conducted by Erich Kleiber, who put his cast through 137 rehearsals to overcome the unprecedented difficulties that dodecatonality brought to opera.

The critics hated and abused it. 'Mountebank,' they shrilled at Berg, 'poisoner of the wells of German music.' But the public, entranced by its air of war weariness, took to *Wozzeck* instantly. Success did not intoxicate the composer, nor did it provoke him into a rush of fresh works. He continued to create slowly, thoroughly, intensively. At forty, he had only ten years left to live, but that decade saw the flowering of four of his most exquisite works: the chamber concerto, the *Lyric Suite*, the violin concerto and his second opera, *Lulu*, the latter two preoccupying him in the year of his death. *Lulu*, saga of a *femme fatale* who leads her lovers to their doom, was begun in 1928 but, as it neared completion, prospects for production in Germany receded when the Nazis rose to power. Berg set it aside to compose, with remarkable rapidity, a violin concerto 'to the memory of an angel', moved by the death of Manon Gropius, Alma's beautiful eighteen-year-old daughter by her second husband. Four months later, Berg too was dead, of blood poisoning, his *Lulu* still unfinished.

The bereaved Helene quickly came into conflict with Berg's musical associates. Anton von Webern, who was to have conducted the posthumous world première of the violin concerto in Barcelona, stormed out of the third rehearsal after having failed to obtain the complex effects he required from uncomprehending Catalan musicians. He locked himself in his hotel room and refused to give up his conductor's score, shouting, 'It must not take place.' He relinquished it only when the widow went on her knees to him in supplication. A Freudian friend observed that Berg's death had induced in Webern a state of temporary paranoia.

Helene meanwhile tried to have *Lulu* completed. The first two acts were intact and the vocal score of Act Three was all but complete. She was confident that Schoenberg would render it as closely as was possible to her husband's intentions. When he returned the material untouched, offended by an anti-semitic allusion, Helene felt abandoned. She is said to have consulted Zemlinsky and also Webern, but in vain.

As an interim solution, she allowed the first two acts to be performed on their own and the vocal score of the third to be published. But after seventy pages of Act Three had come off the presses in Vienna, printing stopped. The publishers were becoming nervous about producing potentially offensive material at a time when Nazi Germany was making clear its intentions to engorge itself on Austria. Helene, too, was having sudden second thoughts about the opera.

Exactly when and why the widow changed her mind is only coming to light in the years since her death in 1976. After the première of the first two acts in Zurich in 1937, she said she still hoped to see *Lulu* completed. Yet shortly afterwards she imposed an irrevocable ban on any further work on the score. A copy of the vocal score of Act Three was left with the publishers, but Helene stipulated firmly in her will that 'No one is to be allowed to examine the manuscript of Act Three of *Lulu*, nor to study the photocopy.' Clearly she had discovered something that had to be suppressed, even at the cost of destroying Berg's masterpiece.

Speculation about Berg's secret circulated spasmodically while Helene was alive, but was not voiced openly. The publishers, under enormous pressure from musicians to open their Pandora's Box, admitted certain trusted musicologists to examine the forbidden manuscript under the strictest secrecy. They found that Act Three had been left almost ready for production by Berg. Aware that Helene's ban would not withstand a legal challenge after her death, the publishers quietly commissioned Friedrich Cerha, an Austrian composer, to complete the work discreetly. A decent interval was allowed to elapse after Helene died; in 1979, Pierre Boulez conducted the première of the complete *Lulu* in Paris, amid anticipation that a great truth would be revealed.

But the reason for Helene's obduracy was not immediately evident in the performed completion. Erotic and violent though it was, with the alluring Lulu coming to grief in London at the hands of an ersatz Jack the Ripper, the third act was not discernibly more lurid or provocative than the previous two. Its singular novelty was a thematic affinity that could be discerned with the *Lyric Suite*, a blatantly romantic piece which Berg had dedicated, mystifyingly, to his colleague Zemlinsky, reputedly the ugliest man in Austria. It cannot have been the musical allusion which aroused the musically-disinterested Helene's suspicions and if she did spot a link between *Lulu* and the *Lyric Suite* it must have arisen from something Berg had written on the manuscript score. Whatever the case, it is plain that from some clue in these two masterpieces she came to discover that her 'perfect' husband had spent the last ten years of his life, creatively his most fertile, deeply in love with another woman. She was, as Helene must certainly have found out, Hanna Fuchs-Robettin, wife of a music-loving industrialist with whom Berg lodged when he visited Prague. Hanna was also the sister of Franz Werfel, lover and subsequently third husband of Alban and Helene's best friend, the ubiquitous Alma Mahler-Werfel. It was Alma who had introduced Berg to Hanna (known to her friends as Mopinka), Alma who arranged for him to stay at her house, Alma who arranged to convey secret messages between them, Alma who helped allay Helene's suspicions.

For Helene Berg was no fool and in the ever-loving letters she got from her husband in Prague she could sense his distraction. The timorous adulterer set her mind to rest:

It goes against the grain, really, to have to 'reassure' you about me and Mopinka. Perhaps I'll just say that faithfulness is one of my main qualities (I'm sure I must have been a dog in a previous incarnation). . . Faithfulness towards you, and also towards myself, Music, Schoenberg (and *he* makes this really hard for one) . . . So: being of such a conservative disposition, how could I help, my darling, be anything but faithful to you and remain faithful for ever?

But he was also writing to Mopinka:

Not a day passes, not half a day, not a night, when I do not think of you . . . (my) one and only eternal love . . .

His own long-lost handwritten score of the *Lyric Suite* demonstrates that he was trying to paint himself, Hanna, and her two children in the music, weaving their initials A.B. and H.F. into its themes and secretly dedicating the original not to Zemlinsky, but as 'a small monument to a great love'. The shock of discovering Berg's duplicity must have been devastating to Helene. *Lulu*'s eroticism, a quality seemingly so foreign to her own cool nature but so abundant in Alma's and Hanna's, must suddenly have appeared sinister and threatening to the widow. Unable to suppress the *Lyric Suite* or burn the opera in its entirety, she slaked her fury by silencing — forever, she hoped — *Lulu*'s revealing climax. No other target for her anger remained: Berg was dead, Alma, Werfel and Hanna had all fled to America. With queenly pride, Helene admitted her discovery of Berg's transgression to no one and proceeded in stately fashion to her grave, at the great age of ninety-one, the timeless survivor of a legendary love and a perfect marriage.

No sooner was she laid to rest, than the musical world witnessed some of its most unseemly recent scenes. Every major opera house besieged Berg's publishers for the right to stage the première of the complete *Lulu*. Legal threats flew thick and fast. Those who lost the battle to Boulez, began a merciless campaign of deprecation against Cerha's completed score; a leading Viennese composer said it should be destroyed. Others maintained that Helene's wishes should have been respected, regardless. Meanwhile teams of musicologists scoured the globe for clues to the reason for *Lulu*'s suppression. The secret of Berg and Hanna, known only to five or six of their closest intimates, was revealed by a chance remark of Zemlinsky's about the *Lyric Suite*. Hanna was dead by then, but her daughter was traced to a town in New Jersey. Among a pile of old papers, she found the all-revealing original score of the *Lyric Suite* that the composer had given to his great love, her mother.

This opened a whole new line of detective inquiry. Who, after all, was Lulu? Was she the vice-regal Helene? Or the voluptuous Hanna? Or the versatile Alma? And why did Berg himself not finish the work when he had time enough, even by his own leisurely habits, to do so? Was it that he could not bear to see the object of his love and his fantasies, whoever of the three she was, succumbing so brutally to an assassin?

The *Lulu* argument will rage for years to come. It is a war, that, like the best of music's conflicts, will respect no ceasefire, honour no armistice. The capacity to create discord, long after a composer and his protagonists are dead and buried, is a primary source of music's vitality at the close of the twentieth century, when its greatest glories are no more than a faint memory. It is discord, in this day as in Shakespeare's, that keeps music alive:

> The skies, the fountains, every region near
> Seem'd all one musical cry: I never heard
> So musical a DISCORD, such sweet thunder.

AUTHOR'S ACKNOWLEDGEMENTS

The author wishes to acknowledge the following sources from which extracts have been quoted: Jean Cocteau: *Cocteau's World* (tr. Crosland), Peter Owen, 1972; Henry Pleasants: *Vienna's Golden Years of Music*, Penguin Books Ltd., 1963; Alexander Werth: *Musical Uproar in Moscow*, Turnstile Press, 1948; ed. Louis Cheslock *H.L. Mencken On Music*, Alfred A. Knopf Inc., 1961; Gray and Heseltine: *Gesualdo, Musician and Murderer*, Kegan Paul, 1926; Nicolas Slonimsky: *Music since 1900*, 3rd edition, Cassell, 1971.

The author is also grateful to the following people and organisations for permission to reproduce material from their collections: Dover Publications Inc. for the illustrations on pages 19, 99, 165, and 174; Gesellschaft der Musikfreunde in Wien for the illustrations on pages 90, 152, 160 and 219; Michael Sisca, La Follia di New York for the illustrations on pages 76, 82 and 141; Bild-Archiv der Österreichischen Nationalbibliothek, Wien for the illustrations on pages 21 and 229; The Illustrated London News Picture Library for the illustrations on pages 27 and 136; Weidenfeld and Nicolson Archives for the illustrations on pages 31, 67, 196 and 217; the Mansell Collection for the illustrations on pages 80, 109, 146, 170, 185 and 191; the Board of the British Library for the illustration on page 1; *Time* for the illustration on page 55; BBC Hulton Picture Library for the illustration on page 101; Mme Vera Stravinsky for the illustration on page 121.

Discord arose from a long-standing fascination with the memoirs and correspondence of great musicians. These writings, together with accounts by their wives and friends (among which Alma Mahler's portrait of her first marriage is pre-eminent), give the most vivid expression to the struggles that dominated their lives. While lacking in objectivity, they afford intimate peculiarities that no detached biographer could otherwise discover and it is regrettable that many of these books are rejected by scholars on grounds of alleged inaccuracy or musical irrelevance. There exists a neglected wealth of remarkable musical literature and I have consequently felt it useful to provide an extensive (albeit, for reasons of space, selective) catalogue of the principal works consulted, in order to help readers pursue their own explorations.

The bibliography is arranged alphabetically under the main characters, listing (a) autobiographical and eye-witness writings; (b) early biographies founded on interviews with the musician's acquaintances; (c) modern studies. A separate section (B) lists some general background works. Wherever a book has appeared in translation, I have given the English title and publication dates.

With regard to twentieth-century controversies, many of which are still unfolding, I have been privileged to examine certain of the issues with those involved, discussing Shostakovich, for example, with Mstislav Rostropovich and Maxim Shostakovich in personal interviews and at press conferences. In others, I happened to be present as a journalist at a vital moment — as, for instance, at Heifetz's momentous reconciliation concert in Jerusalem. Above all, I have sought out original material in newspaper and broadcasting archives, relying principally on *The Times* and the BBC, to which I extend grateful thanks, but also consulting back issues of newspapers and magazines from the USA, Austria, France, Germany and Israel. Additional mention should be made of television and film sources, such as Hans-Jürgen Syberberg's five-hour filmed interview with the unrepentant Winifred Wagner, which gives a unique insight into the role Bayreuth played in the Nazi State, and Lotte Lenya's broadcast memoirs of Kurt Weill, which contribute a human glimpse into an otherwise elusive personality.

*denotes those subjects where additional non-book sources have been used.

ARDITI, Luigi: *My reminiscences.* London 1896.

BACH, Johann Sebastian

    David, H.T. & Mendel, A. (eds): *The Bach reader, a life of Johann Sebastian Bach in letters and documents.* New York 1945.

    Forkel, J.N. (1749-1818): *Johann Sebastian Bach, His life, art and work.* Leipzig 1802. London 1920 (trans. C.S. Terry).

BEECHAM, (Sir) Thomas: *A mingled chime; An autobiography.* London 1944.

    Cardus, (Sir) Neville: *Autobiography.* London 1947.

    Coates, Eric: *Suite in four movements.* London 1953.

BEETHOVEN, Ludwig van: *Letters* (coll., trans. & ed. Emily Anderson). London 1961.

    Czerny, Carl: *Errinerungen aus meinem Leben.* Baden-Baden 1860.

    Sonneck, O.G. (ed.): *Beethoven, impressions by his contemporaries.* New York 1926.

    Spohr, Louis: *Autobiography* (English trans., 2 vols). London 1865.

    Thayer, Alexander Wheelock (1817-1897): *Life of Beethoven* (ed. Krehbiel, 3 vols). New York 1921. (Authoritative study based on numerous interviews with acquaintances and contemporaries of Beethoven.)

    Wagner, Richard: *Beethoven.* Munich 1870. (Controversial analysis.)

*BERG, Alban: *Letters to his wife* (trans. Grun). London 1971. (Carefully selected by Helene.)

    Carner, Mosco: *Alban Berg.* London 1975.

    Werfel-Mahler, Alma Maria: *Mein Leben.* Frankfurt 1960. (Abridged in English under the title *And the bridge is love.* London 1961.)

    Monson, Karen: *Alban Berg.* London 1979.

    Russell, John: *Erich Kleiber.* London 1956.

BERLIOZ, Hector: *Mémoires, correspondance inédite.* Paris 1870, 1879. (The writings of the greatest musical raconteur first appeared in English translation by R. & E. Holmes in 1884. I have borrowed, with permission, from Dent's popular Everyman 1912 edition in a vivacious translation by Katharine F. Boult. More comprehensive versions have since appeared in translations by Ernest Newman, 1934, and David Cairns, 1969.)

Evenings in the orchestra. Paris 1852. London 1963.

    Hallé, (Sir) Charles: *Life and letters.* London 1896.

    Heine, Heinrich: *Self-portrait and other prose writings.* (trans. Ewen). New Jersey 1948.

    Barzun, Jacques: *Berlioz and the romantic century* (2 vols). New York 1950.

BRAHMS, Johannes

Barkan, Hans (trans./ed.): *Johannes Brahms and Theodor Billroth, letters from a musical friendship.* New York 1957.

Litzmann, B. (trans./ed.): *Letters of Johannes Brahms and Clara Schumann* (2 vols). London 1927.

Henschel, (Sir) George: *Musings and memories of a musician.* London 1918.

Newcomb, Ethel: *Leschetizky as I knew him.* New York 1921.

Schumann, Eugenie: *Memoirs* (trans. M. Busch). London 1927.

Smyth (Dame) Ethel: *Impressions that remained* (2 vols). London 1920.

Gal, Hans: *Johannes Brahms, his works and personality* (trans. Stein). New York 1963

Schauffler, R.H.: *The unknown Brahms.* New York 1933. (Personal details retrieved from gossip of surviving acquaintances.)

Specht, Richard: *Johannes Brahms* (trans. Blom). London 1930.

BRUCKNER, Anton

Lochner, L.P.: *Fritz Kreisler.* New York 1951.

Newlin, Dika: *Bruckner, Mahler, Schoenberg.* New York 1947, R1978.

Schönzeler, Hans-Hubert: *Bruckner.* New York 1970.

Wolff, Werner: *Anton Bruckner, rustic genius.* New York 1942.

BÜLOW, Hans von: *Letters to Richard Wagner, Cosima and others* (trans./ed. Scott Goddard). New York 1931.

Bülow, Marie von: *Hans von Bülow's Leben in seinem Briefen dargestellt.* Leipzig 1921.

Strauss, Richard: *Recollections and reflections* (trans. Lawrence, ed. Schuh). London 1953.

BURNEY, Charles: *Music, men and manners in France and Italy, 1770.* London 1771. (Sparkling observations on musical practices and malpractice.)

BUSCH, Fritz: *Pages from a musician's life* (trans. Strachey). London 1953. (Conductor's struggles in Weimar and early-Nazi Germany.)

*CALLAS, Maria

Ardoin, J.: *The Callas legacy.* New York 1977.

Gobbi, Tito: *My life.* London 1979.

Stassinopoulos, A.: *Maria Callas.* London 1980.

CARUSO, Enrico: *Caricatures by Caruso.* New York 19 .

Caruso, D.: *Enrico Caruso, his life and death.* New York 1945.

Key, P.V.R.: *Caruso.* New York 1923.

CHALIAPIN, Fyodor: *Man and mask* (trans. P. Megroz). New York 1932.
    An autobiography, as told to Maxim Gorky (trans./ed. N. Froud & J. Hanley). London 1968.
    Hurok, Sol: *Impresario; a memoir*. New York 1946.

CHERUBINI, Luigi
    Crowest, F.J.: *Maria Luigi Carlo Zenobi Salvatore Cherubini, 1760-1842*. London 1890.

CHOPIN, Frederic: *Selected correspondence* (trans./ed. A. Hedley). London 1962.
    Niecks, F.: *Frederic Chopin as a man and musician*. London 1902.
    Jordan, R.: *Nocturne, a life of Chopin*. London 1975.

CUZZONI, Francesca
    Edwards, H. Sutherland: *The prima donna from the 17th to 19th century*. London 1888.
    Famous first representations. London 1886.
    Ferris, G.T.: *Great singers*. New York 1891.
    Pleasants, Henry: *The great singers*. London 1967.

DEBUSSY, Achille-Claude: *On music; the critical writings* (trans./ed. Smith). London 1977.
    Garden, Mary & Biancolli, L.: *Mary Garden's story*. London 1952. (The singer's somewhat prim memories of the Pelleas scandal and Debussy's marriages.)
    Leblanc, Georgette: *Souvenirs (1895-1918); my life with Maeterlinck* (trans. Flanner). New York 1932.
    Wood, Henry J.: *My Life of music*. London 1938. (Debussy in London.)

    Lockspeiser, E.: *Debussy, his life and mind* (2 vols). London 1966.
    Thompson, O.: *Debussy, man and artist*. New York 1940.
    Vallas, L.: *Claude Debussy, musicien français*. Paris 1921.

DITTERSDORF, Karl Ditters von (1739-1799): *Autobiography*. London 1896. (Musings of eighteenth-century composer, with enlightening observations on castrati and court quarrels.)

DORATI, Antal: *Notes of seven decades*. London 1979.

*FURTWÄNGLER, Wilhelm: *Concerning music* (trans. Lawrence). London 1953.
    Geissmar, Berta: *The baton and the jackboot*. London 1944. (Invaluable recollections of music in the early Nazi period and Furtwängler's stance, written by his inseparable assistant.)
    Riess, C: *Wilhelm Furtwängler, a biography*. (trans. Goldsmith).

London 1955. (Based on interviews and Wilhelm Furtwängler's own papers.)

Speer, Albert: *Inside the Third Reich*. London 1969.

Gillis, Daniel: *Furtwängler and America*. New York 1970.

Schoenberg, Harold: *The great conductors*. New York 1964.

(*see also* Karajan and Toscanini)

GATTI-CASAZZA, Giulio: *Memories of opera*. New York 1941. (Working with Toscanini, Puccini, Chaliapin, Caruso &c.)

GESUALDO, Don Carlo

Gray, Cecil & Heseltine, Peter: *Carlo Gesualdo, Prince of Venosa, musician and murderer*. London 1926. (Containing Gray's entertaining translation of contemporary accounts of the murders.)

Watkins, G.: *Gesualdo, the man and his music*. London 1973.

GIGLI, Beniamino: *Memoirs* (trans. Silone). New York 1957.

Jeritza, Maria: *Sunlight and song*. (trans. Martens). New York 1924. (Describes Gigli, but makes no mention of her assault on him.)

GILBERT, William Schwenk

Dark, S. & Grey, R. (eds): *William Schwenk Gilbert, his life and letters*. London 1924.

Pearson, Hesketh: *Gilbert and Sullivan, a biography*. London 1946.

(*see also* Sullivan)

GLUCK, Christoph Willibald von: *Collected correspondence and papers* (ed. H. Müller von Asow). London 1962.

Newman, Ernest: *Gluck and the opera*. London 1895.

GOTTSCHALK, Louis Moreau: *Notes of a pianist* (trans. Peterson). Pennsylvania 1881.

GRIEG, Edvard

Finck, H.T.: *Grieg*. New York 1906. (Based on personal acquaintance.)

HANDEL, George Frideric

Burney, Charles: *An account of the musical performances in Westminster Abbey . . . in commemoration of Handel*. London 1785.

Coxe, W.: *Anecdotes of G. F. Handel and John Christopher Smith*. London 1799.

Mainwaring, J.: *Memoirs of the life of the late George Frideric Handel*. London 1760.

Mattheson, Johann: *George Friederich Händels Lebensbeschreibung*. Hamburg 1761. (Quoted in Streatfield.)

Deutsch, Otto Erich: *Handel, a documentary biography*. London 1955.

Streatfield, R.A.: *Handel.* London 1909. (Enduringly readable biography.)

HANSLICK, Eduard: *The beautiful in music* (trans. Cohen, from the 7th edition. Leipzig 1885). London 1891.
Aus meinem Leben. Berlin 1894.
Pleasants, Henry (coll., trans. & ed.): *Vienna's golden years of music, 1850-1900.* London (rev. edn) 1963. (A representative selection of Hanslick's critical writings, including several of the best on Wagner and Brahms and the acid condemnation of Bruckner's 8th, in a fluent translation.)

Deas, Stewart: *In defence of Hanslick.* London 1940/1972. (Pioneering work of advocacy.)
Gay, Peter: *Freud, Jews and other Germans.* New York 1978. (Contains incisive analysis of the Brahms-Wagner conflict of ideas and Hanslick's pivotal role within it; also vital research on Hermann Levi.)

HAUK, Minnie (Baroness de Wartegg): *Memories of a singer.* New York 1925.
(*see also* Mapleson)

HAYDN, (Franz) Josef
Dies, A.C.: *Biographische Nachrichten von Josef Haydn.* Vienna 1810.
Griesinger, G.A.: *Biographische Notizen über Josef Haydn.* Vienna 1809. (Both works available in edited modern Eng. trans. in: Gotwals, V.: *Haydn: Two contemporary portraits.* Madison 1968.)
Landon, H.C.R.: *The collected correspondence and London notebooks of Josef Haydn.* London 1959.

Landon, H.C.R.: *Haydn: Chronicle and Works* (5 vols). London 1976-81. (Definitive modern biography.)

*HEIFETZ, Jascha
Axelrod, H.R.: *Heifetz.* Neptune City 1976. (Includes excerpts from interviews.)
Rubinstein, Arthur: *My many years.* New York 1979. (Personal anecdotes.)

HINDEMITH, Paul
Skelton, Geoffrey: *Paul Hindemith.* London 1975.

JARNOVICK (Giornovichi), Giovanni
Kelly, Michael: *Reminiscences* (2 vols). London 1826.
Dubourg, G.: *Famous violinists.* London 1854.
Pincherle, Marc: *The world of the virtuoso.* (trans. Brockway). London 1964.

JOACHIM, Joseph: *Letters* (trans. Bickley). London 1914.
  Moser, A.: *Joseph Joachim, a biography 1831-1899* (trans. Durham).
  London 1901.

*KARAJAN, Herbert von
  Culshaw, John: *Putting the record straight.* London 1981. (Recording
    impressions.)
  Galway, James: *An autobiography.* London 1980.
  Robinson, Paul: *Karajan.* London 1975. (Unauthorized biographical
    essay.)
  Speer, Albert: Spandau; the secret diaries (trans. Winston). New York
    1976.
  (*see also* Furtwängler)

*KLEMPERER, Otto: *Minor recollections.* London 1964.
  Heyworth, P.: *Conversations with Klemperer.* London 1973.

*KOUSSEVITSKY, Serge
  Bowers, F.: *Scriabin, a biography* (2 vols). Tokyo 1970.
  (*see also* Rachmaninov)

LIND, Jenny
  Barnum, P.T.: *Struggles and triumphs.* Buffalo 1889.
  Chorley, H.F.: *30 years' musical recollections.* London 1862.
  Lumley, Benjamin: *Reminiscences of the opera.* London 1864.
  Maretzek, Max: *Crotchets and quavers.* New York 1855. (Opera
    manager's view.)
  Rockstro, W.S.: *Jenny Lind* (2 vols). London 1891. (The classic study.)

LISZT, Franz: *Letters* (coll./ed. La Mara; trans. Bache). London 1894.
  Fay, Amy: *Music study in Germany.* London 1896. (A pupil's
    impression.)
  Huneker, James: *Franz Liszt.* London 1911. (First-hand impressions
    from multiple sources.)
  Lenz, Wilhelm von: *The great piano virtuosos of our time from personal
    acquaintance.* New York 1899.
  Weingartner, Felix: *Buffets and rewards.* London 1937. (English
    abridgement of the conductor's memoirs, containing lively accounts
    of his adoption by Liszt as a protégé, life at Bayreuth, Liszt's death,
    Hermann Levi and Cosima Wagner. Essential reading on musical
    life, 1880-1930.)

  Newman, Ernest: *The man Liszt.* London 1934. (Intensely readable,
    debunks many of the best-loved myths.)

LULLY, Jean-Baptiste
  Prunières, H.: *Lully, biographie critique.* Paris 1927.

Scott, R.H.F.: *Jean-Baptiste Lully*. London 1973.

*MAHLER, Gustav: *Selected letters* (ed. Alma Mahler, 1st edn Vienna 1924; enlarged and trans. 1st English edn, ed. Martner). London 1979.

Mahler, Alma: *Gustav Mahler, memories and letters* (trans. Creighton). London 1946, R1968. (The extraordinary biography of Mahler by his wife.)

Bauer-Lechner, Natalie: *Recollections of Gustav Mahler* (trans. Newlin). London 1980. (Faithful jottings of a female acolyte, subsequently displaced by Alma.)

Karpath, Ludwig: *Begegnung mit dem Genius*. Vienna 1934. (Critic's gossipy memoirs of the Mahler and post-Mahler eras.)

Slezak, Leo: *Song of motley; being the reminiscences of a hungry tenor*. New York 1938.

Walter, Bruno: *Gustav Mahler* (trans. Lindt). New York 1947. (Assessment by his assistant conductor.)

Briefe, 1894-1962. Frankfurt 1969.

Theme and Variations (trans. Galston). London 1947. (Autobiography, containing fine portraits of Mahler and his circle in Vienna, as well as memories of music in inter-War Germany and the rise of Hitler.)

Blaukopf, Kurt: *Mahler, a documentary biography* (trans. Ford). London 1976.

Cooke, Deryck: *Gustav Mahler, an introduction to his music*. London 1980.

de la Grange, Henry: *Mahler, vol 1*. London 1973. (Massively comprehensive modern biography. Volume 2 in preparation. Essential reading.)

Reik, Theodor: *The haunting melody*. New York 1953. (Incisive psychoanalytical study by a pupil of Freud of Mahler's mental state and its influence on his compositions.)

Cooke, Deryck (ed.): *Tenth Symphony in Deryck Cooke's performing version*. London 1964.

Schalk, Franz (ed.): *Tenth Symphony in facsimile edition with introduction by Alma Mahler*. Vienna 1924.

MALIBRAN, Maria

Edwards, H.S.: *History of the opera* (2 vols). London 1862.

Pougin, A.: *Maria Malibran, the story of a great singer*. London 1911.

Smart, (Sir) George: *Leaves from his journal*. London 1907. (Contains probably the most reliable eye-witness account of the manner of Malibran's death.)

*MANN, Thomas: *Death in Venice*, London 1913.
  Doctor Faustus, London 1949.
  A Sketch of my life (trans. Lowe-Porter). New York 1960.
  Letters 1889-1955 (trans. Winston). New York 1971.
  The Story of a Novel: The genesis of Doctor Faustus (trans. Winston).
    New York 1961.
  Mann, Katia: *Unwritten memories* (trans. Hannum; ed. E. Plessen &
    Michael Mann). London 1975. (His widow's dismissive version of
    the fracas with Schoenberg and oversimplified account of his conflict
    with the Nazis.)
  (*see also* Mahler, Schoenberg, Wagner)

MAPLESON, (Colonel) Henry: *Memoirs, 1848-88* (2 vols). London 1888.
  ed. & abr. Rosenthal. London 1966. (Opera manager's life.)

MELBA, (Dame) Nellie: *Melodies and memories*. London 1925.
  Finck, H.T.: *My adventures in the golden age of music*. New York
    1926.
  Klein, H.: *Great women singers of my time*. London 1933.

  Hetherington, J.: *Melba, a biography*. London 1967. (Strong Australian
    material.)
  Wechsberg, Joseph: *Red plush and black velvet; Dame Nellie Melba
    and her times*. London 1962. (Excellent chapter on the Vienna
    claques.)

MENDELSSOHN, Felix
  Hiller, F.: *Mendelssohn, letters and recollections*. London 1874.
    (Includes anecdotes of Chopin, Berlioz and Liszt.)
  Hensel, S.: *The Mendelssohn family, 1729-1847*. London 1881.

MEYERBEER, Giacomo
  Gruneisen, C.L.: *Memoir of Meyerbeer*. London 1848.
  Pougin, A.: *Meyerbeer, notes biographiques*. Paris 1864.
  Wagner, Richard: *Mein Leben*. Munich 1911.

MILHAUD, Darius: *Notes without music* (trans. Evans). London 1952.
    (Subdued account of *Les Six*, but invaluable for observation of the
    death of Satie.)

MOZART, Wolfgang Amadeus: *Letters* (trans. Emily Anderson; 3 vols).
    London 1966. (Immature, lewd, inspired and dejected correspond-
    ence.)
  Kelly, M.: *Reminiscences*. London 1826. (Personal descriptions of
    Mozart and the intrigues he encountered.)
  Ponte, Lorenzo da: *Memoirs* (trans. Sheppard). New York 1929.
    (Librettist's story.)

Deutsch, O.E.: Mozart, a documentary biography (trans. Blom). London 1965.

Holmes, Edward: *The Life of Mozart.* London 1848.

Levey, Michael: *The Life and Death of Mozart.* London 1971.

Shaeffer, Peter: *Amadeus.* London 1980 (Script of popular play on Mozart's death.)

NATHAN, Isaac

Mackerras, Catherine: *Hebrew melodist; life of Isaac Nathan.* London 1963. (Painstaking biography by his granddaughter.)

Phillips, Olga Somech: *Isaac Nathan, Friend of Byron.* London 1943.

NEWMAN, Ernest: *Essays from the world of music* (2 vols). London 1958.

OFFENBACH, Jacques: *Orpheus in America* (trans. MacLintock). London 1958. (Travelogue.)

Brindejont-Offenbach, Jacques: *Offenbach, mon grand-père.* Paris 1940.

Faris, Alexander: *Jacques Offenbach.* London 1980. (Best modern biography.)

PADEREWSKI, Ignacy Jan

& Lawton, Mary: *The Paderewski memoirs.* London 1939.

Rubinstein, Arthur: *My young years.* London 1973.

Schonberg, Harold C.: *The great pianists.* New York 1968.

PAGANINI, Niccolò

Fétis, F.-J.: *Biographical notice of N. Paganini.* London 1852.

Day, L.: *Paganini of Genoa.* London 1929.

PALESTRINA, Giovanni Pierluigi da

Pyne, Z.K.: *Palestrina; his life and times.* London 1922.

PATTI, Adelina

Ganz, Wilhelm: *Memories of a musician; reminiscences of 70 years of musical life.* London 1913.

Klein, Hermann: *The reign of Patti.* London 1920.

Lauw, Louisa: *14 years with Adelina Patti.* London 1884.

Mapleson, J.: *Memoirs.* London 1888.

Santley, (Sir) Charles: *Reminiscences of my life.* London 1909.

*PROKOFIEV, Serge: *Prokofiev by Prokofiev, a composer's memoir* (trans. Daniels). London 1979. (Dreary ramblings, filtered through the Soviet sanitizer.)

American Russian Institute of Southern California, Hollywood: *On Soviet Music, documents and discussion* (trans. Groth). Hollywood 1948. (Contain's Prokofiev's self-abasing letter to the Central Committee.)

Krebs, S.: *Soviet composers and the development of Soviet music.* London 1970.

Slonimsky, Nicholas: *Lexicon of musical invective.* New York 1953. (Prokofiev and the critics.)

Stravinsky, Igor (& Craft, Robert): *Memories and commentaries.* London 1960.

(*see also* Shostakovich)

PUCCINI, Giacomo: *Letters* (trans. Makin; ed. Adami). London 1937.
Carner, Mosco: *Puccini* (2nd edn). London 1975. (The standard biography.)
Seligman, Vincent: *Puccini among friends.* London 1938.

*RACHMANINOV, Sergey: *Recollections* (told to Oskar von Riesemann). London 1934.
Chasins, Abram: *Speaking of pianists.* New York 1959.

Bertensson, J.: *Sergey Rachmaninov.* London 1965.

RAMEAU, Jean-Philippe
Girdlestone, C.: *Rameau.* London 1957.

*RAVEL, Maurice
Long, Marguerite: *At the piano with Ravel* (trans. Senior-Ellis). London 1973.
Roland-Manuel: *Maurice Ravel.* London 1947.
Stuckenschmidt, H.H.: *Ravel.* London 1969.

ROSSINI, Gioacchino
Beyle, Marie-Henri (Stendhal): *La Vie de Rossini.* Paris 1823.
(Adapted for an English readership, London 1824. Although a modern and more faithful translation exists, I have included excerpts from the 1824 version, since it seems more in the spirit of the times. Stendhal was not entirely accurate about his subject, but always entertaining.)
Michotte, E: *Souvenirs personels. La visite de R. Wagner à Rossini (1860).* Paris 1906. (Personal reminiscences of Rossini by one of his social circle. Includes tales of his meetings with Beethoven and Salieri and a witnessed account of his long conversation with Wagner. An English translation has appeared in recent years.)
Saint-Saens, Camille: *Musical memories* (trans. Rich). Boston 1919.

Weinstock, H.: *Rossini.* New York 1968. (Fine modern biography.)

SALIERI, Antonio
Moscheles, Ignaz: *Recent music and musicians; as described in the diaries and correspondence of Ignaz Moscheles.* London 1873. (Report of his deathbed visit to Salieri.)

Pushkin, Alexander: *Mozart and Salieri.* 1830. (Work of fiction set to opera in 1898 by Rimsky-Korsakov.)
Beethoven, L. van: *Letters, journals and conversations* (trans./ed. Michael Hamburger). London 1966.
(*see also* Mozart, Rossini)

*SATIE, Erik: *Memoires d'un amnésique.* Paris 1953.
Cocteau, Jean: *Cock and harlequin* (trans. R. Myers). London 1921.
Harding, James: *Satie.* London 1975.
Templier, E.: *Erik Satie* (trans. French). Cambridge, Massachusets, 1969.
Shattock, R.: *The banqueting years.* London 1959.
(*see also* Debussy, Milhaud)

*SCHOENBERG, Arnold: *Letters* (trans. Wilkins & Kaiser; ed. Stein). London 1965.
Harmonielehre. Vienna 1911. (Schoenberg's major theoretical treatise. The first complete English translation, by Roy E. Carter, appeared only in 1978.)
Newlin, Dika: *Schoenberg remembered; diaries and recollections 1938-76.* New York 1980. (Starry-eyed jottings by an adolescent pupil in California, but frequently insightful and revealing.)
Viertel, Salka: *The kindness of strangers.* New York 1969. (California memoirs by exiled Viennese salon hostess, friend of Schoenberg, Mann and Brecht.)
Werfel-Mahler, Alma Maria: *And the bridge is love.* London 1961. (Important glimpses, but unintimate.)

Armitage, Merle (ed.): *Schoenberg, Articles 1929-1937.* New York 1937. (Tribute volume, containing writings by Schoenberg and his admirers, as well as a selection of the most violent critical barrages.)
Reich, Willi: *Schoenberg, a critical biography.* London 1971.
Stuckenschmidt, H.H.: *Arnold Schoenberg, his life, work and world* (trans. Searle). London 1977.
Wellesz, Egon: Schönberg (trans. Kerridge). New York 1925.
(The three major biographies are all by ex-pupils who have remained too close to their master to be ideally objective. Wellesz's is an interesting early view, now outdated. Reich assembles excellent material and Stuckenschmidt is painstakingly comprehensive.)
Comini, Alessandra: *The fantastic art of Vienna.* New York 1978. (Contains paintings by Schoenberg and Gerstel and a brief assessment of their relationship.)
Graf, Max: *Modern music; composers and music of our time.* New York 1946. (Lucid account of Schoenberg's development by ex-Vienna critic.)

SCHUBERT, Franz
  Deutsch, O.E.: *Schubert, a documentary biography* (trans. Blom). London 1946.

SCHUMANN, Clara and Robert
  Schumann, Robert: *On music and musicians.* (ed. Wolff). London 1947. (Essays.)
  de Lara, Adeline: *Finale.* London 1955. (Pupil of Clara describes her milieu.)
  Litzmann, B.: *Clara Schumann, an artist's life.* London 1913.
  May, Florence: *The girlhood of Clara Schumann.* London 1912. (By a pupil of Brahms.)
  Niecks, F.: *Robert Schumann* (ed. C. Niecks). London 1925. (Based on several first hand accounts.)
  Schumann, Eugenic: *Memoirs* (trans. Busch). London 1927. (Daughter's tales.)

SHAW, George Bernard: *Shaw's music* (ed. Don H. Laurence). Vol 1 1876-1890; Vol. II 1890-1893; Vol. III 1893-1950. London 1981. (Modern edition of Shaw's critical writings.)

*SHOSTAKOVICH, Dmitri
  Volkov, Solomon: *Testimony, the memoirs of Shostakovich* (trans. Bouis, as related to and edited by Volkov). London 1979. (The controversial 'memoirs' smuggled out to the West. Maxim Shostakovich, son of the composer, described it to me as 'a book *about* Shostakovich, not *by* him'. He does not dispute its general accuracy, just the misanthropic tone of the discourse.)
  Sollertinsky, Dmitri Ludmilla: *Pages from the life of Dmitri Shostakovich* (trans. Hobbs & Midgley). New York 1980. (The official Soviet whitewash with no reference to Stalin.)
  Werth, Alexander: *Musical uproar in Moscow.* London 1949. (Indispensable journalist's report of Stalin's second repression of music, containing a transcript of the deliberations of the Central Committee and the 'confessions' it obtained.)
  Olkhovsky, Andrey: *Music under the Soviets.* London 1955. (Study of 20th-century music in the USSR.)
  (*see also* Prokofiev)

SOUSA, John Philip: *Marching along.* New York 1928.

SPOHR, Louis: *Autobiography* (2 vols, Eng trans.). London 1865. (Among the most informative 19-century musical memoirs.)

STRADELLA, Alessandro
  Stendhal: *Life of Rossini.* London 1824. (Contains the account of his murder quoted in Chapter 10.)

*STRAUSS family (Johann I, Johann II, Josef, Eduard)
Strauss, Eduard: *Erinnerungen*. Vienna 1906.

Fantel, Hans: *The waltz kings, father and son, and their romantic age*. Newton Abbott 1972.
Gartenberg, E.: *Johann Strauss, the end of an era*. Pennsylvania 1974.
Wechsberg, Joseph: *The waltz emperors*. London 1973.

*STRAUSS, Richard: *Recollections and reflections* (trans. Lawrence; ed. Schuh). London 1953. (Sharp portrayal of the latter stages of the Wagner-Brahms war.)
Correspondence with Hugo von Hoffmannsthal (trans. Hammelman & Osers). Cambridge, 1961. (Step-by-step creation of the operas.)
A confidential matter: correspondence with Stefan Zweig 1931-5 (trans. Knight). California 1978. (The intensive last collaboration and its destruction by the Nazis.)
Beecham, (Sir) Thomas: *A mingled chime*. London 1944.
Kessler, Count Harry: *The diaries of a cosmopolitan 1918-1937* (trans. C. Kessler). London 1971. (Socialite's view of Dr and Mrs Strauss.)
Lehmann, Lotte: *Singing with Richard Strauss* (trans. Pawel). London 1964.
On wings of song; an autobiography. London 1939.
Zweig, Friederike Maria: *Stefan Zweig* (trans. McArthur). London 1946.
Zweig, Stefan: *The world of yesterday*. London 1943.

Del Mar, Norman: *Richard Strauss, a critical commentary on his life and works* (3 vols). London 1962-72.
Jefferson, Alan: *Richard Strauss*. London 1975.

*STRAVINSKY, Igor: *Chronicle of my life*. London 1936. (Stravinsky's own account of the night of the Rite.)
Cocteau, Jean: *Cock and harlequin* (trans. Myers). London 1921.
Craft, Robert: *Conversations with Igor Stravinsky*. London 1959.
Chronicle of a friendship, 1948-71. London 1972.
de Falla, Manuel: *On music and musicians* (trans. Urman). London R1979.
Rubinstein, Arthur: *My many years*. London 1979.

SULLIVAN, (Sir) Arthur
Sullivan, H. & Newman Flower: *Sir Arthur Sullivan, his life, letters and diaries*. London 1950.
Graves, C.L.: *The life and letters of Sir George Grove*. London 1903.
(*see also* Gilbert)

TCHAIKOVSKY, Pyotr Ilyich *Life and letters* (ed. Modeste Tchaikovsky; trans. Newmarch). (2 vols). New York R1973.

Brown, D.: *Tchaikovsky, vol 1, 1840-74.* London 1978.

TETRAZZINI, Luisa: *My life of song.* London 1921.
Gaisberg, Fred: *Music on record.* London 1946 (Record producer's fascinating memoirs, containing account of Tetrazzini's elopement.)
Newton, Ivor: *At the piano.* London 1966. (By her accompanist.)

*TOSCANINI, Arturo
Boult, (Sir) Adrian: *My own trumpet.* London 1973.
Clemens, Clara: *My husband Gabrilowitsch.* New York 1938.
Respighi, Elsa: *Ottorino Respighi.* Milan, London, 1954. (Clemens and Respighi both contain first-hand information of Toscanini's persecution in Fascist Italy.)
Wagner, Friedelind and Cooper, P.: *The royal family of Bayreuth.* London 1944. (Insider's account of Toscanini and the Nazis. Essential reading.)

Sachs, Harvey: *Toscanini.* London 1978. (Outstanding modern biography.)

VERDI, Giuseppe: *Letters* (trans./ed. Charles Osborne). London 1971.
Pougin, A.: *Verdi, anecdotic memoirs.* London 1887.
Walker, F.: *The man Verdi.* London 1962.

VIVALDI, Antonio
Marcello, Benedetto: *Il teatro alla moda.* Venice 1720; rev. edn 1887.
Kendall, Alan: *Vivaldi.* London 1978.

*WAGNER, Richard: *Mein Leben* (*My life*). Munich/London 1911. (His life story up to 1865, dictated to Cosima and published 28 years after his death. Though tailored to suit his self-image — and Cosima's sensibilities — it still reads entertainingly in parts, especially on the Dresden uprising.)
Prose works (trans. Ellis, 8 vols). London 1895. (Includes the diatribes on *Jews in Music* and the *Artwork of the Future.* William Ashton Ellis has tried to translate them into an English approximation of Wagner's dense prose and the result is often stultifying. Though several of the essays have appeared since in shorter collections, editors have generally held to the original translation. So have I, except in the most impenetrable where I have substituted modern English for clarity.)
Correspondence with: Liszt (London 1897). August Röckel (London 1897). Minna Wagner (London 1908, 1950). Mathilde Wesendonck (London 1905).
Ganz, Wilhelm: *Memories of a musician.* London 1913.
Neumann, Angelo: *Reminiscences of Richard Wagner.* New York 1908. (By his impresario.)

Nietzsche, Friederich: *The case of Wagner* (trans. Common). London 1899. (The philosopher's savage attack on his fallen idol.)
Praeger, F.: *Richard Wagner as I knew him*. London 1892. (By an English admirer who attempts, most entertainingly, to explain away the Master's moral inconsistencies.)
Wagner, Cosima: *Diaries* (2 vols). (trans. Skelton; ed. Georg-Dellin). London 1978-80.

Gal, Hans: *Richard Wagner* (trans. Schönzeler). London 1976. (Fine, brief modern study.)
Newman, Ernest: *The life of Richard Wagner* (4 vols). London 1933-46. (The most erudite and impressive of the major biographies.)
Zuckerman, E.: *The first 100 years of Wagner's Tristan*. New York 1962. (Examines the imputed dangers of singing Wagner.)

*WAGNER family (from 1883 to the present)
Culshaw, John: *Ring resounding*. London 1967. (Record producer's impressions of Bayreuth in the immediate post-War period.)
Leider, Frida: *Playing my part* (trans. Osborne). London 1966. (Singing at Bayreuth 1928-38.)
Mayer, Hans: *Richard Wagner in Bayreuth 1876-1976* (trans. Zipes). Stuttgart 1976.
Skelton, Geoffrey: *Wagner at Bayreuth*. London
Wieland Wagner, the positive sceptic. London 1971.
Wagner, Friedelind & Cooper, P.: *The royal family of Bayreuth*. London 1944.
Weingartner, Felix: *Buffets and rewards*. (trans. Wolff). London 1937.

WEBER, Carl Maria von
Weber, Max Maria von: *Weber, the life of an artist*. London 1865. (By his son.)

*WEBERN, Anton von
Moldenhauer, Hans: *The death of Anton Webern*. London 1962.
Anton Webern, a chronicle of his life and work. London 1978.
Monson, Karen: *Alban Berg*. London 1979.

*WEILL, Kurt
Brecht, Bertolt: *Diaries*. London 1977.
Jarman, Douglas: Kurt Weill, an illustrated biography. Unpublished manuscript.
Kowalke, Kim H.: *Kurt Weill in Europe*. Michigan 1980.
Sanders, Ronald: *The days grow short*. London 1980.

WOLF, Hugo: *The music criticism of Hugo Wolf* (trans., ed. & annot. Henry Pleasants). New York 1979.
Walker, F.: *Hugo Wolf, a biography*. London 1951.

(B) *General works*

Arundell, Dennis: *The critic at the opera.* London 1957.

Burney, Charles: *A general history of music from the earliest ages to the present period* (4 vols). London 1776-89.

Casanova, Jaques: *Memoirs.* Paris 1880.

Conquest, Robert: *The Great Terror, Stalin's purge of the thirties.* London 1968.

Eaton, Quaintance: *Opera caravan: adventures of the Metropolitan on tour 1883-1956.* New York 1957.

Edgcumbe, Richard: *Musical reminiscences of the Earl of Mount Edgcumbe.* London 1834.

Gartenberg, E.: *Vienna, its musical heritage.* Pennsylvania 1968.

Gattey, Charles Neilson: *Queens of Song.* London 1979.

Graf, Max: *Composer and Critic; 200 years of music criticism.* New York 1947.

Grunberger, Richard: *The social history of the Third Reich.* London 1971.

Grunfeld, Frederic: *Prophets without honour.* New York 1979. (Valuable study of Jewish artists in Nazi Europe.)

Heriot, Angus: *The castrati in opera.* London 1956 (Definitive.)

Holde, Artur: *Jews in music.* London 1959.

Jenks, W.A.: *Vienna and the young Hitler.* New York 1960.

Jones, Ernest: *The life and work of Sigmund Freud* (ed. Trilling & Marcus) (3 vols). London 1953-7.

Kolodin, I.: *The Metropolitan Opera, 1883-1950.* London 1940.

Kralik, H.: *The Vienna Philharmonic.* Vienna 1955.

Mandelstam, Nadezhda: *Hope against hope.* London 1970. (Account of Stalinist persecution.)

Mencken, H.L.: *On music.* New York 1961.

Pleasants, Henry: *The great singers.* London 1967.

Nettl, Paul: *The book of musical documents.* New York 1948.

Prawy, Marcel.: *The Vienna Opera.* London 1970.

Rushmore, R.: *The singing voice.* London 1969.

Sadie, S. (ed.): *The New Grove dictionary of music and musicians.* 6th edn, (20 vols). London 1981.

Schnitzler, Arthur: *My youth in Vienna* (trans. Hutter). London 1971.

Scholes, Percy: *The Mirror of Music 1844-1944. A century of musical life in Britain as reflected in the Musical Times* (2 vols). London 1947. *Oxford Companion to Music.* Oxford 1963.

Schorske, Carl E.: *Fin de siècle Vienna; politics and culture.* London 1978.

Schwarz, Doris. *Music and musical life in Soviet Russia, 1917-1970.* London 1972.

Strunk, Oliver (ed.): *Source readings in music history.* New York 1950.

Slonimsky, Nicholas: *Music since 1900.* 3rd edn, London 1971. (Faithful
  chronicle of the modern era by ardent modernist.)
Twain, Mark: *A tramp abroad.* New York
Wulf, J.: *Musik im dritten Reich.* Hamburg 1966.

INDEX